Great Short Stories
of the World

Great Short Stories of the World

A Collection of Complete Short Stories Chosen from the Literatures of all Periods and Countries

by

BARRETT H. CLARK

MAXIM LIEBER

Volume I

ABI PRINTS & PUBLISHING CO.

New Delhi

GREAT SHORT STORIES OF THE WORLD

ISBN-81-86787-10-0 (Vol. I)
81-86787-13-5 (Set)

First Published: London, 1926

Reprinted in **2006** by:
ABI PRINTS & PUBLISHING CO.
Pooja Apartments, 4B, Ansari Road, New Delhi - 110 002 (India)
Tel.: 23287589, 23255799; Fax: 91-11-23270385
E-mail: aryanbooks@vsnl.com

Printed in India at B.B.N. Printers, New Delhi

Preface

THIS collection marks the first attempt to bring together in a single volume a characteristic group of the outstanding examples of the Short Story as it has been practised by writers of almost every race, from the earliest days of civilization down to the present century. Its purpose is not to shew, by a series of texts chosen on academic grounds, how the form developed, but to bring together the best examples of every form by which men have endeavoured to entertain and instruct their fellows.

No art is more spontaneous than that of the short story, and though it may be proved that lyric poetry came earlier to the dignity of literature, it is certain that stories of some sort were told as soon as man became articulate. The period covered in the present collection embraces nearly five thousand years, but there can be no reasonable doubt that the Egyptian tales that open the volume, the first of their kind known to us, are the finished products of an art that was practised thousands of years before these were written. And since the beginning of civilization as we know it, there has been no break in the tradition of tale-telling: the demand for stories is as strong and insatiable in man to-day as it was before he discovered how to make stone weapons.

Of recent years there has been a good deal of theorizing about the Short Story as an art form. A whole literature of theory has come into being in order to explain the work of Maupassant and Poe and O. Henry, as well as to guide the would-be writer. Several theorists have maintained that the Short Story (as opposed to the story that is short) is an invention of the Nineteenth Century, that it must be unified, that it must concern itself with but a single anecdote or episode or situation, that it must be of a certain length; in a word, that it must conform to certain *a priori* principles. These theories are often interesting and ingenious, but so far as they have influenced the writers of stories, they are of little importance.

The editors of this collection have approached their task of selection with open minds: they have not allowed themselves to be influenced by any theory of what a short story should be, except that which requires that it be interesting of its kind. While it is quite true that Maupassant was a more highly inspired artist than say the Seventeenth Century Dutchman Jacob Cats, it does not follow that Cats' fable which is printed in the pages that follow, is not a story because *The Necklace* is a masterpiece.

So, without confining themselves to any theory of classification, the editors have chosen a wide variety of stories designed to appeal to the general reader, and perhaps to the student as well, in the belief that what has delighted the Chinese from time immemorial, the ancient Egyptians, the Jewish shepherds and warriors of Biblical times, the Greeks of Homer's days and the Romans of Cæsar's, will appeal with equal force to the inhabitants of the civilized world of the Twentieth Century.

Despite the indefatigable efforts of editors and publishers in unearthing the little-known or quite forgotten tales of certain countries or peoples, and despite the bewilderingly numerous collections of stories published in sets of many volumes, it has never before been possible for the reader to make the acquaintance of so many stories as are here brought together within the covers of a single volume. It has even been necessary to translate the work of several writers unknown to readers of English, and in many cases to make known through translation some particular story hitherto not accessible. The volume, therefore, besides being the first to include examples of stories of practically the entire world, introduces several new writers to English and American readers. Among the stories that appear here for the first time in English are those by the Hungarians Mikszath and Molnar; the Spanish-Americans Darío, Blanco-Fombóna and García-Calderón; the Dutchman Heijermans; the Pole Prus; the Bulgarian Elin-Pelin; the Jugoslavs Matoš, Lazarevich, and Cankar; and the Belgian Lemonnier.

That *Great Short Stories of the World* is not as nearly perfect a collection as the editors and publisher would have liked to make it is a foregone conclusion. Has ever any anthology entirely pleased its maker? Has it ever pleased every critic and every reader? It is hardly necessary to state that the first limitation imposed upon the editors was that of space. It was not, of course, possible to include more than a comparatively small number of the great stories available; it was not possible to include many stories which, like Vigny's *Laurette,* were too long; it was inadvisable to reprint too many of the stories that were in every other collection, but on the other hand it would not have done to omit all the recognized masterpieces, like Maupassant's *Necklace.* To include stories even from those countries which had made the most important contributions to the world's store of tales was in itself a hazardous undertaking, but when it came to selecting precisely what stories should be chosen to give an adequate notion of the richness and variety of a country like France, it seemed at first a rather hopeless task. How, for instance, was it possible to give the reader a fair notion of the beautiful stories of the Thirteenth and Fourteenth Centuries? It was imperative that out of a possible hundred only two or three should be chosen.

In the case of modern writers, the difficulties were much greater. Every one has his favourite authors and favourite stories. It was not the intention of the editors to bring this collection up to the minute: the works of our immediate contemporaries are easily accessible. If certain contemporaries like Cabell and Anderson, Bojer and Gorky are included, it is either because they have their roots in the Nineteenth Century or that they represent in a general way some modern trend that seems more or less permanent, and because their work is intrinsically worth printing in a collection of this sort.

Finally, came considerations of copyright. In almost every instance both publishers and writers have been helpful in allowing copyright stories to be reprinted, but occasionally it has been necessary to omit the work of certain authors because either the publisher or the agent was unable to see his way clear to coöperating with the editors.

Although the final selection of all stories is a matter for which the editors are alone responsible, the lists were submitted to and passed upon by a number of specialists, particularly in the case of those sections whose literature was little known. These persons have enabled the editors to make their work more inclusive and more genuinely representative of all peoples and nations than would otherwise have been possible. But while every effort has been made to show, both by the stories themselves and by the brief notes, what each nation and race has contributed to the art of the Short Story, the attitude of the editors throughout has been that of every true teller of tales: it is their wish that these stories shall be read and enjoyed by the general public. They were written not for critics and historians, editors of anthologies and specialists, but for all mankind. They have tried to bear in mind that the Short Story is a "tale which holdeth children from play and old men from the chimney corner."

To many publishers, both English and American, thanks are due for their courtesy and assistance in the use of copyright material. Specific acknowledgment is made in connection with the separate stories. For constant and invaluable assistance of every sort the editors take this occasion to thank Cecile S. Clark, Irma Lieber, and Mr. Guy Holt. A number of authors have themselves granted permission to reprint and in some instances given valuable advice regarding what stories to use. Acknowledgment is hereby gratefully made to Maxim Gorky, George Moore,

James Branch Cabell, Per Hallström, Johan Bojer, Arthur Morrison, and Abraham Raisin. Among the many advisers and translators who have helped in the preparation of one or more sections, the editors are especially grateful to Miss Hanna Astrup Larsen, Dr. Isaac Goldberg, Dr. A. C. van P. Huizinga, Mrs. Velma S. Howard, Prof. Sarka B. Hrbkova, Mr. Gray Casement, Mr. Rajner Hlacha, Mr. Ivan Mladineo, Mr. Adamantios Polisoides, and Mr. George Gorn.

THE EDITORS

October, 1925.

PUBLISHER'S NOTE

Contents

Vol. I

CONTENTS

Great Short Stories
of the World

Ancient Egypt

INTRODUCTION

IN determining the development of the short story in Egypt, it is necessary to study the inscriptions on papyri and stone monuments, a process which the archæologists are better fitted to accomplish than the literary historians, for there appears to have been little development in the form, and the earliest do not differ radically from the later stories, such as the two here included.

The few Egyptian tales that have survived may date back as early as the Thirtieth Century B.C. So far as can be determined, they are indigenously Egyptian, having Egyptian names, backgrounds, and customs. They are not only an invaluable commentary on the lives of the men of those times, but also genuinely moving and interesting stories.

The tales from Egypt possess an extraordinary interest in that they are the very earliest examples that we possess. That they were the earliest in order of composition is naturally an open question: before the year 3000 B.C. we can only conjecture. How many thousands of years before that time the plots were invented we cannot know, but the art with which *The Two Brothers* and *Setna and the Magic Book* are contrived indicates that they are comparatively late products.

By the time Egypt was conquered by Alexander the Great, the ancient literature of the country had been superseded.

THE TWO BROTHERS

(ANPU AND BATA)

(Anonymous: about 1400 B.C.)

THE manuscript of this story, one of the oldest in the world, came from the workshop of the scribe Anena, who flourished in the reigns of Rameses II, Menephtah, and Setui II. The work of an unknown author, it is one of the finest examples of the short story in existence. The theme, which has been used numberless times, is easily recognizable as that of the story of Potiphar's wife. It has also been used in *The History of Prince Amziad and Prince Aisad* in *The Arabian Nights*, and later by Dante in *The Divine Comedy*.

As in all great art, we are here impressed by the modernity of the author's attitude, which is only another way of saying that he understood his characters and was an accomplished artist.

The translation here used is that by William Flinders Petrie in *Egyptian Tales*, Vol. 2, published in 1895 by Methuen & Co., by whose permission it is here reprinted. The original manuscript is a part of the so-called Madame d'Orbiney Papyrus. There is no title in the original story, but the transcriber has named it *Anpu and Bata*.

THE TWO BROTHERS

(ANPU AND BATA)

ONCE there were two brethren, of one mother and one father; Anpu was the name of the elder, and Bata was the name of the younger. Now, as for Anpu he had a house, and he had a wife. But his little brother was to him as it were a son; he it was who made for him his clothes; he it was who followed behind his oxen to the fields; he it was who did the plowing; he it was who harvested the corn; he it was who did for him all the matters that were in the field. Behold, his younger brother grew to be an excellent worker, there was not his equal in the whole land; behold, the spirit of a god was in him.

Now after this the younger brother followed his oxen in his daily manner; and every evening he turned again to the house, laden with all the herbs of the field, with milk and with wood, and with all things of the field. And he put them down before his elder brother, who was sitting with his wife; and he drank and ate, and he lay down in his stable with the cattle. And at the dawn of day he took bread which he had baked, and laid it before his elder brother; and he took with him his bread to the field, and he drave his cattle to pasture in the fields. And as he walked behind his cattle, they said to him, "Good is the herbage which is in that place"; and he listened to all that they said, and he took them to the good place which they desired. And the cattle which were before him became exceeding excellent, and they multiplied greatly.

Now at the time of plowing his elder brother said unto him: "Let us make ready for ourselves a goodly yoke of oxen for plowing, for the land has come out from the water: it is fit for plowing. Moreover, do thou come to the field with corn, for we will begin the plowing in the morrow morning." Thus said he to him; and his younger brother did all things as his elder brother had spoken unto him to do them.

And when the morn was come, they went to the fields with their things; and their hearts were pleased exceedingly with their task in the beginning of their work. And it came to pass after this that as they were in the field they stopped for corn, and he sent his younger brother, saying, "Haste thou, bring to us corn from the farm." And the younger brother found the wife of his elder brother, as she was sitting tying her hair. He said to her: "Get up, and give to me corn, that I may run to the field, for my elder brother hastened me; do not delay." She said to him: "Go, open the bin, and thou shalt take to thyself according to thy will, that I may not drop my locks of hair while I dress them."

The youth went into the stable; he took a large measure, for he desired to take much corn; he loaded it with wheat and barley; and he went out carrying it. She said to him, "How much of the corn that is wanted, is that which is on thy shoulder?" He said to her: "Three bushels of barley, and two of wheat, in all five; these are what are upon my shoulder." Thus said he to her. And she conversed with him, saying, "There is great strength in thee, for I see thy might every day." And her heart knew him with the knowledge of youth. And she arose and came to him, and conversed with him, saying, "Come, stay with me, and it shall be well for thee, and I will make for thee beautiful garments." Then the youth became like a panther of the south with fury at the evil speech which she had made to him; and she feared greatly. And he spake unto her, saying: "Behold, thou art to me as a mother, thy husband is to me as a father, for he who is elder than I has brought me up. What is this wickedness that thou hast said to me? Say it not to me again. For I will not tell it to any man, for I will not let it be uttered by the mouth of any man." He lifted up his burden, and he went to the field and came to his elder brother; and they took up their work, to labor at their task.

Now afterward, at eventime, his elder brother was returning to his house; and the younger brother was following after his oxen, and he loaded himself with all the things of the field; and he brought his oxen before him, to make them lie down in their stable which was in the farm. And behold the wife of the elder brother was afraid for the words which she had said. She took a parcel of fat, she became like one who is evilly beaten, desiring to say to her husband, "It is thy younger brother who has done this wrong." Her husband returned in the even, as was his wont of every day; he came unto his house; he found his wife ill of violence; she did not give him water upon his hands as he used to have, she did not make a light before him, his house was in darkness, and she was lying very sick. Her husband said to her, "Who has spoken with thee?" Behold she said: "No one has spoken with me except thy younger brother. When he came to take for thee corn he found me sitting alone; he said to me, 'Come, let us stay together, tie up thy hair.' Thus spake he to me. I did not listen to him, but thus spake I to him: 'Behold, am I not thy mother, is not thy elder brother to thee as a father?' And he feared, and he beat me to stop me from making report to thee, and if thou lettest him live I shall die. Now behold he is coming in the evening; and I complain of these wicked words, for he would have done this even in daylight."

And the elder brother became as a panther of the south; he sharpened his knife; he took it in his hand; he stood behind the door of his stable to slay his younger brother as he came in the evening to bring his cattle into the stable.

Now the sun went down, and he loaded himself with herbs in his daily manner. He came, and his foremost cow entered the stable, and she said to her keeper, "Behold thou thy elder brother standing before thee with his knife to slay thee; flee from before him." He heard what his first cow had said; and the next entering, she also said likewise. He looked beneath the door of the stable; he saw the feet of his elder brother; he was standing behind the door, and his knife was in his hand. He cast down his load to the ground, and betook himself to flee swiftly; and his elder brother pursued after him with his knife. Then the younger brother cried out unto Ra Harakhti, saying, "My good Lord! Thou art he who divides the evil from the good." And Ra stood and heard all his cry; and Ra made a wide water between him and his elder brother, and it was full of crocodiles; and the one brother was on one bank, and the other on the other bank; and the elder brother smote twice on his hands at not slaying him. Thus did he. And the younger brother called to the elder on the bank, saying: "Stand still until the dawn of day; and when Ra ariseth, I shall judge with thee before him, and he discerneth between the good and the evil. For I shall not be with thee any more forever; I shall not be in the place in which thou art; I shall go to the valley of the acacia."

Now when the land was lightened, and the next day appeared, Ra Harakhti arose, and one looked unto the other. And the youth spake with his elder brother, saying: "Wherefore camest thou after me to slay me in craftiness, when thou didst not hear the words of my mouth? For I am thy brother in truth, and thou art to me as a father, and thy wife even as a mother: is it not so? Verily, when I was sent to bring for us corn, thy wife said to me, 'Come, stay with me'; for behold this has been turned over unto thee into another wise." And he caused him to understand of all that happened with him and his wife. And he swore an oath by Ra Harakhti, saying, "Thy coming to slay me by deceit with thy knife was an abomination." Then the youth took a knife, and cut off of his flesh, and cast it into the water, and the fish swallowed it. He failed; he became faint; and his elder brother cursed his own heart greatly; he stood weeping for him afar off; he knew not how to pass over to where his younger brother was, because of the crocodiles. And the younger brother called unto him, saying: "Whereas thou hast devised an evil thing, wilt thou not also devise a good thing, even like that which I would do unto thee? When thou goest to thy house thou must look to thy cattle, for I shall not stay in the place where thou art; I am going to the valley of the acacia. And now as to what thou shalt do for me; it is even that thou shalt come to seek after me, if thou perceivest a matter, namely, that there are things happening unto me. And this is what shall come to pass, that I shall draw out my soul, and I shall put it upon the top of the flowers of the acacia, and when the acacia is cut down, and it falls to the ground, and thou comest to seek for it, if thou searchest for it seven years do not let thy heart be wearied. For thou wilt find it, and thou must put it in a cup of cold water, and expect that I shall live again, that I may make answer to what has been done wrong. And thou shalt know of this, that is to say, that things are happening to me, when one shall give to thee a cup of beer in thy hand, and it shall be troubled; stay not then, for verily it shall come to pass with thee."

And the youth went to the valley of the acacia; and his elder brother went unto his house; his hand was laid on his head, and he cast dust on his head; he came to his house, and he slew his wife, he cast her to the dogs, and he sat in mourning for his younger brother.

Now many days after these things, the younger brother was in the valley of the acacia; there was none with him; he spent his time in hunting the beasts of the desert, and he came back in the even to lie down under the acacia, which bore his soul upon the topmost flower. And after this he built himself a tower with his own hands, in the valley of the acacia; it was full of all good things, that he might provide for himself a home.

And he went out from his tower, and he met the Nine Gods, who were walking forth to look upon the whole land. The Nine Gods talked one with another, and they said unto him: "Ho! Bata, bull of the Nine Gods, art thou remaining alone? Thou hast left thy village for the wife of Anpu, thy elder brother. Behold his wife is slain. Thou hast given him an answer to all that was transgressed against thee." And their hearts were vexed for him exceedingly. And Ra Harakhti said to Khnumu, "Behold, frame thou a woman for Bata, that he may not remain alive alone." And Khnumu made for him a mate to dwell with him. She was more beautiful in her limbs than any woman who is in the whole land. The essence of every god was in her. The seven Hathors came to see her: they said with one mouth, "She will die a sharp death."

And Bata loved her very exceedingly, and she dwelt in his house; he passed his time in hunting the beasts of the desert, and brought and laid them before her. He said: "Go not outside, lest the sea seize thee; for I cannot rescue thee from it, for I am a woman like thee; my soul is placed on the head of the flower of the acacia; and if another find it, I must fight with him." And he opened unto her his heart in all its nature.

Now after these things Bata went to hunt in his daily manner. And the young girl went to walk under the acacia which was by the side of her house. Then the sea saw her, and cast its waves up after her. She betook herself to flee from before it. She entered her house. And the sea called unto the acacia, saying, "Oh, would that I could seize her!" And the acacia brought a lock from her hair, and the sea carried it to Egypt, and dropped it in the place of the fullers of Pharaoh's linen. The smell of the lock of hair entered into the clothes of Pharaoh; and they were wroth with the fullers of Pharaoh, saying, "The smell of ointment is in the clothes of Pharaoh." And the people were rebuked every day, they knew not what they should do. And the chief fuller of Pharaoh walked by the bank, and his heart was very evil within him after the daily quarrel with him. He stood still, he stood upon the sand opposite to the lock of hair, which was in the water, and he made one enter into the water and bring it to him; and there was found in it a smell, exceeding sweet. He took it to Pharaoh; and they brought the scribes and the wise men, and they said unto Pharaoh: "This lock of hair belongs to a daughter of Ra Harakhti: the essence of every god is in her, and it is a tribute to thee from another land. Let messengers go to every strange land to seek her: and as for the messenger who shall go to the valley of the acacia, let many men go with him to bring her." Then said his Majesty, "Excellent exceedingly is what has been said to us"; and they sent them. And many days after these things the people who were sent to strange lands came to give report unto the King: but there came not those who went to the valley of the acacia, for Bata had slain them, but let one of them return to give a report to the King. His Majesty sent many men and soldiers, as well as horsemen, to bring her back. And there was a woman among them, and to her had been given in her hand beautiful ornaments of a woman. And the girl came back with her, and they rejoiced over her in the whole land.

And his Majesty loved her exceedingly, and raised her to high estate; and he spake unto her that she should tell him concerning her husband. And she said, "Let the acacia be cut down, and let one chop it up." And they sent men and soldiers with their weapons to cut down the acacia; and they came to the acacia, and they cut the flower upon which was the soul of Bata, and he fell dead suddenly.

And when the next day came, and the earth was lightened, the acacia was cut down. And Anpu, the elder brother of Bata, entered his house, and washed his hands; and one gave him a cup of beer, and it became troubled; and one gave him another of wine, and the smell of it was evil. Then he took his staff, and his sandals, and likewise his clothes, with his weapons of war; and he betook himself forth to the valley of the acacia. He entered the tower of his younger brother, and he found him lying upon his mat; he was dead. And he wept when he saw his younger brother verily lying dead. And he went out to seek the soul of his younger brother under the acacia tree, under which his younger brother lay in the evening. He spent three years in seeking for it, but found it not. And when he began the fourth year, he desired in his heart to return into Egypt; he said, "I will go to-morrow morn." Thus spake he in his heart.

Now when the land lightened, and the next day appeared, he was walking under the acacia; he was spending his time in seeking it. And he returned in the evening, and labored at seeking it again. He found a seed. He returned with it. Behold this was the soul of his younger brother. He brought a cup of cold water, and he cast the seed into it: and he sat down, as he was wont. Now when the night came his soul sucked up the water; Bata shuddered in all his limbs, and he looked on his elder brother; his soul was in the cup. Then Anpu took the cup of cold water, in which the soul of his younger brother was; Bata drank it, his soul stood again in its place, and he became as he had been. They embraced each other, and they conversed together.

And Bata said to his elder brother: "Behold I am to become as a great bull, which bears every good mark; no one knoweth its history, and thou must sit upon my back. When the sun arises I shall be in the place where my wife is, that I may return answer to her; and thou must take me to the place where the King is. For all good things shall be done for thee; for one shall lade thee with silver and gold, because thou bringest me to Pharaoh, for I become a great marvel, and they shall rejoice for me in all the land. And thou shalt go to thy village."

And when the land was lightened, and the next day appeared, Bata became in the form which he had told to his elder brother. And Anpu sat upon his back until the dawn. He came to the place where the King was, and they made his Majesty to know of him; he saw him, and he was exceeding joyful with him. He made for him great offerings, saying, "This is a great wonder which has come to pass." There were rejoicings over him in the whole land. They presented unto him silver and gold for his elder brother, who went and stayed in his village. They gave to the bull many men and many things, and Pharaoh loved him exceedingly above all that is in this land.

And many days after these things, the bull entered the purified place; he stood in the place where the princess was; he began to speak with her, saying, "Behold, I am alive indeed." And she said to him, "And, pray, who art thou?" He said to her, "I am Bata. I perceived when thou causedst that they should destroy the acacia of Pharaoh, which was my abode, that I might not be suffered to live. Behold, I am alive indeed, I am as an ox." Then the princess feared exceedingly for the words that her husband had spoken to her. And he went out from the purified place.

And his Majesty was sitting, making a good day with her: she was at the table of his Majesty, and the King was exceeding pleased with her. And she said to his Majesty, "Swear to me by God, saying, 'What thou shalt say, I will obey it for thy sake.'" He hearkened unto all that she said, even this. "Let me eat of the liver of the ox, because he is fit for naught." Thus spake she to him. And the King was exceeding sad at her words, the heart of Pharaoh grieved him greatly. And after the land was lightened, and the next day appeared, they proclaimed a great feast with offerings to the ox. And the King sent one of the chief butchers of his Majesty, to cause the ox to be sacrificed. And when he was sacrificed, as he was upon the shoulders of the people, he shook his neck, and he threw two drops of blood over against the two doors of his Majesty. The one fell upon the one side, on the great door of Pharaoh, and the other upon the other door. They grew as two great Persea trees, and each of them was excellent.

And one went to tell unto his Majesty, "Two great Persea trees have grown, as a great marvel of his Majesty, in the night by the side of the great gate of his Majesty." And there was rejoicing for them in all the land, and there were offerings made to them.

And when the days were multiplied after these things, his Majesty was adorned with the blue crown, with garlands of flowers on his neck, and he was upon the chariot of pale gold, and he went out from the palace to behold the Persea trees: the princess also was going out with horses behind his Majesty. And his Majesty sat beneath one of the Persea trees, and it spake thus with his wife: "Oh, thou deceitful one, I am Bata, I am alive, though I have been evilly entreated. I knew who caused the acacia to be cut down by Pharaoh at my dwelling. I then became an ox, and thou causedst that I should be killed."

And many days after these things the princess stood at the table of Pharaoh, and the King was pleased with her. And she said to his Majesty, "Swear to me by God, saying, 'That which the princess shall say to me I will obey it for her.'" And he hearkened unto all she said. And he commanded, "Let these two Persea trees be cut down, and let them be made into goodly planks." And he hearkened unto all she said. And after this his Majesty sent skilful craftsmen, and they cut down the Persea trees of Pharaoh; and the princess, the royal wife, was standing looking on, and they did all that was in her heart unto the trees. But a chip flew up, and it entered into the mouth of the princess; she swallowed it, and after many days she bore a son. And one went to tell his Majesty, "There is born to thee a son." And they brought him, and gave to him a nurse and servants; and there were rejoicings in the whole land. And the King sat making a merry day, as they were about the naming of him, and his Majesty loved him exceedingly at that moment, and the King raised him to be the royal son of Kush.

Now after the days had multiplied after these things, his Majesty made him heir of all the land. And many days after that, when he had fulfilled many years as heir, his Majesty flew up to heaven. And the heir said, "Let my great nobles of his Majesty be brought before me, that I may make them to know all that has happened to me." And they brought also before him his wife, and he judged with her before him, and they agreed with him. They brought to him his elder brother; he made him hereditary prince in all his land. He was thirty years King of Egypt, and he died, and his elder brother stood in his place on the day of burial.

Excellently finished in peace, for the ka of the scribe of the treasury Kagabu, of the treasury of Pharaoh, and for the scribe Hora, and the scribe Meremapt. Written by the scribe Anena, the owner of this roll. He who speaks against this roll, may Tahuti smite him.

SETNA AND THE MAGIC BOOK

(Anonymous: about 1400 B.C.)

THE manuscript of this story was found during the Nineteenth Century in the tomb of a Coptic monk. Nothing is known of the author, but it is assumed that he lived not long after the time of the probable origin of the Egyptian short story. *Setna and the Magic Book* is one of those wonder tales that have from time immemorial evoked the admiration of the world, and particularly of the Orientals. Whether or not the Egyptians actually believed all they were told in a fairy tale is an idle conjecture: but it seems probable that the strange happenings described in this story were accepted by many. Even the present age of science has not entirely banished a belief in magic: some of the finest of modern tales are based upon an ineradicable belief in the supernatural.

The translation here used is that by William Flinders Petrie in *Egyptian Tales*, Vol. 2, published in 1895 by Methuen and Co., by whose permission it is here reprinted. The original manuscript is a part of the so-called Doulaq Papyrus. There is no title to the original story, the title here used being that given it by the transcriber.

SETNA AND THE MAGIC BOOK

THE mighty King User.maat.ra (Rameses the Great) had a son named Setna Kha.em.uast who was a great scribe, and very learned in all the ancient writings. And he heard that the magic book of Thoth, by which a man may enchant heaven and earth, and know the language of all birds and beasts, was buried in the cemetery of Memphis. And he went to search for it with his brother An.he.hor.eru; and when they found the tomb of the King's son, Na.nefer.ka.ptah, son of the King of Upper and Lower Egypt, Mer.neb.ptah, Setna opened it and went in.

Now in the tomb was Na.nefer.ka.ptah, and with him was the *ka* of his wife Ahura; for though she was buried at Koptos, her *ka* dwelt at Memphis with her husband, whom she loved. And Setna saw them seated before their offerings, and the book lay between them. And Na.nefer.ka.ptah said to Setna, "Who are you that break into my tomb in this way?" He said, "I am Setna, son of the great King User.maat.ra, living forever, and I come for that book which I see between you." And Na.nefer.ka.ptah said, "It cannot be given to you." Then said Setna, "But I will carry it away by force."

Then Ahura said to Setna, "Do not take this book; for it will bring trouble on you, as it has upon us. Listen to what we have suffered for it."

AHURA'S TALE

"We were the two children of the King Mer.neb.ptah, and he loved us very much, for he had no others; and Na.nefer.ka.ptah was in his palace as heir over all the land. And when we were grown, the King said to the Queen, 'I will marry Na.nefer.ka.ptah to the daughter of a general, and Ahura to the son of another general.' And the Queen said, 'No; he is the heir, let him marry his sister, like the heir of a king; none other is fit for him.' And the King said, 'That is not fair; they had better be married to the children of the general.'

"And the Queen said, 'It is you who are not dealing rightly with me.' And the King answered, 'If I have no more than these two children, is it right that they should marry one another? I will marry Na.nefer.ka.ptah to the daughter of an officer, and Ahura to the son of another officer. It has often been done so in our family.'

"And at a time when there was a great feast before the King, they came to fetch me to the feast. And I was very troubled, and did not behave as I used to do. And the King said to me, 'Ahura, have you sent someone to me about this sorry matter, saying, "Let me be married to my elder brother"?' I said to him, 'Well, let me marry the son of an officer, and he marry the daughter of another officer, as it often happens so in our family.' I laughed, and the King laughed. And the King told the steward of the palace, 'Let them take Ahura to the house of Na.nefer.ka.ptah to-night, and all kinds of good things with her.' So they brought me as a wife to the house of Na.nefer.ka.ptah; and the King ordered them to give me presents of silver and gold, and things from the palace.

"And Na.nefer.ka.ptah passed a happy time with me, and received all the presents from the palace; and we loved one another. And when I expected a child, they told the King, and he was most heartily glad; and he sent me many things, and a present of the best silver and gold and linen. And when the time came, I bore this little child that is before you. And they gave him the name of Mer-ab, and registered him in the book of the 'House of life.'

"And when my brother Na.nefer.ka.ptah went to the cemetery of Memphis, he did nothing on earth but read the writings that are in the catacombs of the kings, and the tablets of the 'House of life,' and the inscriptions that are seen on the monuments, and he worked hard on the writings. And there was a priest there called Nesi-ptah; and as Na.nefer.ka.ptah went into a temple to pray, it happened that he went behind this priest, and was reading the inscriptions that were on the chapels of the gods. And the priest mocked him and laughed. So Na.nefer.ka.ptah said to him, 'Why are you laughing at me?' And he replied, 'I was not laughing at you, or if I happened to do so, it was at your reading writings that are worthless. If you wish so much to read writings, come to me, and I will bring you to the place where the book is which Thoth himself wrote with his own hand, and which will bring you to the gods. When you read but two pages in this you will enchant the heaven, the earth, the abyss, the mountains, and the sea; you shall know what the birds of the sky and the crawling things are saying; you shall see the fishes of the deep, for a divine power is there to bring them up out of the depth. And when you read the second page, if you are in the world of ghosts, you will become again in the shape you were in on earth. You will see the sun shining in the sky, with all the gods, and the full moon.'

"And Na.nefer.ka.ptah said; 'By the life of the King! Tell me of anything you want done, and I'll do it for you, if you will only send me where this book is.' And the priest answered Na.nefer.ka.ptah, 'If you want to go to the place where the book is, you must give me 100 pieces of silver for my funeral, and provide that they shall bury me as a rich priest.' So Na.nefer.ka.ptah called his lad and told him to give the priest 100 pieces of silver; and he made them do as he wished, even everything that he asked for. Then the priest said to Na.nefer.ka.ptah: 'This book is in the middle of the river at Koptos, in an iron box; in the iron box is a bronze box; in the bronze box is a sycamore box; in the sycamore box is an ivory and ebony box; in the ivory and ebony box is a silver box; in the silver box is a golden box, and in that is the book. It is twisted all round with snakes and scorpions and all the other crawling things around the box in which the book is; and there is a deathless snake by the box.' And when the priest told Na.nefer.ka.ptah, he did not know where on earth he was, he was so much delighted.

"And when he came from the temple he told me all that had happened to him. And he said: 'I shall go to Koptos, for I must fetch this book; I will not stay any longer in the north.' And I said, 'Let me dissuade you, for you prepare sorrow and you will bring me into trouble in the Thebaid.' And I laid my hand on Na.nefer.ka.ptah, to keep him from going to Koptos, but he would not listen to me; and he went to the King, and told the King all that the priest had said. The King asked him, 'What is it that you want?' and he replied, 'Let them give me the royal boat with its belongings, for I will go to the south with Ahura and her little boy Mer-ab, and fetch this book without delay.' So they gave him the royal boat with its belongings, and we went with him to the haven, and sailed from there up to Koptos.

"Then the priests of Isis of Koptos, and the high-priest of Isis, came down to us without waiting, to meet Na.nefer.ka.ptah, and their wives also came to me. We went into the temple of Isis and Harpokrates; and Na.nefer.ka.ptah brought an ox, a goose, and some wine, and made a burnt-offering and a drink-offering before Isis of Koptos and Harpokrates. They brought us to a very fine house, with all good things; and Na.nefer.ka.ptah spent four days there and feasted with the priests of Isis of Koptos, and the wives of the priests of Isis also made holiday with me.

"And the morning of the fifth day came; and Na.nefer.ka.ptah called a priest to him, and made a magic cabin that was full of men and tackle. He put the spell upon it, and put life in it, and gave them breath, and sank it in the water. He filled the royal boat with sand, and took leave of me, and sailed from the haven: and I sat by the river at Koptos that I might see what would become of him. And he said, 'Workmen, work for me, even at the place where the book is.' And they toiled by night and by day; and when they had reached it in three days, he threw the sand out, and made a shoal in the river. And then he found on it entwined serpents and scorpions and all kinds of crawling things around the box in which the book was; and by it he found a deathless snake around the box. And he laid the spell upon the entwined serpents and scorpions and all kinds of crawling things which were around the box, that they should not come out. And he went to the deathless snake, and fought with him, and killed him; but he came to life again, and took a new form. He then fought again with him a second time; but he came to life again, and took a third form. He then cut him in two parts, and put sand between the parts, that he should not appear again.

"Na.nefer.ka.ptah then went to the place where he found the box. He uncovered a box of iron, and opened it; he found then a box of bronze, and opened that; then he found a box of sycamore wood, and opened that; again, he found a box of ivory and ebony, and opened that; yet, he found a box of silver, and opened that; and then he found a box of gold; he opened that, and found the book in it. He took the book from the golden box, and read a page of spells from it. He enchanted the heaven and the earth, the abyss, the mountains, and the sea; he knew what the birds of the sky, the fish of the deep, and the beasts of the hills all said. He read another page of the spells, and saw the sun shining in the sky, with all the gods, the full moon, and the stars in their shapes; he saw the fishes of the deep, for a divine power was present that brought them up from the water. He then read the spell upon the workmen that he had made, and taken from the haven, and said to them, 'Work for me, back to the place from which I came.' And they toiled night and day, and so he came back to the place where I sat by the river of Koptos; I had not drunk nor eaten anything, and had done nothing on earth, but sat like one who is gone to the grave.

"I then told Na.nefer.ka.ptah that I wished to see this book, for which we had taken so much trouble. He gave the book into my hands; and when I read a page of the spells in it I also enchanted heaven and earth, the abyss, the mountains, and the sea. I also knew what the birds of the sky, the fishes of the deep, and the beasts of the hills all said. I read another page of the spells, and I saw the sun shining in the sky with all the gods, the full moon, and the stars in their shapes; I saw the fishes of the deep, for a divine power was present that brought them up from the water. As I could not write, I asked Na.nefer.ka.ptah, who was a good writer, and a very learned one; he called for a new piece of papyrus, and wrote on it all that was in the book before him. He dipped it in beer, and washed it off in the liquid; for he knew that if it were washed off, and he drank it, he would know all that there was in the writing.

"We returned back to Koptos the same day, and made a feast before Isis of Koptos and Harpokrates. We then went to the haven and sailed, and went northward of Koptos. And as we went on Thoth discovered all that Na.nefer.ka.ptah had done with the book; and Thoth hastened to tell Ra, and said, 'Now know that my book and my revelation are with Na.nefer.ka.ptah, son of the King Mer.neb.ptah. He has forced himself into my place, and robbed it, and seized my box with the writings, and killed my guards who protected it.' And Ra replied to him, 'He is before you, take him and all his kin.' He sent a power from heaven with the command, 'Do not let Na.nefer.ka.ptah return safe to Memphis with all his kin.' And after this hour, the little boy Mer-ab, going out from the awning of the royal boat, fell into the river: he called on Ra, and everybody who was on the bank raised a cry. Na.-nefer.ka.ptah went out of the cabin, and read the spell over him; he brought his body up because a divine power brought him to the surface. He read another spell over him, and made him tell of all that happened to him, and of what Thoth had said before Ra.

"We turned back with him to Koptos. We brought him to the Good House, we fetched the people to him, and made one embalm him; and we buried him in his coffin in the cemetery of Koptos like a great and noble person.

"And Na.nefer.ka.ptah, my brother, said: 'Let us go down, let us not delay, for the King has not yet heard of what has happened to him, and his heart will be sad about it.' So we went to the haven, we sailed, and did not stay to the north of Koptos. When we were come to the place where the little boy Mer-ab had fallen into the water, I went out from the awning of the royal boat, and I fell into the river. They called Na.nefer.ka.ptah, and he came out from the cabin of the royal boat; he read a spell over me, and brought my body up, because a divine power brought me to the surface. He drew me out, and read the spell over me, and made me tell him of all that had happened to me, and of what Thoth had said before Ra. Then he turned back with me to Koptos, he brought me to the Good House, he fetched the people to me, and made one embalm me, as great and noble people are buried, and laid me in the tomb where Mer-ab my young child was.

"He turned to the haven, and sailed down, and delayed not in the north of Koptos. When he was come to the place where we fell into the river, he said to his heart: 'Shall I not better turn back again to Koptos, that I may lie by them? For, if not, when I go down to Memphis, and the King asks after his children, what shall I say to him? Can I tell him, "I have taken your children to the Thebaid, and killed them, while I remained alive, and I have come to Memphis still alive"?' Then he made them bring him a linen cloth of striped byssus; he made a band, and bound the book firmly, and tied it upon him. Na.nefer.ka.-ptah then went out of the awning of the royal boat and fell into the river. He cried on Ra; and all those who were on the bank made an outcry, saying: 'Great woe! Sad woe! Is he lost, that good scribe and able man that has no equal?'

"The royal boat went on, without anyone on earth knowing where Na.nefer.ka.ptah was. It went on to Memphis, and they told all this to the King. Then the King went down to the royal boat in mourning, and all the soldiers and high-priests of Ptah were in mourning, and all the officials and courtiers. And when he saw Na.nefer.ka.ptah, who was in the inner cabin of the royal boat—from his rank of high scribe—he lifted him up. And they saw the book by him; and the King said, 'Let one hide this book that is with him.' And the officers of the King, the priests of Ptah, and the high-priest of Ptah, said to the King, 'Our Lord, may the King live as long as the sun! Na.nefer.ka.ptah was a good scribe, and a very skilful man.' And the King had him laid in his Good House to the sixteenth day, and then had him wrapped to the thirty-fifth day, and laid him out to the seventieth day, and then had him put in his grave in his resting-place.

"I have now told you the sorrow which has come upon us because of this book for which you ask, saying, 'Let it be given to me.' You have no claim to it; and, indeed, for the sake of it, we have given up our life on earth."

And Setna said to Ahura, "Give me the book which I see between you and Na.nefer.ka.ptah; for if you do not I will take it by force." Then Na.nefer.ka.ptah rose from his seat and said: "Are you Setna, to whom my wife has told of all these blows of fate, which you have not suffered? Can you take this book by your skill as a good scribe? If, indeed, you can play games with me, let us play a game, then, of 52 points." And Setna said, "I am ready," and the board and its pieces were put before him. And Na.nefer.ka.ptah won a game from Setna; and he put the spell upon him, and defended himself with the game board that was before him, and sunk him into the ground above his feet. He did the same at the second game, and won it from Setna, and sunk him into the ground to his waist. He did the same at the third game, and made him sink into the ground up to his ears. Then Setna struck Na.nefer.ka.ptah a great blow with his hand. And Setna called his brother An.he.hor.eru and said to him, "Make haste and go up upon earth, and tell the King all that has happened to me, and bring me the talisman of my father Ptah, and my magic books."

And he hurried up upon earth, and told the King all that had happened to Setna. The King said, "Bring him the talisman of his father Ptah, and his magic books." And An.he.hor.eru hurried down into the tomb; he laid the talisman on Setna, and he sprang up again immediately. And then Setna reached out his hand for the book, and took it. Then—as Setna went out from the tomb—there went a Light before him, and Darkness behind him. And Ahura wept at him, and she said: "Glory to the King of Darkness! Hail to the King of Light! all power is gone from the tomb." But Na.nefer.ka.ptah said to Ahura: "Do not let your heart be sad; I will make him bring back this book, with a forked stick in his hand, and a fire-pan on his head." And Setna went out from the tomb, and it closed behind him as it was before.

Then Setna went to the King, and told him everything that had happened to him with the book. And the King said to Setna, "Take back the book to the grave of Na.nefer.ka.ptah, like a prudent man, or else he will make you bring it with a forked stick in your hand, and a fire-pan on your head." But Setna would not listen to him; and when Setna had unrolled the book he did nothing on earth but read it to everybody.

After that it happened one day, when Setna was walking near the temple of Ptah, he saw a woman of such beauty that another could not be found to equal her. On her there was much gold, and with her were fifty-two servants. From the time that Setna beheld her, he no longer knew the part of the world he lived in. He called his page, saying, "Do not delay going to the place where that woman is and finding out who she is." The young page made no delay. He addressed the maidservant who walked behind her, and questioned her, "What person is that?" She said to him, "She is Tbubui, daughter of the prophet of Bastit, who now goes to make her prayer before Ptah." When the young man had returned to Setna, he recounted all the words she had said to him without exception. Setna said to the young man, "Go and say thus to the maidservant, 'Setna-Khamois, son of the Pharaoh Usimares it is who sends me, saying, "I will give thee ten pieces of gold that thou mayest pass an hour with me. If there is necessity to have recourse to violence he will do it, and he will take thee to a hidden place, where no one in the world will find thee."' When the young man had returned to the place where Tbubui was, he addressed the maidservant, and spake with her, but she exclaimed against his words, as though it were an insult to speak them. Tbubui said to the young man, "Cease to speak to that wretched girl; come and speak to me." The young man approached the place where Tbubui was; he said to her, "I will give thee ten pieces of gold if thou wilt pass an hour with Setna-Khamois, the son of Pharaoh Usimares. If there is necessity to have recourse to violence, he will do so, and will take thee to a hidden place where no one in the world will find thee." Tbubui said, "Go, say to Setna, 'I am a hierodule, I am no mean person; if thou dost desire to have thy pleasure of me, thou shalt come to Bubastis into my house. All will be ready there, and thou shalt have thy pleasure of me, and no one in the world shall know it, and I shall not have acted like a woman of the streets." When the page had returned to Setna, he repeated to him all the words that she had said without exception, and he said, "Lo, I am satisfied." But all who were with Setna began to curse.

Setna caused a boat to be fetched, he embarked, and delayed not to arrive at Bubastis. He went to the west of the town, until he came to a house that was very high; it had a wall all round it, it had a garden on the north side, there was a flight of steps in front of it. Setna inquired saying, "Whose is this house?" They said to him, "It is the house of Tbubui." Setna entered the grounds, and he marveled at the pavilion situated in the garden while they told Tbubui; she came down, she took the hand of Setna, and she said to him, "By my life! the journey to the house of the priest of Bastit, lady of Ankhutaui, at which thou art arrived, is very pleasant to me. Come up with me." Setna went up by the stairway of the house with Tbubui. He found the upper story of the house sanded and powdered with sand and powder of real lapis lazuli and real turquoise. There were several beds there, spread with stuffs of royal linen, and also many cups of gold on a stand. They filled a golden cup with wine and placed it in the hand of Setna and Tbubui said to him, "Will it please thee to rest thyself?" He said to her, "That is not what I wish to do." They put scented wood on the fire, they brought perfumes of the kind that are supplied to Pharaoh, and Setna made a happy day with Tbubui. "Let us accomplish that for which we have come here." She said to him, "Thou shalt arrive at thy house, that where thou art. But for me, I am a hierodule, I am no mean person. If thou desirest to have thy pleasure of me, thou shalt make me a contract of sustenance, and a contract of money on all the things and all the goods that are thine." He said to her, "Let the scribe of the school be brought." He was brought immediately, and Setna caused to be made in favor of Tbubui a contract for maintenance, and he made her in writing a dowry of all the things, all the goods that were his. An hour passed, one came to say this to Setna, "Thy children are below." He said, "Let them be brought up." Tbubui arose; she put on a robe of fine linen and Setna beheld all her limbs through it, and his desire increased yet more than before. Setna said to Tbubui, "Let us accomplish now that for which I came." She said to him, "Thou shalt arrive at thy house, that where thou art. But for me, I am a hierodule; I am no mean person. If thou desirest to have thy pleasure of me, thou wilt cause thy children to subscribe to my writing that they may not seek a quarrel with my children on the subject of thy possessions." Setna had his children fetched and made them subscribe to the writing. Setna said to Tbubui, "Let me now accomplish that for which I came." She said to him, "Thou shalt arrive at thy house, that where thou art. But for me, I am a hierodule; I am no mean person. If thou dost desire to have thy pleasure of me, thou shalt cause thy children to be slain, so that they may not seek a quarrel with my children on account of thy possessions." Setna said, "Let the crime be committed on them of which the desire has entered thy heart." She caused the children of Setna to be slain before him, she had them thrown out below the window, to the dogs and cats, and they ate their flesh, and he heard them while he was drinking with Tbubui. Setna said to Tbubui, "Let us accomplish that for which we have come here, for all that thou hast said before me has been done for thee." She said to him, "Come into this chamber." Setna entered the chamber; he lay down on a bed of ivory and ebony, in order that his love might be rewarded, and Tbubui lay down by the side of Setna. He stretched out his hand to touch her; she opened her mouth widely and uttered a loud cry.

When Setna came to himself he was in a place of a furnace without any clothing on his back. After an hour Setna perceived a very big man standing on a platform, with quite a number of attendants beneath his feet, for he had the semblance of a Pharaoh. Setna was about to raise himself but he could not arise for shame, for he had no clothing on his back. This Pharaoh said, "Setna, what is the state in which you are?" He said, "It is Na.nefer.ka.ptah who has had all this done to me." This Pharaoh said, "Go to Memphis; thy children, lo! they wish for thee. Lo! they are standing before Pharaoh." Setna spake before this Pharaoh, "My great lord the king—mayest thou have the duration of Ra—how can I arrive at Memphis, for I have no raiment in the world on my back?" This Pharaoh called a page who was standing near him and commanded him to give a garment to Setna. This Pharaoh said, "Setna, go to Memphis. Thy children, behold they live, behold they are standing before the king."

So Setna went to Memphis, and embraced his children for that they were alive. And the King said to him, "Were you not drunk to do so?" Then Setna told all things that had happened with Tbubui and Na.nefer.ka.ptah. And the King said, "Setna, I have already lifted up my hand against you before, and said, 'He will kill you if you do not take back the book to the place you took it from.' But you have never listened to me till this hour. Now, then, take the book to Na.nefer.ka.ptah, with a forked stick in your hand, and a fire-pan on your head."

So Setna went out from before the King, with a forked stick in his hand, and a fire-pan on his head. He went down to the tomb in which was Na.nefer.ka.ptah. And Ahura said to him, "It is Ptah, the great god, that has brought you back safe." Na.nefer.ka.ptah laughed, and he said, "This is the business that I told you before." And when Setna had praised Na.nefer.ka.ptah, he found it as the proverb says, "The sun was in the whole tomb." And Ahura and Na.nefer.ka.ptah besought Setna greatly. And Setna said, "Na.nefer.ka.ptah, is it aught disgraceful (that you lay on me to do)?" And Na.nefer.ka.ptah said, "Setna, you know this, that Ahura and Mer-ab, her child, behold! they are in Koptos; bring them here into this tomb, by the skill of a good scribe. Let it be impressed upon you to take pains, and to go to Koptos to bring them here." Setna then went out from the tomb to the King, and told the King all that Na.nefer.ka.ptah had told him.

The King said, "Setna, go to Koptos and bring back Ahura and Mer-ab." He answered the King, "Let one give me the royal boat and its belongings." And they gave him the royal boat and its belongings, and he left the haven, and sailed without stopping till he came to Koptos.

And they made this known to the priests of Isis at Koptos and to the high-priest of Isis; and behold they came down to him, and gave him their hand to the shore. He went up with them and entered into the temple of Isis of Koptos and of Harpokrates. He ordered one to offer for him an ox, a goose, and some wine, and he made a burnt-offering and a drink-offering before Isis of Koptos and Harpokrates. He went to the cemetery of Koptos with the priests of Isis and the high-priest of Isis. They dug about for three days and three nights, for they searched even in all the catacombs which were in the cemetery of Koptos; they turned over the steles of the scribes of the "double house of life," and read the inscriptions that they found on them. But they could not find the resting-place of Ahura and Mer-ab.

Now Na.nefer.ka.ptah perceived that they could not find the resting-place of Ahura and her child Mer-ab. So he raised himself up as a venerable, very old ancient, and came before Setna. And Setna saw him, and Setna said to the ancient: "You look like a very old man; do you know where is the resting-place of Ahura and her child Mer-ab?" The ancient said to Setna: "It was told by the father of the father of my father to the father of my father, and the father of my father has told it to my father; the resting-place of Ahura and of her child Mer-ab is in a mound south of the town of Pehemato." And Setna said to the ancient, "Perhaps we may do damage to Pehemato, and you are ready to lead one to the town for the sake of that." The ancient replied to Setna: "If one listens to me, shall he therefore destroy the town of Pehemato! If they do not find Ahura and her child Mer-ab under the south corner of their town may I be disgraced." They attended to the ancient, and found the resting-place of Ahura and her child Mer-ab under the south corner of the town of Pehemato. Setna laid them in the royal boat to bring them as honored persons, and restored the town of Pehemato as it originally was. And Na.nefer.ka.ptah made Setna to know that it was he who had come to Koptos, to enable them to find out where the resting-place was of Ahura and her child Mer-ab.

So Setna left the haven in the royal boat, and sailed without stopping, and reached Memphis with all the soldiers who were with him. And when they told the King he came down to the royal boat. He took them as honored persons escorted to the catacombs, in which Na.nefer.ka.ptah was, and smoothed down the ground over them.

This is the completed writing of the tale of Setna Kha.em.uast, and Na.nefer.ka.ptah, and his wife Ahura, and their child Mer-ab. It was written in the thirty-fifth year, the month Tybi.

Ancient Greece

INTRODUCTION

THERE is no land without its story-tellers, and in the dawn of Hellenic civilization we find the half-legendary author of the *Iliad* and the *Odyssey* telling tales—some of them so long and elaborate as to be called epics, and some of them brief enough to be classed as short stories. Though the actual composition of the earliest Greek stories dates from a thousand or fifteen hundred years after the Egyptian tales, there is no doubt that they were sung or recited centuries before the great epics assumed the form in which they are now known.

The poet Hesiod, somewhat later than Homer, but before the opening of the Golden Age of Greek literature (Fifth Century, B.C.), inserted into his longer mythical and didactic works episodes which are, as a matter of fact, short stories, though they are inferior in workmanship to the ingenious tales with which Herodotus enlivens the pages of his fascinating *History*. Herodotus was much more of an artist than a mere recorder of facts. He was determined at all costs to make his work readable. Other and later historians strove to imitate him, and their books are full of anecdotes and episodes many of which might be extracted to demonstrate the gradual development of the form. Plutarch, in particular, was fond of relating incidents to illustrate the *Lives* of his heroes.

Though the fable probably originated in India, it was given a particular form in the so-called Beast Fable of the Greeks. This is a short story told in order to point a moral, in which respect it is not essentially different from most other stories, ancient and modern. It was in Greece that a collection of beast fables accumulated, and was attributed to a certain Æsop, of whom we have no authentic knowledge. That they are short and deal ostensibly with animals instead of human beings in no way prevents their inclusion in a collection of this sort. The best of them are masterpieces in the art of condensed narrative. Though the works attributed to Æsop are now lost, they have been preserved in translated or adapted form by the Latin fabulist, Phædrus.

It was after the close of the great epoch of Greek literature that the art of prose fiction arose in Greece. Antonius Diogenes, Xenophon of

Ephesus, Achilles Tatius, Lucian, Parthenius, Longus, and Heliodorus belong more especially among the writers of pure fiction. There were occasional exceptions, like Apollonius of Rhodes, who sought inspiration in the myths of the past, and developed the more or less crude incidents of the ancients into comely, if occasionally affected, stories. But the romance itself was originated by Xenophon of Ephesus, Longus, and Heliodorus, and later developed by Achilles Tatius and Chariton. Still, the short story as an independent form was apparently not recognized. In *The Robbers of Egypt*, which is the first chapter of Heliodorus' *Æthiopian Romance*, we find a complete and unified short story. The *Daphnis and Chloe* of Longus is an early example of the "long-short" story.

Long before the final extinction of Greek romance the Greek forms had been carried over into the Roman world, where they were to flourish for a time, disappear, and then a thousand years later bloom again under the touch of the Italians.

HOMER

(About 1000 B.C.)

THE first mention of Homer dates from the Seventh Century B.C., but when he lived, or indeed whether he ever lived at all, are questions that have never been solved. *The Iliad* and *The Odyssey* were probably composed about a thousand years before the Christian era. The short story, as we know it, was not of course a recognized literary form, but *Eumæus' Tale*, in *The Odyssey*, happens to be an excellent example. It is told to Odysseus by the old swineherd.

The present version, purposely reduced by the editors to more or less colloquial prose, is based upon three translations. There is no title in the original.

EUMÆUS' TALE

(From *The Odyssey*, Book XV)

"THERE is an island over beyond Ortygia—perchance thou hast heard tell of it—where the sun turns. It is a goodly island, though not very vast, with rich herds and flocks, and much grain and wine. There is no dearth, and no illness visits poor mortals. When men grow old there, Apollo of the Silver Bow, in company with Artemis, comes to them and kills them gently with his shafts. On the island are two cities, which divide all the land between them. My father was king over all, Ctesius son of Ormenus, a godlike man.

"To this land came the Phœnicians, famous sailors greedy for merchandise, bringing many things in their dark ship. There was in my father's palace a Phœnician woman, tall and lovely, and skilful in making beautiful things with her hands; her the Phœnicians deceived by their guile. As she was washing clothes near the hollow ship, one of them conquered her; love beguiles many women, even the noblest. The Phœnician asked her who she was and from what land, and she straightway showed him the high palace of my father, and said, 'I come from Sidon, rich in bronze, and am the daughter of the wealthy Arybas. The Taphians, who are pirates, seized me as I was coming from the fields, brought me to this land, and sold me for a great price to my present master.' Then he who had conquered her said in answer, 'Wouldst thou return once more to thy home with us, to see again the high palace of thy father, and see thy mother? They are yet alive, and are reputed to be wealthy.'

"Then the woman made answer to him and said, 'This may be, if you sailors will swear to bring me home safely.' Thus she answered, and the sailors swore as she bade them, and after they had sworn, the woman spake to them: 'Say naught now; let none of you speak to me when you see me in the street, or even by the well, lest it be known and told to the old man here, and he suspect me and tie me fast and bring death to you all. But keep in mind the plan, and hasten to bring your freight for the homeward voyage. When your ship is full laden, send a messenger quickly to the palace for me, and I will bring gold, all I can lay hand upon. And there is more, besides, that I would bring with me: I am nursing a child for my master, a darling boy who runs about with me; I would bring him with me on the ship. He should bring a high price, if you sell him among men of other lands and other speech.'

"Then she departed to the fair halls. But the sailors remained among us a whole year, and gathered great wealth for their hollow ship, and when it was laden and ready to sail, a messenger was sent to tell the woman. A crafty man with a golden and amber chain came to the halls of my father. My mother and the maidens in the palace were looking upon the chain and holding it, offering the man a price for it, while he made signs in silence to the woman. Then he betook himself to the hollow ship. The woman then took me by the hand and led me out of the house. At the doorway she found the cups and tables of the guests who had feasted and waited upon my father: they had gone out to the meeting-place where councils were held. And the woman concealed three cups in her bosom, and carried them away, while I followed her innocently. The sun sank and darkness came. Going quickly, we reached the harbor and the swift ship of the Phœnicians; the sailors went aboard, taking us with them, and sailed over the ocean, Zeus giving us favoring winds. We sailed continuously day and night for six days, but when Zeus, son of Cronos, brought the seventh, Artemis the huntress struck down the woman and she fell like a swallow to the bottom of the ship. The sailors threw her overboard, to the seals and the fishes, and I sorrowed. With the help of wind and wave they came to Ithaca, where Laertes bought me. It was thus that I first beheld this place."

ÆSOP

(6th Century, B.C.?)

ÆSOP was "not a poet," says Gilbert Murray, "but the legendary author of a particular type of story." This type is known as the Beast Fable, a brief incident related in order to point a simple moral. According to tradition Æsop was a foreign slave of the Sixth Century B.C. Whether the fables of ancient India, such as those in the *Hitopadesa*, influenced the ancient Greeks and Romans is a question still debated by scholars. At any rate there is a striking similarity, both in treatment and subject-matter, between the Fables of Æsop, Phædrus and Avianus, and those which delighted the Indians.

The present translation was made by James and published first in 1848.

THE COUNTRY MOUSE AND THE TOWN MOUSE

ONCE upon a time a Country Mouse who had a friend in town invited him, for old acquaintance' sake, to pay him a visit in the country. The invitation being accepted in due form, the Country Mouse, though plain and rough and somewhat frugal in his nature, opened his heart and store, in honor of hospitality and an old friend. There was not a carefully stored-up morsel that he did not bring forth out of his larder, peas and barley, cheese-parings and nuts, hoping by quantity to make up what he feared was wanting in quality, to suit the palate of his dainty guest. The Town Mouse, condescending to pick a bit here and a bit there, while the host sat nibbling a blade of barley-straw, at length exclaimed, "How is it, my good friend, that you can endure the dullness of this unpolished life? You are living like a toad in a hole. You can't really prefer these solitary rocks and woods to streets teeming with carriages and men. On my honor, you are wasting your time miserably here. We must make the most of life while it lasts. A mouse, you know, does not live forever. So come with me and I'll show you life and the town." Overpowered with such fine words and so polished a manner, the Country Mouse assented; and they set out together on their journey to town. It was late in the evening when they crept stealthily into the city, and midnight ere they reached the great house, where the Town Mouse took up his quarters. Here were couches of crimson velvet, carvings in ivory, everything in short that denoted wealth and luxury. On the table were the remains of a splendid banquet, to procure which all the choicest shops in the town had been ransacked the day before. It was now the turn of the courtier to play the host; he places his country friend on purple, runs to and fro to supply all his wants, presses dish upon dish and dainty upon dainty, and as though he were waiting on a king, tastes every course ere he ventures to place it before his rustic cousin. The Country Mouse, for his part, affects to make himself quite at home, and blesses the good fortune that had wrought such a change in his way of life; when, in the midst of his enjoyment, as he is thinking with contempt of the poor fare he has forsaken, on a sudden the door flies open, and a party of revellers returning from a late entertainment, bursts into the room. The affrighted friends jump from the table in the greatest consternation and hide themselves in the first corner they can reach. No sooner do they venture to creep out again than the barking of dogs drives them back in still greater terror than before. At length, when things seemed quiet, the Country Mouse stole out from his hiding place, and bidding his friend good-bye, whispered in his ear, "Oh, my good sir, this fine mode of living may do for those who like it; but give me my barley-bread in peace and security before the daintiest feast where Fear and Care are in waiting."

HERODOTUS

(484–424 B.C.)

HERODOTUS, the Father of History, is celebrated as a teller of tales. These he introduced into his *History* partly for purposes of elucidation and example, but partly also because he enjoyed writing them. The story that follows is, according to Professor Murray "all but pure fairy" tale, and is probably based on an Indian original. For the first time in Greek literature we have a short story as unified and free from unessential details as the most rigid modern critic could desire.

The present version, which comprises Chapter CXXI of the

Second Book of the *History*, is from the standard translation by George Rawlinson, first published in 1858. There is no title in the original.

KING RHAMPSINITUS AND THE THIEF

(From the *History*, Book II)

KING RHAMPSINITUS was possessed, they said, of great riches in silver—indeed to such an amount, that none of the princes, his successors, surpassed or even equaled his wealth. For the better custody of this money, he proposed to build a vast chamber of hewn stone, one side of which was to form a part of the outer wall of his palace. The builder, therefore, having designs upon the treasures, contrived, as he was making the building, to insert in this wall a stone which could easily be removed from its place by two men, or even one. So the chamber was finished, and the king's money stored away in it.

Time passed, and the builder fell sick; when finding his end approaching, he called for his two sons, and related to them the contrivance he had made in the king's treasure-chamber, telling them it was for their sakes he had done it, so that they might always live in affluence. Then he gave them clear directions concerning the mode of removing the stone, and communicated the measurements, bidding them carefully keep the secret, whereby they would be Comptrollers of the Royal Exchequer so long as they lived. Then the father died, and the sons were not slow in setting to work; they went by night to the palace, found the stone in the wall of the building, and having removed it with ease, plundered the treasury of a round sum.

When the king next paid a visit to the apartment he was astonished to see that the money was sunk in some of the vessels wherein it was stored away. Whom to accuse, however, he knew not, as the seals were all perfect, and the fastenings of the room secure. Still each time that he repeated his visits, he found that more money was gone. The thieves in truth never stopped, but plundered the treasury ever more and more. At last the king determined to have some traps made, and set near the vessels which contained his wealth. This was done, and when the thieves came, as usual, to the treasure chamber, and one of them entering through the aperture, made straight for the jars, suddenly he found himself caught in one of the traps. Perceiving that he was lost, he instantly called his brother, and telling him what had happened, entreated him to enter as quickly as possible and cut off his head, that when his body should be discovered it might not be recognized, which would have the effect of bringing ruin upon both. The other thief thought the advice good, and was persuaded to follow it; then, fitting the stone into its place, he went home, taking with him his brother's head.

When day dawned, the king came into the room, and marveled greatly to see the body of the thief in the trap without a head, while the building was still whole, and neither entrance nor exit was to be seen anywhere. In this perplexity he commanded the body of the dead man to be hung up outside the palace wall, and set a guard to watch it, with orders that if any persons were seen weeping or lamenting near the place, they should be seized and brought before him. When the mother heard of this exposure of the corpse of her son, she took it sorely to heart, and spoke to her surviving child, bidding him devise some plan or other to get back the body, and threatening that if he did not exert himself she would go herself to the king and denounce him as the robber.

The son said all he could to persuade her to let the matter rest, but in vain: she still continued to trouble him, until at last he yielded to her importunity, and contrived as follows: Filling some skins with wine, he loaded them on donkeys, which he drove before him till he came to the place where the guards were watching the dead body, when, pulling two or three of the skins towards him, he untied some of the necks which dangled by the asses' sides. The wine poured freely out, whereupon he began to beat his head and shout with all his might, seeming not to know which of the donkeys he should turn to first.

When the guards saw the wine running, delighted to profit by the occasion, they rushed one and all into the road, each with some vessel or other, and caught the liquor as it was spilling. The driver pretended anger, and loaded them with abuse; whereon they did their best to pacify him, until at last he appeared to soften, and recover his good humor, drove his asses aside out of the road, and set to work to rearrange their burdens; meanwhile, as he talked and chatted with the guards, one of them began to rally him, and make him laugh, whereupon he gave them one of the skins as a gift. They now made up their minds to sit down and have a drinking-bout where they were, so they begged him to remain and drink with them. Then the man let himself be persuaded, and stayed.

As the drinking went on, they grew very friendly together, so presently he gave them another skin, upon which they drank so copiously that they were all overcome with liquor, and growing drowsy, lay down, and fell asleep on the spot. The thief waited till it was the dead of the night, and then took down the body of his brother; after which, in mockery, he shaved off the right side of all the soldiers' beards, and so left them. Laying his brother's body upon the asses, he carried it home to his mother, having thus accomplished the thing that she had required of him.

When it came to the king's ears that the thief's body was stolen away, he was sorely vexed. Wishing, therefore, whatever it might cost, to catch the man who had contrived the trick, he had recourse (the priest said) to an expedient which I can scarcely credit. He announced that he would bestow his own daughter upon the man who would narrate to her the best story of the cleverest and wickedest thing done by himself. If any one in reply told her the story of the thief, she was to lay hold of him, and not allow him to get away.

The daughter did as her father willed, whereon the thief, who was well aware of the king's motive, felt a desire to outdo him in craft and cunning. Accordingly he contrived the following plan: He procured the corpse of a man lately dead, and cutting off one of the arms at the shoulder, put it under his dress, and so went to the king's daughter. When she put the question to him as she had done to all the rest, he replied that the wickedest thing he had ever done was cutting off the head of his brother when he was caught in a trap in the king's treasury, and the cleverest was making the guards drunk and carrying off the body. As he spoke, the princess caught at him, but the thief took advantage of the darkness to hold out to her the hand of the corpse. Imagining it to be his own hand, she seized and held it fast; while the thief, leaving it in her grasp, made his escape by the door.

The king, when word was brought him of this fresh success, amazed at the sagacity and boldness of the man, sent messengers to all the towns in his dominions to proclaim a free pardon for the thief, and to promise him a rich reward, if he came and made himself known. The thief took the king at his word, and came boldly into his presence; whereupon Rhampsinitus, greatly admiring him, and looking on him as the most knowing of men, gave him his daughter in marriage. "The Egyptians," he said, "excelled all the rest of the world in wisdom, and this man excelled all other Egyptians."

APOLLONIUS OF RHODES

(3d Century, B.C.)

Although he was a late writer in the epic form, Apollonius treated ancient mythical material, but from the standpoint of a scholar and a literary stylist. He left his native land, Rhodes, and settled in Alexandria, then the centre of the cultured world. The tale of Phineus is not new, but the details which embellish it, and the verbal pyrotechnics which he lavished upon it are highly characteristic of the decadent period in which it was written.

The present translation is that of R. C. Seaton, in the Loeb edition, William Heinemann, London, 1912. There is no title to the story in the original.

PHINEUS AND THE HARPIES

(From *The Argonautica*, Book III)

THERE Phineus, son of Agenor, had his home by the sea, Phineus, who above all men endured most bitter woes because of the gift of prophecy which Leto's son had granted him aforetime. And he reverenced not a whit even Zeus himself, for he foretold unerringly to men his sacred will. Wherefore Zeus sent upon him a lingering old age, and took from his eyes the pleasant light, and suffered him not to have joy of the dainties untold that the dwellers-around ever brought to his house when they came to inquire the will of heaven. But on a sudden, swooping through the clouds, the Harpies, with their crooked beaks, incessantly snatched the food away from his mouth and hands, and at times not a morsel of food was left, at others but a little, in order that he might live and be tormented. And they poured forth over all a loathsome stench; and no one dared not merely to carry food to his mouth, but even to stand at a distance, so foully reeked the remnants of the meal. But straightway when he heard the voice and the tramp of the band he knew that they were the men passing by, at whose coming Zeus's oracle had declared to him that he should have joy of his food. And he rose from his couch, like a lifeless dream, bowed over his staff, and crept to the door on his withered feet, feeling the walls; and as he moved, his limbs trembled for weakness and age; and his parched skin was caked with dirt, and naught but the skin held his bones together. And he came forth from the hall and sat on the threshold of the courtyard; and a dark stupor covered him, and it seemed that the earth reeled round beneath his feet, and he lay in a strengthless trance, speechless. But when they saw him they gathered round and marveled, and he at last drew labored breath from the depths of his chest and spoke among them with prophetic utterance:

"Listen, bravest of all the Hellenes, if it be truly ye, whom by a king's ruthless command Jason is leading on the ship Argo in quest of the fleece. It is ye truly. Even yet my soul by its divinations knows everything. Thanks I render to thee, O King, son of Leto, plunged in bitter affliction though I be. I beseech you by Zeus, the god of suppliants, the sternest foe to sinful men, and for the sake of Phœbus and Hera herself under whose especial care ye have come hither, help me, save an ill-fated man from misery, and depart not uncaring, and leaving me thus as ye see. For not only has the Fury set her foot on my eyes and I drag on to the end a weary old age, but besides my other woes a woe hangs over me, the bitterest of all. The Harpies, swooping down from some unseen den of destruction, ever snatch the food from my mouth, and I have no device to aid me. But it were easier, when I long for a meal, to escape my own thoughts than them, so swiftly do they fly through the air. But if haply they do leave me a morsel of food, it reeks of decay and the stench is unendurable, nor could any mortal bear to draw near, even for a moment, no, not if his heart were wrought of adamant. But necessity, bitter and insatiate, compels me to abide, and abiding to put food into my accursed belly. These pests, the oracle declares, the sons of Boreas shall restrain, and no strangers are they that shall ward them off if indeed I am Phineus who was once renowned among men for wealth and the gift of prophecy, and if I am the son of my father Agenor; and when I ruled among the Thracians, by my bridal gifts I brought home their sister Cleopatra to be my wife."

So spake Agenor's son, and deep sorrow seized each of the heroes, and especially the two sons of Boreas. And brushing away a tear, they drew nigh, and Zetes spake as follows, taking in his own the hand of the grief-worn sire:

"Unhappy one, none other of men is more wretched than thou, methinks. Why upon thee is laid the burden of so many sorrows? Hast thou with baneful folly sinned against the gods through thy skill in prophecy? For this are they greatly wroth with thee? Yet our spirit is dismayed within us for all our desire to aid thee, if indeed the god has granted this privilege to us two. For plain to discern to men of earth are the reproofs of the immortals. And we will never check the Harpies when they come, for all our desire, until thou hast sworn that for this we shall not lose the favor of heaven."

Thus he spake; and towards him the aged sire opened his sightless eyes and lifted them up and replied with these words:

"Be silent, store not up such thoughts in thy heart, my child. Let the son of Leto be my witness, he who of his gracious will taught me the lore of prophecy, and be witness the ill-starred doom which possesses me, and this dark cloud upon my eyes, and the gods of the underworld—and may their curse be upon me if I die perjured thus—no wrath of heaven will fall upon you two for your help to me."

Then were those two eager to help him because of the oath. And quickly the younger heroes prepared a feast for the aged man, a last prey for the Harpies; and both stood near him, to smite with the sword those pests when they swooped down. Scarcely had the aged man touched the food when they forthwith, like bitter blasts or flashes of lightning, suddenly darted from the clouds, and swooped down with a yell, fiercely craving for food; and the heroes beheld them and shouted in the midst of their onrush. But they, at the cry, devoured everything and sped away over the sea afar, and an intolerable stench remained. And behind them the two sons of Boreas, raising their swords, rushed in pursuit. For Zeus imparted to them tireless strength; but without Zeus they could not have followed, for the Harpies used ever to outstrip the blasts of the west wind when they came to Phineus, and when they left him. And, as when, upon the mountain-side, hounds, cunning in the chase, run in the track of horned goats or deer, and as they strain a little behind, gnash their teeth upon the edge of their teeth in vain; so Zetes and Calias rushing very near, just grazed the Harpies in vain with their fingertips. And assuredly they would have torn them to pieces despite heaven's will when they had overtaken them far off at the Floating Islands, had not swift Iris seen them and leaped down from the sky from heaven above and checked them with these words:

"It is not lawful, O sons of Boreas, to strike with your swords the Harpies, the hounds of mighty Zeus; but I myself will give you a pledge, that hereafter they shall not draw near to Phineus."

With these words she took an oath by the water of Styx, which to all the gods is most dread and most awful, that the Harpies would never thereafter again approach the home of Phineus, son of Agenor, for so it was fated. And the heroes, yielding to the oath, turned back their flight to the ship. And, on account of this, men called them the Islands of Turning, though aforetime they had called them the Floating Islands. And the Harpies and Iris parted. They entered their den in Minoan Crete; but she sped up to Olympus, soaring aloft on her swift wings.

Meantime the chiefs carefully cleansed the old man's squalid skin, and, with due selection, sacrificed sheep which they had borne away from the spoil of Amycus. And when they had laid a huge supper in the hall, they sat down and feasted, and with them feasted Phineus ravenously, delighting his soul as in a dream. And there, when they had taken their fill of food and drink, they kept awake all night, waiting for the sons of Boreas. And the aged sire himself sat in the midst, near the hearth, telling of the end of their voyage and the completion of their journey.

HELIODORUS

(3d Century, A.D.)

Heliodorus was one of the earliest writers of the novel, or romance. Though he lived long after the close of the Golden Age of Greek literature, he is (together with Longus) the initiator of the novel form. But like many novelists (even modern novelists, who are supposed to know better), he interspersed his romance with episodes which are in themselves short stories. The very first chapter of the *Æthiopian Romance*, which is here reprinted, is such a story.

The present version is slightly modified and modernized from the early English translation by Thomas Underdowne. There is no title to the story in the original.

THE ROBBERS OF EGYPT

(From *The Æthiopica,* or *Æthiopian Romance,* Book I)

AT the first smile of day, when the sun was just beginning to shine on the summits of the hills, men whose custom was to live by rapine and violence ran to the top of a cliff and stretched toward that mouth of the Nile which is called Heracleot. Standing awhile, they viewed the sea underneath them, and when they had looked a good season afar off into the same and could see nothing which could put them in the hope of prey, they cast their eyes toward the neighboring shore, where a ship lay moored, without sailors but full-freighted; which thing they who were afar off might easily conjecture, for the cargo brought the water up to the ship's third loading-line. But on the shore every place was full of men newly slain, some quite dead, some half dead, some whose bodies yet panted and plainly declared that there had been a battle fought of late. There could be seen no signs or tokens of any just quarrel, but only some poor confused remnants of an unlucky banquet which had ended so. For the tables were furnished with delicate dishes, some whereof lay in the hands of those that were slain, having served as weapons in the battle so suddenly begun. Other tables covered such as had crept under them to hide themselves, as they thought. Besides, the cups were overthrown and fallen from the hands, either of them that drank or those who had, instead of stones, used them. For that sudden mischief wrought new devices, and taught them instead of weapons to use their pots. Of those who lay there, one was wounded with an ax, another was hurt with the shells of fishes, whereof on the shore there was great plenty; another was battered with a club, many burnt by fire, and the rest by divers other means, but most of all were slain with arrows. To be brief, God showed a wonderful sight in so small a space, imbruing wine with blood, joining battle with banqueting, mingling indifferently slaughter with drinking, and killing with quaffings, providing such a sight for the thieves of Egypt to gaze at. For they, when they had looked upon these things a good while from the hill, could not understand what that sight meant, forasmuch as they saw some slain there, but the conquerors could they see nowhere. A manifest victory, but no spoils taken away, a ship without mariners, but, as concerning other things, untouched, as if she had been kept with a guard of many men, and lay at road in a peaceful harbor.

But though they knew not what the thing meant, they still had regard for gain, and deeming themselves to be victors, hurried with all speed to seize their booty. They were but a little way from the ship when they saw a sight more perplexing than the rest a great deal. A maid endowed with excellent beauty, who almost might be supposed a goddess, sat upon a rock seeming not a little to be grieved with that present mischance, but for all that of excellent courage. She had a garland of laurel on her head, a quiver on her back; to her left shoulder a bow was fastened, and her left arm hung carelessly down. Her right elbow she rested upon her thigh, holding her cheek in her hand, looking downward without moving her head, beholding a certain young man who lay before her, the which was sore wounded and seemed to lift up himself as if he had been awakened out of a dead sleep, almost of death itself. Yet was he in this case of singular beauty, and although his cheeks were besprinkled with blood, his whiteness did appear so much the more. He was constrained for grief to close his eyes, but the sight of the maiden drew them towards her, and they must needs see, because they saw her. As soon as he came to himself he heaved a deep sigh and uttered these words very faintly, "And art thou safe indeed, my sweetheart?" quoth he. "Or hast thou by thy death augmented the slaughter? Canst thou not endure, even after death, to be separated from me, that now a vision of thy spirit haunts this place of trouble?" "Nay," answered the maid, "on you doth all my estate depend, for good or ill, for this cause, you see"—showing a knife in her hand—"this has hitherto been waiting, and only by the chance of your recovery was restrained."

As soon as she had said thus, she leaped from the stone, and they who were on the hill, as well for wonder as also for the fear they had, as if they had been stricken with lightning, ran every man to hide them in the bushes there beside. For she seemed to them a thing of greater price, and more heavenly when she stood upright, and her arrows with the sudden moving of her body gave a clash on her shoulders, her apparel wrought with gold glistened against the sun, and her hair under the garland, blown about with the wind, covered a great part of her back. The thieves were greatly afraid; and even more than what they saw did their ignorance of what had happened before terrify them. Some of them said indeed it was a goddess—Artemis, or Isis, the lady of the land—others declared it was a priestess of the gods who, replenished with divine fury, had made the great slaughter which there appeared. And they every man gave his verdict, because they knew not yet the truth. But she, hastily running to the young man, embraced him, wept for sorrow, kissed him, wiped away his blood and made pitiful moan, scarcely believing that she held him in her arms. Which things when the Egyptians had seen, they turned their opinions: "And are these," said they, "the works of a goddess? Would a goddess kiss a dead man with such compassion?" They determined therefore with themselves that it was best to take heart of grace, and draw near to find out the truth. When they had therefore encouraged each other a little, they ran down and found the maid busy in dressing the young man's wounds, and coming behind her, suddenly stood still, and durst neither speak nor do anything more for their lives.

When she heard the noise around her, and saw their shadows before her eyes, she lifted herself up a little and looked back, but then at once stooped down again, no whit dismayed by the strange color of their skin, nor yet abashed to see the thieves in harness, but applying herself only to bind up his wounds that lay before her. Such is the force of earnest desire and true love: it despiseth all outward chances, be they pleasant or otherwise, only beholding that which it loveth, and thereabout bestoweth all diligence and travail. But when the thieves passed by and stood before her, and seemed as though they would enterprise somewhat, she lifted herself up again and beholding them black and ill-favored, said: "If you be the spirits of those who are slain here, you trouble us wrongfully, for most of you were slain by your own hands. As for us, if we slew any, we did it but in our own defense to repel the violence which was proffered to my virginity. But if you be men alive, it seemeth you are thieves, and you have come here in good season. Rid us, I pray, from these present miseries, and by death finish this our unhappy tragedy." Thus did she sorrowfully lament. But they, not understanding what she said, left them there, accounting their weakness a sufficient guard, and hastened to the ship, and brought out that which was in the same, paying no regard to other things whereof therein was great store, but every man bearing out as much as he could, of gold, silver, precious stones and silk. And when they thought they had enough, and there was such plenty as might satisfy even a thief's greed, laying their booty on the shore, they fell to dividing it into portions such as they could carry, not according to the worth and value of what they had, but contenting themselves with equality of weight. As for the young man and the maid, they would take order for them afterwards.

In the meantime, another company of thieves, whereof two horsemen were captains, came toward them: which thing as soon as those saw that had been there before, having no courage to oppose them, they ran away as fast as they could, without taking with them any part of the prey, that they might give their enemy no occasion to pursue them. For they were in number but ten, and those who came upon them were three times as many. And so the maid and her companion, though not yet prisoners, were again in durance. But the robbers, although they were eager for the spoil, yet, partly because they knew not what those things signified which they saw, and partly also for fear, stayed themselves a while, thinking that the former slaughter had been made by the thieves that had been there before. But when they beheld the maid in her fine foreign dress, who despised the dangers that hung over her head as if they had been none, and altogether employed her care to ease the young man's wounds, taking his grief as heavily as her own sorrow, they not only marveled at her beauty and high spirit but were wonderfully moved by the comeliness of the wounded man's person. Such was the seemliness of his countenance, and tallness of his stature, as he lay before them. For by this time he was a little mended, and his person had recovered its old handsomeness again. At length, after they had beheld them a good while, he drew near who was their master, and laid hand on the maid, and bade her arise and follow him. She, although she understood not what he said, conjecturing what he wished her to do, drew the young man with her, himself holding her fast, and pointing with a knife to her breast, threatened that she would kill herself if they carried them not away both together. Which thing when the master, partly by her talk but more plainly by her gesture, understood, hoping also to use the young man's help in great affairs when he recovered, he alighted himself from his horse and commanded his harness-bearer likewise so to do, and set his prisoners upon them. Then, ordering the rest when they had gathered up the prey to follow them, he himself like a lackey ran by their side and stayed them upright, if by reason of their infirmity they were likely to fall. Surely this deed was not without glory; for he who was their master now waited upon them, and he who took them prisoners was content to serve them. Such is the impression that nobility makes, and such the force of comeliness, which can subdue the disposition of thieves and bring under the wild and savage.

Ancient Rome

INTRODUCTION

IT is a commonplace of literary history that Roman art was largely imitated or derived from the Greek, and in particular that Roman literature contributed little to the world's store of masterpieces. Yet among the Romans the short story was esteemed more highly and was often more skilfully developed than it was among the Greeks.

The first of the stories chosen is from the historian Livy. Before his day there is very little material from which to select, although if the earlier writers of epic and history were better known to us, we might have found stories in the works of Livius Andronicus, Ennius, and the historians, most of whose writings have been lost. In the *Letters* of Cicero are numerous incidents falling within our category, but none of them of sufficient intrinsic interest to warrant their inclusion in this volume. Livy's *History* abounds in episodes, many of them related with a certain matter-of-factness that characterizes a great deal of Latin prose writing. Still, *Horatius at the Bridge* is a stirring tale rendered doubly effective by its simplicity.

Ovid was a born teller of stories, and though he borrowed largely from the Greeks and was a fastidious poet intent upon achieving a refined and elegant style, the numerous myths which he treats at length in his *Metamorphoses* include half a dozen of the loveliest stories ever written.

Other poets and historians and miscellaneous writers—Valerius Maximus, Varro, Statius, Tacitus and Suetonius—tried their hand at story-telling, and even Vergil in his *Æneid* recounted episodes that are genuine stories, but none of them could rival the technical skill with which the minor poet Phædrus turned the Æsopian fables and everyday incidents of life and history into graceful and appealing tales. Like the earlier fabulists, Phædrus preached little sermons. The most interesting parts of his work are the little anecdotes, like the one included in this volume; these are miniature stories. The other famous Roman fabulist was Avianus who, rediscovered in the Middle Ages, exerted a profound and lasting influence in France and Germany. But his work is neither so finished nor so attractive as that of Phædrus.

Many genuine stories are found in the personal correspondence of the time, chiefly among the published collections of Cicero and Pliny the Younger. Pliny wrote several short stories which he elaborated with conscious skill, for he wrote with a view to publication. Throughout all modern literature we find stories, indeed lengthy stories (see Richardson), related through the medium of letters. This is a deliberate device employed to lend to the narrative an air of actuality. It would be enlightening to know whether Pliny wrote his *Haunted House* as a literary experiment, or whether he really believed the story. But supposing he related it as a fact—supposing even that all the facts were to be proved scientifically correct, would it be any the less a good story?

Petronius belonged to a different world in which Latin prose had lost a good deal of its rigid dignity, and like the literature of the late Hellenistic period in Greece, was characterized by a facile cynicism on the part of the writers, and an over-luxuriance of style. The writers were very numerous, poets, historians, satirists, and even scientists interspersing their writings with tales of haunted houses, ghosts, and all the supernatural apparitions that are the stock-in-trade of the story-writer. Petronius and Apuleius, however, stood head and shoulders above the rest of their contemporaries and followers. *The Matron of Ephesus*, hackneyed though its theme may be, is a masterpiece of satirical fiction, while *The Dream* is one of a dozen tales of mystery and imagination which constitute the chief glory of *The Golden Ass*. That rambling romance, it will be remembered, also contains the enchanting *Cupid and Psyche*, which is far too long for inclusion in a collection of this sort.

Just at what point Roman literature ended is a matter to be determined by the historians, but after the Fifth Century A.D. it becomes increasingly difficult to designate any tale as unmistakably Roman.

Then foreigners began to change the face of the Empire, Christianity damped the ardour of the artist and stifled the imagination of the story-teller. It is not until the dawn of modern times, some six or seven centuries afterward, when the fragments of Roman stories were again taken up and imbedded in the curious mediæval mosaics of the *Gesta Romanorum* and the *Hundred Ancient Tales*, that we realize how the art of tale-telling had never been forgotten.

Throughout the break-up of Rome and the barbarian invasions, through the darkest years of the Tenth Century, the Latin traditions were preserved in the manuscripts of the monasteries, and on the lips of singers, minstrels, acrobats, and actors.

With Apuleius and Petronius the short story, as an art-form, may be said to have achieved a decided technical advance over the efforts of the Greeks. With these later writers the story was told largely for its own sake, and not to illustrate a moral truth or glorify the deeds of the Roman people.

LIVY

(59 B.C.–17 A.D.)

Titus Livius, known to us under the English title of Livy, though born in the provinces at Padua, spent most of his life at the capital, where he was a teacher and writer of history. His *History of Rome* was a monumental work, of which only a part has come down to us. Like practically all the historians of antiquity (and most of the moderns, for that matter) he introduces stories and anecdotes on hearsay evidence, using them in order to glorify his country or to drive home a lesson. *Horatius at the Bridge* is a case in question, and though it may be founded on fact, it is probably apocryphal in detail.

The present translation (including Chapters IX and X of Book II) is a revision of that made by D. Spillan, published in the Bohn edition in 1872. There is no title in the original.

HORATIUS AT THE BRIDGE

(From the *History*, Book II)

By this time the Tarquins had fled to Lars Porsena, king of Clusium. There, with advice and entreaties, they besought him not to suffer them, who were descended from the Etrurians and of the same blood and name, to live in exile and poverty; and advised him not to let this practice of expelling kings to pass unpunished. Liberty, they declared, had charms enough in itself; and unless kings defended their crowns with as much vigor as the people pursued their liberty, the highest must be reduced to a level with the lowest; there would be nothing exalted, nothing distinguished above the rest; hence there must be an end of regal government, the most beautiful institution both among gods and men. Porsena, thinking it would be an honor to the Tuscans that there should be a king at Rome, especially one of the Etrurian nation, marched towards Rome with an army. Never before had such terror seized the Senate, so powerful was the state of Clusium at the time, and so great the renown of Porsena. Nor did they only dread their enemies, but even their own citizens, lest the common people, through excess of fear should, by receiving the Tarquins into the city, accept peace even though purchased with slavery. Many concessions were therefore granted to the people by the Senate during that period. Their attention, in the first place, was directed to the markets, and persons were sent, some to the

Volscians, others to Cumæ, to buy up corn. The privilege of selling salt, because it was farmed at a high rate, was also taken into the hands of the government, and withdrawn from private individuals; and the people were freed from port-duties and taxes, in order that the rich, who could bear the burden, should contribute; the poor paid tax enough if they educated their children. This indulgent care of the fathers accordingly kept the whole state in such concord amid the subsequent severities of the siege and famine, that the highest as well as the lowest abhorred the name of king; nor was any individual afterwards so popular by intriguing practices as the whole Senate was by their excellent government.

Some parts of the city seemed secured by the walls, others by the River Tiber. The Sublician Bridge well-nigh afforded a passage to the enemy, had there not been one man, Horatius Cocles (fortunately Rome had on that day such a defender) who, happening to be posted on guard at the bridge, when he saw the Janiculum taken by a sudden assault and the enemy pouring down thence at full speed, and that his own party, in terror and confusion, were abandoning their arms and ranks, laying hold of them one by one, standing in their way and appealing to the faith of gods and men, he declared that their flight would avail them nothing if they deserted their post; if they passed the bridge, there would soon be more of the enemy in the Palatium and Capitol than in the Janiculum. For that reason he charged them to demolish the bridge, by sword, by fire, or by any means whatever; declaring that he would stand the shock of the enemy as far as could be done by one man. He then advanced to the first entrance of the bridge, and being easily distinguished among those who showed their backs in retreating, faced about to engage the foe hand to hand, and by his surprising bravery he terrified the enemy. Two indeed remained with him from a sense of shame: Sp. Lartius and T. Herminius, men eminent for their birth, and renowned for their gallant exploits. With them he for a short time stood the first storm of the danger, and the severest brunt of the battle. But as they who demolished the bridge called upon them to retire, he obliged them also to withdraw to a place of safety on a small portion of the bridge that was still left. Then casting his stern eyes toward the officers of the Etrurians in a threatening manner, he now challenged them singly, and then reproached them, slaves of haughty tyrants who, regardless of their own freedom, came to oppress the liberty of others. They hesitated for a time, looking round one at the other, to begin the fight; shame then put the army in motion, and a shout being raised, they hurled weapons from all sides at their single adversary; and when they all stuck in his upraised shield, and he with no less obstinacy kept possession of the bridge, they endeavored to thrust him down from it by one push, when the crash of the falling bridge was heard, and at the same time a shout of the Romans raised for joy at having completed their purpose, checked their ardor with sudden panic. Then said Cocles: "Holy Father Tiber, I pray thee, receive these arms, and this thy soldier, in thy propitious stream." Armed as he was, he leaped into the Tiber, and amid showers of darts, swam across safe to his party, having dared an act which is likely to obtain with posterity more fame than credit. The state was grateful for such valor; a statue was erected to him in the comitium, and as much land given to him as he could plow in one day. The zeal of private individuals was also conspicuous among his public honors. For amid the great scarcity, each contributed something, according to his supply, depriving himself of his own support.

OVID

(43 B.C.–18 A.D.?)

PUBLIUS OVIDIUS NASO, better known to readers of English as Ovid, was born not far from Rome, and spent the latter part of his life in exile. *The Metamorphoses*, his most ambitious work, is an attempt to reshape in metrical form the chief stories of Greek mythology, and several from Roman mythology. *Orpheus and Eurydice*, one of the most human of the legends of antiquity, is a graceful piece of writing. Its "point" is as clear and as cleverly turned as you will find in any ancient tale.

The present translation is based by the editors upon two early versions, the one very literal, the other a paraphrase. The story, which has no title in the original, appears in the Tenth Book of the *Metamorphoses*.

ORPHEUS AND EURYDICE

(From *The Metamorphoses*, Book X)

THENCE Hymenæus, clad in a saffron-colored robe, passed through the unmeasured spaces of the air and directed his course to the region of the Ciconians, and in vain was invoked by the voice of Orpheus. He presented himself, but brought with him neither auspicious words, nor a joyful appearance, nor happy omen. The torch he held hissed with a smoke that brought tears to the eyes, though it was without a flame. The issue was more disastrous than the omen; for the new bride, while strolling over the grass attended by a train of Naiads, was killed by the sting of a serpent on her ankle.

After the Rhodopeian bard had bewailed her in the upper realms, he dared, that he might try the shades below as well, to descend to the Styx by the Tænarian Gate, and amid the phantom inhabitants, he went to Persephone and him who held sway over the dark world. Touching the strings of his harp and speaking, he thus addressed them: "Oh, ye deities of the world that lies beneath the earth, to which we all come at last, if I be permitted to speak, laying aside the artful expressions of a deceitful tongue, I have not descended hither from curiosity to see dark Tartarus nor to bind the threefold throat of the Medusæan monster bristling with serpents. My wife is the cause of my coming, into whom a serpent which she trod on suffused its poison, and cut short the thread of her years. I wished to be able to endure this, and I will not deny that I have striven to do so. But love has proved stronger. That god is well-known in the regions above; whether he be so here as well, I am uncertain. Yet I think that even here he is, and if the story of the rape of former days is true, 'twas love that brought you two together. By these places filled with terrors, by this vast chaos and by the silence of these boundless realms, I entreat you, weave over again the quick-spun thread of the life of Eurydice.

"To you we all belong, and having stayed but a little while above, sooner or later we all hasten to your abode. Hither are we all hastening. This is our last home, and you possess indisputable dominion over the human race. She, too, when in due time she shall have completed her allotted number of years, will be under your sway. The enjoyment of her I entreat as a favor, but if the fates deny me this privilege on behalf of my wife, I have determined that I will never return to earth. Triumph, then, in the death of us both!"

As he spoke and touched the strings of his lyre, the bloodless spirits wept. Tantalus no longer caught at the retreating water; the wheel of Ixion stood still in amazement; the birds ceased to tear at the liver of Tityus, and the granddaughters of Belus paused at their urns. Thou, too, Sisyphus, didst seat thyself on the stone. The story is that then for the first time the cheeks of the Eumenides, overcome by the music of Orpheus, were wet with tears; nor could the royal consort, nor he who ruled the infernal regions endure to deny his request. And they called for Eurydice. She advanced at a slow pace from among the shades newly arrived, for she was lame from her wound.

The Rhodopeian hero received her and at the same time was told the condition that he turn not back his eyes until he had passed the Avernian Valley, lest the grant be revoked. They ascended the path in silence, steep, dark, and enveloped in deepening gloom. Now they were arrived at last at a point not far below the verge of the upper earth. Orpheus, fearing lest Eurydice should fall, and impatient to behold her once again, turned his eyes, and at once she sank back again. Hapless woman, stretching out her hands and struggling for the arms of her lover, she caught nothing but empty air. Dying a second time, she complained not of her husband, for why should she complain of being beloved? Then she pronounced the last farewell, which he scarcely heard, and again was she hurried back whence she had come.

And Orpheus was astounded and perplexed by this two-fold death of his wife.

PHÆDRUS

(15 B.C.?–55 A.D.?)

It was the chief distinction of this writer to have collected the *Fables* of Æsop (or whoever it was who wrote Æsop's works) and rewritten them for the Romans. His collection is the earliest of its kind which has survived. Not all his Fables, however, are based upon Æsop. *The Shipwreck of Simonides* is either an original composition or was taken from another source. Phædrus was a Thracian slave, and later a freedman, in the service of the Emperor Augustus. He once declared that the fable was invented as a "device whereby slavery could find a voice," a definition which throws considerable light on Phædrus' life, even if it fails to explain the origin of the Fable form.

The present text was first published in the Bohn edition of Phædrus in 1848.

THE SHIPWRECK OF SIMONIDES

A LEARNED man has always a fund of riches in himself.

Simonides, who wrote such excellent lyric poems, the more easily to support his poverty, began to make a tour of the celebrated cities of Asia, singing the praises of victors for such reward as he might receive. After he had become enriched by this kind of gain, he resolved to return to his native land by sea (for he was born, it is said, in the island of Ceos). Accordingly he embarked in a ship, which a dreadful tempest, together with its own rottenness, caused to founder at sea. Some gathered together their girdles, others their precious effects, which formed the support of their existence. One who was over inquisitive, remarked: "Are you going to save none of your property, Simonides?" He made reply: "All my possessions are about me." A few only made their escape by swimming, for the majority, being weighed down by their burdens, perished. Some thieves too made their appearance, and seized what each person had saved, leaving him naked. Clazomenæ, an ancient city, chanced to be near; to which the shipwrecked persons repaired. Here a person devoted to the pursuits of literature, who had often read the lines of Simonides, and was a very great admirer of him though he had never seen him, knowing from his very language who he was, received him with the greatest pleasure into his house, and furnished him with clothes, money, and attendants. The others meanwhile were carrying about their pictures, begging for victuals. Simonides chanced to meet them; and, as soon as he saw them, remarked: "I told you that all my property was about me; what you have endeavored to save is lost."

PETRONIUS

(Died 66 A.D.)

GAIUS PETRONIUS ARBITER was born some time early during the First Century of the Christian era, and committed suicide in the year 66. Writer, government official, dilettante and friend of Nero, he "had idled into fame," as Tacitus tells us. His best-known work, *The Satyricon*, is a strange straggling sort of satirical novel, into which he introduced this short masterpiece, *The Matron of Ephesus*. The tale is supposed to be in the manner of one of the so-called lost Milesian Tales, a collection renowned for its cynical outlook on humanity in general and woman in particular. This brief story (in one form or another) is to be found running through all literature, especially the literature written by men.

The present version is a revision (by the editors) of two older versions.

THE MATRON OF EPHESUS

(From *The Satyricon*)

A CERTAIN matron of Ephesus was so notably pure that women came from afar to look upon her. When her husband was buried, she was not satisfied with the usual custom of following the body with loosened hair and beating her breast in the presence of the people: she accompanied her dead spouse right into the sepulcher—which was in the Greek style, underground—and there remained to watch and weep by day and by night. Her parents and relations were unable to prevent her from thus torturing herself, and remaining in the sepulcher to die of hunger. The civil officials at last left in despair.

The matron lived through the fifth day without eating, and was grieved for by all as a shining example to all womenkind. A faithful maidservant sat by the wretched woman, shed the appropriate number of tears, and kept the lamp burning.

Word spread through the city, and every one agreed that it was a unique example of conjugal love and fidelity.

Meantime, the provincial governor crucified certain thieves near the sepulcher where the matron was weeping over the body of her late husband, and a soldier was commanded to keep guard over the crosses, to prevent the bodies from being taken down and buried. The following night he perceived a light shining brightly among the trees and heard the moans of the woman. Like all human beings, he was curious, and desired to know who was groaning, and what was the cause of it. He therefore entered the sepulcher, and on seeing a beautiful woman, stopped short and was as deeply moved as though he had seen an omen or a ghost from the nether world. The moment he set eyes on the body and remarked the matron's tears, and her face scarred by the marks of fingernails, he understood: she was desperate in her love for the man who was dead. He then brought his frugal supper into the sepulcher, and begged the matron not to give way so to a grief that was useless, nor break her heart in weeping. All men, he said, had the same fate and the same last resting-place. But she was ill-pleased by such commonplace consolation, and smote her breast more violently than ever, tearing out her hair and throwing it upon the body before her. Still, the young soldier did not leave. He tried to give the woman food. Though she resisted, her maidservant was won over by the smell of the wine, and stretched out her hand for the supper that was offered her. After she was fortified by food and drink, she strove to win over her mistress. "How," she asked, "will you be benefited, if you starve to death and bury yourself alive, dying before Destiny has demanded your soul? Do you imagine that your mourning can be acceptable to the body or the soul of a man who is dead and buried? Why not rather begin your life anew? Why not forget this misguided fidelity—adhered to only by women—and enjoy the daylight as long as the gods allow? This cold body ought to be a warning to you to enjoy life to the utmost."

Now, generally, one gives heed when one is asked to eat food or to live, and the matron was both hungry and thirsty after five days' fasting; she allowed her resolution to be broken. She ate as greedily as the maidservant had eaten. Those who are well-fed are easily tempted, and the soldier set about to conquer the matron's virtue, by the same pleasant and persuasive means he had used before. The chaste matron perceived that he was an attractive young man, and by no means a fool. The maidservant was sympathetic, and quoted the words, "Do you seek to struggle against a passion that is pleasing to you? Do you not remember in whose country you are?"

To make a long story short, having overcome certain of the matron's scruples, the soldier succeeded in overcoming her remaining scruples.

They were together not only on that first night, but on the second and the third. The gates of the sepulcher were closed, so that if any friend or stranger had come, he would have imagined that the very virtuous woman had died in the presence of her husband's body. The soldier was greatly pleased by the matron's charms, and with their uninterrupted love; he bought such delicate viands as his pay would permit, and brought them to the sepulcher when darkness came.

The parents of one of the thieves who had been crucified, perceiving that the soldier was not strictly guarding the crosses, took down the body of their son and buried it. Next morning, seeing the body gone, the soldier knew what his punishment would be, and went and told the woman. He would, he declared, kill himself with his sword rather than be sentenced by a military court, and told her to make room for her lover to lie beside her late husband. But the lady was as compassionate as she was pure. "May the gods forbid," said she, "that I should lay eyes at one time on the corpses of the two men who are dearest to me! It were better to hang up a dead body than to kill a breathing man." And therewith she told the soldier to take the husband's body from its place and put it upon the cross that was vacant. The soldier at once acted upon the matron's clever suggestion, and the next day people wondered how the dead man had been able to crucify himself.

PLINY THE YOUNGER

(62–113 A.D.)

THE *Letters* of Pliny the Younger (known in Latin as C. Plinius Cæcilius Secundus) give a pleasant and varied picture of Roman life at a time when the satirists were depicting it in lurid hues. Pliny was a gentleman of refinement who found time, in spite of his career as a lawyer and a high government official, to write many letters to his friends, with a view, as we happen to know, to publication. Several of these letters are neither more nor less than short stories. *The Haunted House* is simply the recital of an incident in a letter to his friend Sura, and is one of the best of the ancient ghost stories. Needless to say, it is a type that has been used time and again.

The text is from an early English translation, and comprises *Letter 27* of the Seventh Book. There is no title in the original.

THE HAUNTED HOUSE

(*Letter* to Sura, Book VII)

THERE was at Athens a mansion, spacious and commodious, but of evil repute and dangerous to health. In the dead of night there was a noise as of iron, and, if you listened more closely, a clanking of chains was heard, first of all from a distance, and afterwards hard by. Presently a specter used to appear, an ancient man sinking with emaciation and squalor, with a long beard and bristly hair, wearing shackles on his legs and fetters on his hands, and shaking them. Hence the inmates, by reason of their fears, passed miserable and horrible nights in sleeplessness. This want of sleep was followed by disease, and, their terrors increasing, by death. For in the daytime as well, though the apparition had departed, yet a reminiscence of it flitted before their eyes, and their dread outlived its cause. The mansion was accordingly deserted and, condemned to solitude, was entirely abandoned to the dreadful ghost. However, it was advertised, on the chance of some one, ignorant of the fearful curse attached to it, being willing to buy or to rent it. Athenodorus the philosopher came to Athens and read the advertisement. When he had been informed of the terms, which were so low as to appear suspicious, he made inquiries, and learned the whole of the particulars. Yet none the less on that account, nay, all the more readily, did he rent the house. As evening began to draw on, he ordered a sofa to be set for himself in the front part of the house, and called for his notebooks, writing implements, and a light. All his servants he dismissed to the interior apartments, and for himself applied his soul, eyes, and hand to composition, that his mind might not, from want of occupation, picture to itself the phantoms of which he had heard, or any empty terrors. At the commencement there was the universal silence of night. Soon the shaking of irons and the clanking of chains was heard, yet he never raised his eyes nor slackened his pen, but hardened his soul and deadened his ears by its help. The noise grew and approached: now it seemed to be heard at the door, and next inside the door. He looked round, beheld and recognized the figure he had been told of. It was standing and signaling to him with its finger, as though inviting him. He, in reply, made a sign with his hand that it should wait a moment, and applied himself afresh to his tablets and pen. Upon this the figure kept rattling its chains over his head as he wrote. On looking round again, he saw it making the same signal as before, and without delay took up a light and followed it. It moved with a slow step, as though oppressed by its chains, and, after turning into the courtyard of the house, vanished suddenly and left his company. On being thus left to himself, he marked the spot with some grass and leaves which he plucked. Next day he applied to the magistrates, and urged them to have the spot in question dug up. There were found there some bones attached to and intermingled with fetters; the body to which they had belonged, rotted away by time and the soil, had abandoned them thus naked and corroded to the chains. They were collected and interred at the public expense, and the house was ever afterwards free from the spirit, which had obtained due sepulture.

The above story I believe on the strength of those who affirm it. What follows I am myself in a position to affirm to others. I have a freedman, who is not without some knowledge of letters. A younger brother of his was sleeping with him in the same bed. The latter dreamed he saw some one sitting on the couch, who approached a pair of scissors to his head, and even cut the hair from the crown of it. When day dawned he was found to be cropped round the crown, and his locks were discovered lying about. A very short time afterwards a fresh occurrence of the same kind confirmed the truth of the former one. A lad of mine was sleeping, in company with several others, in the pages' apartment. There came through the windows (so he tells the story) two figures in white tunics, who cut his hair as he lay, and departed the way they came. In his case, too, daylight exhibited him shorn, and his locks scattered around. Nothing remarkable followed, except, perhaps, this, that I was not brought under accusation, as I should have been, if Domitian (in whose reign these events happened) had lived longer. For in his desk was found an information against me which had been presented by Carus; from which circumstance it may be conjectured—inasmuch as it is the custom of accused persons to let their hair grow—that the cutting off of my slaves' hair was a sign of the danger which threatened me being averted.

I beg, then, that you will apply your great learning to this subject. The matter is one which deserves long and deep consideration on your part; nor am I, for my part, undeserving of having the fruits of your wisdom imparted to me. You may even argue on both sides (as your way is), provided you argue more forcibly on one side than the other, so as not to dismiss me in suspense and anxiety, when the very cause of my consulting you has been to have my doubts ended.

APULEIUS

(Born *ca.* 125 A.D.)

Lucius Apuleius, author of *The Golden Ass*, was born and educated in northern Africa. He practised law, was an indefatigable traveller, a ceaseless investigator into religious ceremonies and mysteries, and a writer of considerable skill and imagination. Many stories, including *Cupid and Psyche* and *The Dream*, are introduced into the rambling narrative of his celebrated romance. Like many other literary men, he was publicly accused of writing indecent literature. Like Pliny's *Haunted House*, *The Dream* is one of those lurid ghost-stories which apparently pleased the readers of the early Christian era. They continue to do so.

The present text is a modernized version of the classic translation by Adlington, which first appeared in 1566. There is no title in the original.

THE DREAM

(From *The Golden Ass*)

BUT I could in no wise sleep for the great fear which was in my heart, until it was about midnight, and then I began to slumber. But, alas! behold suddenly the chamber doors broke open, and locks, bolts, and posts fell down, that you would verily have thought that some thieves had presently come to have spoiled and robbed us. And my bed whereon I lay, being a truckle-bed, fashioned in the form of a cradle, and one of the feet broken and rotten, by violence was turned upside down, and I likewise was overwhelmed and covered lying in the same. And while I lay on the ground covered in this sort, I peeped under the bed to see what would happen. And behold there entered in two old women, the one bearing a burning torch, and the other a sponge and a naked sword; and so in this habit they stood about, Socrates being fast asleep. Then she which bare the sword said unto the other, "Behold, sister Panthia, this is my dear and sweet heart, this is he who little regarding my love, doth not only defame me with reproachful words, but also intendeth to run away." Which said, she pointed toward me that lay under the bed, and showed me to Panthia. "This is he," quoth she, "which is his counselor, and persuadeth him to forsake me, and now being at the point of death, he lieth prostrate on the ground covered with his bed, and hath seen all our doings, and hopeth to escape scot-free from my hands; but I will cause that he shall repent himself too late, nay rather forthwith, of his former intemperate language, and his present curiosity." Which words when I heard, I fell into a cold sweat, and my heart trembled with fear, insomuch that the bed over me did likewise rattle and shake. Then spake Panthia unto Meroe and said, "Sister, let us by and by tear him in pieces." Then Meroe answered, "Nay, rather let him live, and bury the corpse of this poor wretch in some hole of the earth"; and therewithal she turned up the head of Socrates on the other side, and thrust her sword up to the hilt into the left part of his neck, and received the blood that gushed out, into a pot, that no drop thereof fell beside: which things I saw with mine own eyes; and as I think to the intent that she might alter nothing that pertained to sacrifice, which she accustomed to make, she thrust her hand down into the internals of his body, and searching about at length brought forth the heart of my miserable companion, Socrates, who having his throat cut in such sort, yielded out a dreadful cry and gave up the ghost. Then Panthia stopped the wide wound of his throat with the sponge, and said, "O sponge, sprung and made of the sea, beware that thou pass not by running river." When this was ended, they went their ways, and the doors closed fast, the posts stood in their old places, and the locks and bolts were shut again. But I that lay upon the ground like one without soul, naked and cold, like to one that were more than half dead, yet reviving myself, and appointed as I thought for the gallows, began to say, "Alas! what shall become of me to-morrow, when my companion shall be found murdered here in the chamber? To whom shall I seem to tell any similitude of truth, whenas I shall tell the truth indeed? They will say, 'If thou wert unable to resist the violence of the women, yet shouldst thou have cried for help: wouldst thou suffer the man to be slain before thy face and say nothing? Or why did they not slay thee likewise? why did they spare thee that stood by and saw them commit that horrible fact? Wherefore although thou hast escaped their hands, yet thou shalt not escape ours.'" While I pondered these things with myself the night passed on, and so I resolved to take my horse before day, and go forward on my journey.

Howbeit the ways were unknown to me: and thereupon I took up my packet, unlocked and unbarred the doors, but those good and faithful doors, which in the night did open of their own accord, could then scantly be opened with their keys. And when I was out I cried, "O sirrah hostler, where art thou? Open the stable-door, for I will ride away by and by." The hostler lying behind the stable-door upon a pallet and half asleep, "What (quoth he), do you not know that the ways be very dangerous? what mean you to rise at this time of night? If you, perhaps guilty of some heinous crime, be weary of your life, yet think you not that we are such sots that we will die for you." Then said I, "It is well-nigh day, and moreover, what can thieves take from him that hath nothing? Dost thou not know, fool as thou art, if thou be naked, if ten giants should assail thee, they could not spoil or rob thee?" Whereunto the drowsy hostler, half asleep and turning on the other side, answered, "What know I whether you have murdered your companion whom you brought in yesternight or no, and now seek the means to escape away?"

O Lord, at that time, I remember, the earth seemed to open, and methought I saw at hellgate the dog Cerberus ready to devour me; and then I verily believed that Meroe did not spare my throat moved with pity, but rather cruelly pardoned me to bring me to the gallows. Wherefore I returned to my chamber, and there devised with myself in what sort I should finish my life. And therewithal I pulled out a piece of rope wherewith the bed was corded, and tied one end thereof about a rafter by the window, and with the other end I made a sliding knot, and stood upon my bed, and so put my neck into it, and when I leaped from the bed thinking verily to strangle myself and so die, behold the rope, being old and rotten, burst in the middle, and I fell down tumbling upon Socrates that lay under: and even at that same very time the hostler came in crying with a loud voice and said, "Where are you that made such haste at midnight, and now lies wallowing abed?" Whereupon (I know not whether it was by my fall, or by the great cry of the hostler) Socrates as waking out of a sleep, did rise up first and said, "It is not without cause that strangers do speak evil of all such hostlers, for this caitiff in his coming in, and with his crying out, I think under a color to steal away something, has waked me out of a sound sleep." Then I rose up, joyful with a merry countenance, saying, "Behold, good hostler, my friend, my companion and my brother whom thou didst falsely affirm to be slain by me this night. And therewithal I embraced my friend Socrates and kissed him, and took him by the hand and said, "Why tarry we? Why lose we the pleasure of this fair morning? let us go": and so I took up my packet, and paid the charges of the house and departed.

And we had not gone a mile out of the town but it was broad day, and then I diligently looked upon Socrates' throat to see if I could espy the place where Meroe thrust in her sword; but when I could not perceive any such thing, I thought with myself, What a madman am I, that being overcome with wine yesternight have dreamed such terrible things! behold, I see Socrates is sound, safe and in health. Where is his wound? where is the sponge? where is his great and new cut? And then I spake to him and said, "Verily it is not without occasion that physicians of experience do affirm, that such as fill their gorges abundantly with meat and drink shall dream of dire and horrible sights. For I myself, not tempering my appetite yesternight from pots of wine, did seem to see this night strange and cruel visions, that even yet I think myself sprinkled and wet with human blood." Whereunto Socrates laughing made answer, "Nay verily, I myself dreamed this night that my throat was cut, and that I felt the pain of the wound, and that my heart was pulled out of my belly, and the remembrance thereof makes me now to fear, for my knees do so tremble that I can scarce go any further; and therefore I would fain eat somewhat to strengthen and revive my spirits."

Then said I, "Behold here thy breakfast"; and therewithal I opened my scrip that hanged upon my shoulder, and gave him bread and cheese, and we sat down under a great plane tree, and I ate part with him. And while I beheld him eating greedily, I perceived that he waxed meager and pale, and that his lively color faded away, insomuch that being in great fear, and remembering those terrible furies of whom I lately dreamed, the first morsel of bread that I put in my mouth (which was but very small) did so stick in my jaws, that I could neither swallow it down, nor yet yield it up, and moreover the small time of our being together increased my fear: and what is he that seeing his companion die in the highway before his face, would not greatly lament and be sorry? But when that Socrates had eaten sufficiently, he waxed very thirsty, for indeed he had well-nigh devoured all a whole cheese: and behold evil fortune! there was behind the plane tree a pleasant running water as clear as crystal, and I said unto him, "Come hither, Socrates, to this water and drink thy fill." And then he rose and came to the river, and kneeled down upon the side of the bank to drink; but he had scarce touched the water with his lips, whenas behold the wound of his throat opened wide, and the sponge suddenly fell into the water, and after issued out a little remnant of blood, and his body being then without life, had fallen into the river, had I not caught him by the leg and so pulled him up. And after that I had lamented a good space the death of my wretched companion, I buried him in the sands there by the river.

Biblical Literature

INTRODUCTION

IT is not surprising that the stories scattered so profusely through the *Bible*, the *Apocrypha*, and the *Talmud*, should be mostly moral tales. They were told in order to illustrate a theological or ethical contention or law, to glorify the race or nation to which the teller belonged, to attract and hold the interest of the listener. All of them were related by Jews, and all, even the parables of Jesus, bear the imprint of the Oriental imagination. The stories of *Ruth* and *Susanna*, from the *Old Testament* and the *Apocrypha*, are the earliest examples in this little group of Biblical tales. *Ruth* is the type of story that could easily be expanded into a novel, while *Susanna* conforms more exactly to the modern conception of what a short story ought to be. These two have been chosen from a great storehouse of prose narrative, which was designed in the first place to appeal to simple-minded shepherds and tradespeople.

In the *New Testament* we find among many other beautiful stories the parables. These are in reality fables, told by Jesus for exactly the same reason that the fables of Æsop or of Phædrus were told, to drive home a moral lesson. If Jesus spoke his parables exactly as they are written, he must be accounted one of the world's greatest artists. *The Prodigal Son* is a perfect model of the short story. The other tale included here, *The Raising of Lazarus*, though somewhat longer and more diffuse, is no less perfect.

The Talmud, which is the orthodox Jewish commentary on the *Old Testament*, bristles with short moral tales. To develop the art of the Jewish short story would necessitate tracing it from the earliest chapters of the *Old Testament*, through *The Talmud*, with all its accumulation of commentary upon commentary, through a long period of oral tradition, up to modern times. There are still sporadic writers in the Hebrew language, though for the most part the modern Jewish writers (when they have not, like Israel Zangwill, written in the language of the country of their adoption) have employed the modern Yiddish dialect.

The literature of the *New Testament* (which was written in late Greek) is difficult to classify. It is Jewish, of course, but permeated by a distinctly non-Hebraic spirit. The influence exerted by the narratives of the *New Testament* has been enormous, but it is rather religious and theological than artistic. The spirit of this literature has penetrated the thought, life, habits, and art of the entire Occidental world.

THE BOOK OF RUTH

(From the *Old Testament*)

INTO the extremely complicated questions of authorship, origin, and development of the Old Testament it is not necessary to enter. *Ruth* is one of the most beautifully conceived and finely written narratives of all Biblical literature. Although it has its place in the ethical scheme of the Old Testament, it seems to have been written with an artistic zest and freedom from constraint that are rare in the religious literature of any race.

The text used here is that printed in Volume IV of *Ancient Hebrew Literature*, in Everyman's Library, published in 1907 by J. M. Dent and Sons, by whose permission it is here included. (The last sentence has been omitted, as it has nothing to do with the story.)

THE BOOK OF RUTH

NOW it came to pass in the days when the judges ruled, that there was a famine in the land. And a certain man of Beth-lehem-judah went to sojourn in the country of Moab, he, and his wife, and his two sons. And the name of the man was Elimelech, and the name of his wife Naomi, and the name of his two sons Mahlon and Chilion, Ephrathites of Beth-lehem-judah. And they came into the country of Moab, and continued there.

And Elimelech Naomi's husband died; and she was left, and her two sons. And they took them wives of the women of Moab; the name of the one was Orpah, and the name of the other Ruth: and they dwelled there about ten years. And Mahlon and Chilion died also both of them; and the woman was left of her two sons and her husband.

Then she arose with her daughters-in-law, that she might return from the country of Moab: for she had heard in the country of Moab how that the Lord had visited His people in giving them bread. Wherefore she went forth out of the place where she was, and her two daughters-in-law with her; and they went on the way to return unto the land of Judah. And Naomi said unto her two daughters-in-law:—"Go, return each to her mother's house: the Lord deal kindly with you, as ye have dealt with the dead, and with me. The Lord grant you that ye may find rest, each of you in the house of her husband." Then she kissed them; and they lifted up their voice, and wept. And they said unto her:—"Surely we will return with thee unto thy people."

And Naomi said:—"Turn again, my daughters: why will ye go with me? are there yet any more sons in my womb, that they may be your husbands? Turn again, my daughters, go your way; for I am too old to have an husband. If I should say, I have hope, if I should have an husband also to-night, and should also bear sons; would ye tarry for them till they were grown? would ye stay for them from having husbands? nay, my daughters; for it grieveth me much for your sakes that the hand of the Lord is gone out against me."

And they lifted up their voice, and wept again: and Orpah kissed her mother-in-law; but Ruth clave unto her. And she said:—"Behold, thy sister-in-law is gone back unto her people, and unto her gods: return thou after thy sister-in-law." And Ruth said:—"Intreat me not to leave thee, or to return from following after thee: for whither thou goest, I will go; and where thou lodgest, I will lodge: thy people shall be my people, and thy God my God: where thou diest, will I die, and there will I be buried: the Lord do so to me, and more also, if ought but death part thee and me."

When she saw that she was steadfastly minded to go with her, then she left speaking unto her. So they two went until they came to Beth-lehem. And it came to pass, when they were come to Beth-lehem, that all the city was moved about them, and they said:—"Is this Naomi?" And she said unto them:—"Call me not Naomi, call me Mara: for the Almighty hath dealt very bitterly with me. I went out full, and the Lord hath brought me home again empty: why then call ye me Naomi, seeing the Lord hath testified against me, and the Almighty hath afflicted me?"

So Naomi returned, and Ruth the Moabitess, her daughter-in-law, with her, which returned out of the country of Moab: and they came to Beth-lehem in the beginning of barley harvest. And Naomi had a kinsman of her husband's, a mighty man of wealth, of the family of Elimelech; and his name was Boaz. And Ruth the Moabitess said unto Naomi:—"Let me now go to the field, and glean ears of corn after him in whose sight I shall find grace." And she said unto her:—"Go, my daughter." And she went, and came, and gleaned in the field after the reapers: and her hap was to light on a part of the field belonging unto Boaz, who was of the kindred of Elimelech.

And, behold, Boaz came from Beth-lehem, and said unto the reapers:—"The Lord be with you." And they answered him:—"The Lord bless thee." Then said Boaz unto his servant that was set over the reapers:—"Whose damsel is this?" And the servant that was set over the reapers answered and said:—"It is the Moabitish damsel that came back with Naomi out of the country of Moab: and she said, I pray you, let me glean and gather after the reapers among the sheaves: so she came, and hath continued even from the morning until now, that she tarried a little in the house." Then said Boaz unto Ruth:—"Hearest thou not, my daughter? Go not to glean in another field, neither go from hence, but abide here fast by my maidens: let thine eyes be on the field that they do reap, and go thou after them: have I not charged the young men that they shall not touch thee? and when thou art athirst, go unto the vessels, and drink of that which the young men have drawn." Then she fell on her face, and bowed herself to the ground, and said unto him: —"Why have I found grace in thine eyes, that thou shouldest take knowledge of me, seeing I am a stranger?" And Boaz answered and said unto her:—"It hath fully been shewed me, all that thou hast done unto thy mother-in-law since the death of thine husband: and how thou hast left thy father and thy mother, and the land of thy nativity, and art come unto a people which thou knewest not heretofore. The Lord recompense thy work, and a full reward be given thee of the Lord God of Israel, under whose wings thou art come to trust."

Then she said:—"Let me find favor in thy sight, my lord; for that thou hast comforted me, and for that thou hast spoken friendly unto thine handmaid, though I be not like unto one of thine handmaidens." And Boaz said unto her:—"At mealtime come thou hither, and eat of the bread, and dip thy morsel in the vinegar." And she sat beside the reapers: and he reached her parched corn, and she did eat, and was sufficed, and left. And when she was risen up to glean, Boaz commanded his young men, saying:—"Let her glean even among the sheaves, and reproach her not: and let fall also some of the handfuls of purpose for her, and leave them, that she may glean them, and rebuke her not."

So she gleaned in the field until even, and beat out that she had gleaned: and it was about an ephah of barley. And she took it up, and went into the city: and her mother-in-law saw what she had gleaned: and she brought forth, and gave to her that she had reserved after she was sufficed. And her mother-in-law said unto her:—"Where hast thou gleaned to-day? and where wroughtest thou? blessed be he that did take knowledge of thee." And she shewed her mother-in-law with whom she had wrought, and said:—"The man's name with whom I wrought to-day is Boaz." And Naomi said unto her daughter-in-law:—"Blessed be he of the Lord, who hath not left off His kindness to the living and to the dead." And Naomi said unto her:—"The man is near of kin unto us, one of our next kinsmen." And Ruth the Moabitess said:—"He said unto me also, Thou shalt keep fast by my young men, until they have ended all my harvest." And Naomi said unto Ruth her daughter-in-law:—"It is good, my daughter, that thou go out with his maidens, that they meet thee not in any other field." So she kept fast by the maidens of Boaz to glean unto the end of barley harvest and of wheat harvest; and dwelt with her mother-in-law.

Then Naomi her mother-in-law said unto her:—"My daughter, shall I not seek rest for thee, that it may be well with thee? And now is not Boaz of our kindred, with whose maidens thou wast? Behold, he winnoweth barley to-night in the threshing-floor. Wash thyself therefore, and anoint thee, and put thy raiment upon thee, and get thee down to the floor: but make not thyself known unto the man, until he shall have done eating and drinking. And it shall be, when he lieth down, that thou shalt mark the place where he shall lie, and thou shalt go in, and uncover his feet, and lay thee down; and he will tell thee what thou shalt do." And she said unto her:—"All that thou sayest unto me I will do."

And she went down unto the floor, and did according to all that her mother-in-law bade her. And when Boaz had eaten and drunk, and his heart was merry, he went to lie down at the end of the heap of corn: and she came softly, and uncovered his feet, and laid her down. And it came to pass at midnight, that the man was afraid, and turned himself: and, behold, a woman lay at his feet. And he said:—"Who art thou?" And she answered:—"I am Ruth thine handmaid: spread therefore thy skirt over thine handmaid; for thou art a near kinsman." And he said:—"Blessed be thou of the Lord, my daughter: for thou hast shewed more kindness in the latter end than at the beginning, inasmuch as thou followedst not young men, whether poor or rich. And now, my daughter, fear not; I will do to thee all that thou requirest: for all the city of my people doth know that thou art a virtuous woman. And now it is true that I am thy near kinsman: howbeit there is a kinsman nearer than I. Tarry this night, and it shall be in the morning, that if he will perform unto thee the part of a kinsman, well; let him do the kinsman's part: but if he will not do the part of a kinsman to thee, then will I do the part of a kinsman to thee, as the Lord liveth: lie down until the morning."

And she lay at his feet until the morning: and she rose up before one could know another. And he said:—"Let it not be known that a woman came into the floor." Also he said:—"Bring the vail that thou hast upon thee, and hold it." And when she held it, he measured six measures of barley, and laid it on her: and she went into the city. And when she came to her mother-in-law, she said:—"Who art thou, my daughter?" And she told her all that the man had done to her. And she said:—"These six measures of barley gave he me; for he said to me, Go not empty unto thy mother-in-law." Then said she:—"Sit still, my daughter, until thou know how the matter will fall: for the man will not be in rest, until he have finished the thing this day."

Then went Boaz up to the gate, and sat him down there: and, behold, the kinsman of whom Boaz spake came by; unto whom he said:—"Ho, such a one! turn aside, sit down here." And he turned aside, and sat down. And he took ten men of the elders of the city, and said:—"Sit ye down here." And they sat down. And he said unto the kinsman:—"Naomi, that is come again out of the country of Moab, selleth a parcel of land, which was our brother Elimelech's: and I thought to advertise thee, saying, Buy it before the inhabitants, and before the elders of my people. If thou wilt redeem it, redeem it: but if thou wilt not redeem it, then tell me, that I may know: for there is none to redeem it beside thee; and I am after thee." And he said:—"I will redeem it." Then said Boaz:—"What day thou buyest the field of the hand of Naomi, thou must buy it also of Ruth the Moabitess, the wife of the dead, to raise up the name of the dead upon his inheritance." And the kinsman said:—"I cannot redeem it for myself, lest I mar mine own inheritance: redeem thou my right to thyself; for I cannot redeem it." Now this was the manner in former time in Israel concerning redeeming and concerning changing, for to confirm all things; a man plucked off his shoe, and gave it to his neighbor: and this was a testimony in Israel. Therefore the kinsman said unto Boaz:—"Buy it for thee." So he drew off his shoe.

And Boaz said unto the elders, and unto all the people:—"Ye are witnesses this day, that I have bought all that was Elimelech's, and all that was Chilion's and Mahlon's, of the hand of Naomi. Moreover, Ruth the Moabitess, the wife of Mahlon, have I purchased to be my wife, to raise up the name of the dead upon his inheritance, that the name of the dead be not cut off from among his brethren, and from the gate of his place: ye are witnesses this day." And all the people that were in the gate, and the elders, said:—"We are witnesses. The Lord make the woman that is come into thine house like Rachel and like Leah, which two did build the house of Israel: and do thou worthily in Ephratah, and be famous in Beth-lehem: and let thy house be like the house of Pharez, whom Tamar bare unto Judah, of the seed which the Lord shall give thee of this young woman."

So Boaz took Ruth, and she was his wife: and when he went in unto her, the Lord gave her conception, and she bare a son. And the women said unto Naomi:—"Blessed be the Lord, which hath not left thee this day without a kinsman, that his name may be famous in Israel. And he shall be unto thee a restorer of thy life, and a nourisher of thine old age: for thy daughter-in-law, which loveth thee, which is better to thee than seven sons, hath born him." And Naomi took the child, and laid it in her bosom, and became nurse unto it. And the women her neighbors gave it a name, saying:—"There is a son born to Naomi"; and they called his name Obed: he is the father of Jesse, the father of David.

THE HISTORY OF SUSANNA

(From *The Apocrypha*)

SUSANNA was originally a part of the Book of Daniel, but was set apart as apocryphal, because it "was not in Hebrew." It is none the less a story of remarkable vividness, told with skill and dramatic power.

The text used here is that printed in Volume IV of *Ancient Hebrew Literature*, in Everyman's Library, published in 1907 by J. M. Dent and Sons, by whose permission it is here included.

THE HISTORY OF SUSANNA

THERE dwelt a man in Babylon, called Joakim: and he took a wife, whose name was Susanna, the daughter of Chelcias, a very fair woman, and one that feared the Lord. Her parents also were righteous, and taught their daughter according to the law of Moses. Now Joakim was a great rich man, and had a fair garden joining unto his house: and to him resorted the Jews; because he was more honorable than all others. The same year were appointed two of the ancients of the people to be judges, such as the Lord spake of, that wickedness came from Babylon from ancient judges, who seemed to govern the people. These kept much at Joakim's house: and all that had any suits in law came unto them.

Now when the people departed away at noon, Susanna went into her husband's garden to walk. And the two elders saw her going in every day, and walking; so that their lust was inflamed toward her. And they perverted their own mind, and turned away their eyes, that they might not look unto heaven, nor remember just judgments. And albeit they both were wounded with her love, yet durst not one shew another his grief. For they were ashamed to declare their lust, that they desired to have to do with her. Yet they watched diligently from day to day to see her. And the one said to the other:—"Let us now go home: for it is dinner time." So when they were gone out, they parted the one from the other, and turning back again they came to the same place; and after that they had asked one another the cause, they acknowledged their lust: then appointed they a time both together, when they might find her alone.

And it fell out, as they watched a fit time, she went in as before with two maids only, and she was desirous to wash herself in the garden: for it was hot. And there was nobody there save the two elders, that had hid themselves, and watched her. Then she said to her maids:—"Bring me oil and washing balls, and shut the garden doors, that I may wash me." And they did as she bade them, and shut the garden doors, and went out themselves at privy doors to fetch the things that she had commanded them: but they saw not the elders, because they were hid.

Now when the maids were gone forth, the two elders rose up, and ran unto her, saying:—"Behold, the garden doors are shut, that no man can see us, and we are in love with thee; therefore consent unto us, and lie with us. If thou wilt not, we will bear witness against thee, that a young man was with thee: and therefore thou didst send away thy maids from thee." Then Susanna sighed, and said:—"I am straitened on every side: for if I do this thing, it is death unto me: and if I do it not, I cannot escape your hands. It is better for me to fall into your hands, and not do it, than to sin in the sight of the Lord." With that Susanna cried with a loud voice: and the two elders cried out against her. Then ran the one, and opened the garden door. So when the servants of the house heard the cry in the garden, they rushed in at a privy door, to see what was done unto her. But when the elders had declared their matter, the servants were greatly ashamed: for there was never such a report made of Susanna.

And it came to pass the next day, when the people were assembled to her husband Joakim, the two elders came also full of mischievous imagination against Susanna to put her to death: and said before the people, "Send for Susanna, the daughter of Chelcias, Joakim's wife." And so they sent. So she came with her father and mother, her children, and all her kindred. Now Susanna was a very delicate woman, and beauteous to behold. And these wicked men commanded to uncover her face (for she was covered) that they might be filled with her beauty. Therefore her friends and all that saw her wept. Then the two elders stood up in the midst of the people, and laid their hands upon her head. And she weeping looked up toward heaven: for her heart trusted in the Lord. And the elders said:—"As we walked in the garden alone, this woman came in with two maids, and shut the garden doors, and sent the maids away. Then a young man, who there was hid, came unto her, and lay with her. Then we that stood in a corner of the garden, seeing this wickedness, ran unto them. And when we saw them together, the man we could not hold: for he was stronger than we, and opened the door, and leaped out. But having taken this woman, we asked who the young man was, but she would not tell us: these things do we testify."

Then the assembly believed them, as those that were the elders, and judges of the people: so they condemned her to death. Then Susanna cried out with a loud voice, and said:—"O everlasting God, that knowest the secrets, and knowest all things before they be: Thou knowest that they have borne false witness against me, and, behold, I must die; whereas I never did such things as these men have maliciously invented against me." And the Lord heard her voice. Therefore when she was led to be put to death, the Lord raised up the holy spirit of a youth, whose name was Daniel: who cried with a loud voice:—"I am clear from the blood of this woman." Then all the people turned them toward him, and said:—"What mean these words that thou hast spoken?"

So he standing in the midst of them said:—"Are ye such fools, ye sons of Israel, that without examination or knowledge of the truth ye have condemned a daughter of Israel? Return again to the place of judgment: for they have borne false witness against her." Wherefore all the people turned again in haste, and the elders said unto him:—"Come, sit down among us, and shew it us, seeing God hath given thee the honor of an elder." Then said Daniel unto them:—"Put these two aside one far from another, and I will examine them." So when they were put asunder one from another, he called one of them, and said unto him:—"O thou that art waxen old in wickedness, now thy sins which thou hast committed aforetime are come to light: for thou hast pronounced false judgment, and hast condemned the innocent, and hast let the guilty go free; albeit the Lord saith, The innocent and righteous shalt thou not slay. Now then, if thou hast seen her, tell me, Under what tree sawest thou them companying together?" Who answered:—"Under a mastic tree." And Daniel said:—"Very well; thou hast lied against thine own head; for even now the angel of God hath received the sentence of God to cut thee in two."

So he put him aside, and commanded to bring the other, and said unto him:—"O thou seed of Canaan, and not of Juda, beauty hath deceived thee, and lust hath perverted thine heart. Thus have ye dealt with the daughters of Israel, and they for fear companied with you: but the daughter of Juda would not abide your wickedness. Now therefore tell me, Under what tree didst thou take them companying together?" Who answered:—"Under an holm tree." Then said Daniel unto him:—"Well; thou hast also lied against thine own head: for the angel of God waiteth with the sword to cut thee in two, that He may destroy you." With that all the assembly cried out with a loud voice, and praised God, who saveth them that trust in Him.

And they arose against the two elders, for Daniel had convicted them of false witness by their own mouth: and according to the law of Moses they did unto them in such sort as they maliciously intended to do to their neighbor: and they put them to death. Thus the innocent blood was saved the same day. Therefore Chelcias and his wife praised God for their daughter Susanna, with Joakim her husband, and all the kindred, because there was no dishonesty found in her.

From that day forth was Daniel had in great reputation in the sight of the people.

THE PRODIGAL SON

(From the *New Testament*, Luke XV)

THE PRODIGAL SON is a parable, spoken by Jesus in praise of forgiveness. It is one of the great stories of the world, and is justly regarded as a perfect model of the art of story-telling.

The present text is taken from the King James version. There is no title to the story in the original.

THE PRODIGAL SON

AND he said, A certain man had two sons: and the younger of them said to his father, Father, give me the portion of goods that falleth to me. And he divided unto them his living. And not many days after the younger son gathered all together, and took his journey into a far country, and there wasted his substance with riotous living. And when he had spent all, there arose a mighty famine in that land; and he began to be in want. And he went and joined himself to a citizen of that country; and he sent him into his fields to feed swine. And he would fain have filled his belly with the husks that the swine did eat: and no man gave unto him. And when he came to himself, he said, How many hired servants of my father's have bread enough and to spare, and I perish with hunger! I will arise and go to my father, and will say unto him, Father, I have sinned against heaven, and before thee, and am no more worthy to be called thy son: make me as one of thy hired servants. And he arose, and came to his father. But when he was yet a great way off, his father saw him, and had compassion, and ran, and fell on his neck, and kissed him. And the son said unto him, Father, I have sinned against heaven, and in thy sight, and am no more worthy to be called thy son. But the father said to his servants, Bring forth the best robe, and put it on him; and put a ring on his hand, and shoes on his feet: and bring hither the fatted calf, and kill it; and let us eat, and be merry: For this my son was dead, and is alive again; he was lost, and is found. And they began to be merry.

Now his elder son was in the field: and as he came and drew nigh to the house, he heard music and dancing. And he called one of the servants, and asked what these things meant. And he said unto him, Thy brother is come; and thy father hath killed the fatted calf, because he hath received him safe and sound. And he was angry, and would not go in: therefore came his father out, and entreated him. And he answering said to his father, Lo these many years do I serve thee, neither transgressed I at any time thy commandment: and yet thou never gavest me a kid, that I might make merry with my friends: but as soon as this thy son was come, which hath devoured thy living with harlots, thou hast killed for him the fatted calf. And he said unto him, Son, thou art ever with me, and all that I have is thine. It was meet that we should make merry, and be glad: for this thy brother was dead, and is alive again; and was lost, and is found.

THE RAISING OF LAZARUS

(From the *New Testament*, John XI)

THOUGH this story is part of the larger narrative of the Gospel of St. John, it is a perfect example of the short story. The details that lead up to the dramatic climax are at first sight not entirely relevant. It is only after the story has been read in its entirety that we perceive the consummate art of the preparatory sentences. Balzac was, many centuries later, to apply this method to the writing of his novels.

The text is taken from the King James version. There is no title to the story in the original.

THE RAISING OF LAZARUS

NOW a certain man was sick, named Lazarus, of Bethany, the town of Mary and her sister Martha. (It was that Mary which anointed the Lord with ointment, and wiped his feet with her hair, whose brother Lazarus was sick.) Therefore, his sister sent unto him saying, Lord, behold, he whom thou lovest is sick. When Jesus heard that, he said, This sickness is not unto death, but for the glory of God, that the Son of God might be glorified thereby.

Now Jesus loved Martha, and her sister, and Lazarus. When he had heard therefore that he was sick, he abode two days still in the same place where he was. Then after that saith he to his disciples, Let us go into Judæa again. His disciples say unto him, Master, the Jews of late sought to stone thee; and goest thou thither again? Jesus answered, Are there not twelve hours in the day? If any man walk in the day, he stumbleth not, because he seeth the light of this world. But if a man walk in the night, he stumbleth, because there is no light in him. These things said he: and after that he saith unto them, Our friend Lazarus sleepeth; but I go, that I may awake him out of sleep. Then said his disciples,

Lord, if he sleep, he shall do well. Howbeit Jesus spake of his death: but they thought that he had spoken of taking of rest in sleep. Then Jesus said unto them plainly, Lazarus is dead. And I am glad for your sakes that I was not there, to the intent ye may believe; nevertheless let us go unto him. Then said Thomas, which is called Didymus, unto his fellow disciples, Let us also go, that we may die with him.

Then when Jesus came, he found that he had lain in the grave four days already. Now Bethany was nigh unto Jerusalem about fifteen furlongs off: and many of the Jews came unto Martha and Mary, to comfort them concerning their brother. Then Martha, as soon as she heard that Jesus was coming, went and met him, but Mary sat still in the house. Then said Martha unto Jesus, Lord, if thou hadst been here, my brother had not died. But I know, that even now, whatsoever thou wilt ask of God, God will give it thee. Jesus saith unto her, Thy brother shall rise again. Martha saith unto him, I know that he shall rise again in the resurrection at the last day. Jesus said unto her, I am the resurrection and the life: he that believeth in me, though he were dead, yet shall he live: and whosoever liveth and believeth in me shall never die. Believest thou this? She saith unto him, Yea, Lord; I believe that thou art the Christ, the son of God, which should come into the world. And when she had so said, she went her way, and called Mary her sister secretly, saying, The Master is come, and calleth for thee. As soon as she heard that, she arose quickly and came unto him.

Now Jesus was not yet come into the town, but was in that place where Martha met him. The Jews then which were with her in the house, and comforted her, when they saw Mary, that she rose up hastily and went out, followed her saying, She goeth unto the grave to weep there. Then when Mary was come where Jesus was, and saw him, she fell down at his feet, saying unto him, Lord, if thou hadst been here, my brother had not died. When Jesus therefore saw her weeping, and the Jews also weeping which came with her, he groaned in the spirit, and was troubled, and said, Where have ye laid him? They said unto him, Lord, come and see. Jesus wept. Then said the Jews, Behold how he loved him! And some of them said, Could not this man, which opened the eyes of the blind, have caused that even this man should not have died? Jesus therefore again groaning in himself cometh to the grave. It was a cave, and a stone lay upon it. Jesus said, Take ye away the stone. Martha, the sister of him that was dead, saith unto him, Lord, by this time he stinketh: for he hath been dead four days. Jesus saith unto her, Said I not unto thee, that, if thou wouldest believe, thou shouldest see the glory of God? Then they took away the stone from the place where the dead was laid. And Jesus lifted up his eyes, and said, Father, I thank thee that thou hast heard me. And I knew that thou hearest me always: but because of the people which stand by I said it, that they may believe that thou hast sent me. And when he thus had spoken, he cried with a loud voice, Lazarus, come forth.

And he that was dead, came forth, bound hand and foot with grave-clothes. And his face was bound about with a napkin. Jesus saith unto them, Loose him, and let him go. Then many of the Jews which came to Mary, and had seen the things which Jesus did, believed on him.

RABBI AKIVA

(From *The Talmud*)

The Talmud is a great collection of law, ritual, precept, and example, which was composed during the period extending from the First Century B.C. to the Fourth Century A.D. The work was the result of a vast amount of compilation begun, so far as the actual writing is concerned, in the year 219 A.D. by Rabbi Jehudah Hanassi. About the year 500 A.D. it was complete, having been combined with a good deal of material brought together since the first parts were written down. The colossal work is interspersed throughout with parables, like *Rabbi Akiva* and *The Jewish Mother*, all of which were used for purposes of illustration.

The texts of these stories are based, by the editors, upon two early translations. There are no titles to the stories in the original.

RABBI AKIVA

THE Rabbis tell us that once the Roman Government made a decree forbidding Israel to study the law. Thereupon Pappus, son of Yehudah, one day found Rabbi Akiva teaching it openly to many whom he had gathered round him to hear it. "Akiva," he said, "dost not thou fear the Government?" "Listen," was the reply, "and I will tell thee how it is through a parable. It is the same with me as with the fishes which a fox, walking by a river's bank, saw darting distractedly to and fro in the stream; and, speaking to them, inquired, 'From what, pray, are ye fleeing?' 'From the nets,' they answered, 'which the sons of men have set to snare us.' 'Why, then,' rejoined the fox, 'not try the dry land with me, where we can live together, as our fathers managed to live before us?' 'Surely,' they exclaimed, 'thou art not he of whom we have heard as the most cunning of animals; for in this thing thou art not wise, but foolish. For if we have cause to fear where it is natural for us to live, how much more reason have we to do so where we must die!' Exactly so," continued Akiva, "is it with us who study the law, in which it is written, 'He is thy life and the length of thy days'; for if we suffer while studying the law, how much more shall we suffer if we neglect it?" Not many days afterward it is related that Rabbi Akiva was arrested and thrown into prison. It so happened that they led him out for execution just at the time when "Hear, O Israel!" was being repeated, and as they gashed his flesh with currycombs, and as he was with long-drawn breath uttering the word One, his soul departed from him. Then there came forth a voice from heaven saying, "Blessed art thou, Rabbi Akiva, for thy soul and the word One left thy body together."

THE JEWISH MOTHER

(From *The Talmud*)

ONCE upon a time a Jewish mother together with her seven sons suffered martyrdom at the hands of the Emperor. The sons, ordered by the latter to do homage to the Imperial idols, declined, and justified their disobedience by each quoting a simple text from the Scriptures. When the seventh was brought forth, it is said that Cæsar, for appearance' sake, offered to spare him if he would only stoop and pick up a ring from the ground which had been dropped on purpose. "Alas for thee, oh, Cæsar!" replied the boy; "if thou art so zealous for thine honor, how much more so ought we to be for that of the Holy One—blessed be He!" When he was led away to the place of execution, his mother begged and obtained leave to give him a last kiss. "Go, my child," she said, "and say to Abraham, Thou didst build an altar for the sacrifice of one son, but I have raised altars for seven sons." Then she turned away and threw herself headlong from the roof and died. The echo of a voice was heard exclaiming, "The joyful mother of children."

Ancient India

INTRODUCTION

SANSKRIT is the classical language of the Hindus of ancient India. Practically the whole of that extraordinary literature which began with the *Vedas* and culminated some time before the close of the Middle Ages, was written in Sanskrit.

Our knowledge of the earliest period is vague. The *Vedas* were composed perhaps before the days of Homer. Beginning perhaps about 500 B.C. and extending to about the time of Christ, is the period of the epics, during which the *Mahabharata* and *Ramayana* were probably written. Both these monumental poems are full of episodes containing at least the material for short stories.

But for the purpose of this volume, the outstanding contribution of the ancient Hindus were the fables and tales, most of which are found in large collections. The earliest of these is doubtless the *Jataka*, or Buddhist "birth-stories," which were in existence at least as early as the Fourth Century B.C. The *Panchatantra* may be as old as the *Jataka* stories; both are rooted in a common source. Many centuries later an unknown author revised certain parts of the *Panchatantra* and produced the book known as the *Hitopadesa*, which may be as recent as the Fourteenth Century A.D.

Most of these stories are directly didactic, but for the historian in search of the origin of certain types, the question of the fable and its Indian or Greek origin, is one of the most fascinating in all literature. There are those who claim that the tales in the *Panchatantra* and the *Jataka* stories are the source of all the fables in the Occident, and others who believe that it was the Hindus who took the fable form from the Ancient Greeks.

Of the other collections of stories the most varied is the famous *Katha-sarit-Sagara*, or *Ocean of Streams of Stories*, written about 1070 A.D. by Somadeva. This was based upon a much earlier collection, which is now lost.

The influence of the Sanskrit tales on the art of the story is almost impossible to estimate: translations and revisions of Sanskrit tales and fables were made as early as the Sixth Century B.C., and modern research is demonstrating beyond any doubt the fact that the Ancient Hindus have furnished ideas and literary forms to other nations ever since the dawn of history.

THE ASS IN THE LION'S SKIN

(Anonymous: 500 B.C.?–380 B.C.?)

THE *Jataka* or "Birth-story" is found in one form or another in several collections, one of which was well known as early as the Fourth Century B.C. It is a brief incident, usually in fable form, showing one incarnation of the Buddha, and drawing from the fable a little moral. The *Jataka* may actually have influenced the ancient Greeks and given rise to the Æsop legends, but whether or not that is true, they constitute the "oldest, most complete, and most important collection of folk-lore extant."

Nothing whatsoever is known of the author or authors of the particular collection from which this story is taken. It is reprinted from *Buddhist Birth Stories* [*Nidana-Katha*], by T. W. Rhys Davids, London, 1880, by permission of the publishers, Kegan Paul, Trench, Trübner and Co.

THE ASS IN THE LION'S SKIN

(From the *Jataka* Collections)

ONCE upon a time, while Brahma-datta was reigning in Benares, the future Buddha was born one of a peasant family; and when he grew up, he gained his living by tilling the ground.

At that time a hawker used to go from place to place, trafficking in goods carried by an ass. Now at each place he came to, when he took the pack down from the ass's back he used to clothe him in a lion's skin, and turn him loose in the rice and barley-fields, and when the watchmen in the fields saw the ass, they dared not go near him, taking him for a lion. So one day the hawker stopped in a village; and while he was getting his own breakfast cooked, he dressed the ass in a lion's skin and turned him loose in a barley-field. The watchmen in the field dared not go up to him; but going home, they published the news. Then all the villagers came out with weapons in their hands; and blowing chanks, and beating drums, they went near the field and shouted. Terrified with the fear of death, the ass uttered a cry—the cry of an ass!

And when he knew him then to be an ass, the future Buddha pronounced the first stanza:

"This is not a lion's roaring,
Nor a tiger's, nor a panther's;
Dressed in a lion's skin,
'Tis a wretched ass that roars!"

But when the villagers knew the creature to be an ass, they beat him till his bones broke; and, carrying off the lion's skin, went away. Then the hawker came, and seeing the ass fallen into so bad a plight, pronounced the second stanza:

"Long might the ass,
Clad in a lion's skin,
Have fed on barley green,
But he brayed,
And that moment he came to ruin."

And even while he was yet speaking the ass died on the spot!

THE DOVE AND THE CROW

(Anonymous: 2nd Century B.C. or later)

It is thought that the collection of fables now known as the *Panchatantra* had assumed definite shape at least as early as the Sixth Century A.D., and it is possible that it dates back to the Second Century B.C. Nothing is known of the author. The little stories that make up the collection are mostly Beast Fables, which were originally designed to instruct young princes. "Panchatantra" means "five books."

The present story, from the second book or *Tantra*, is reprinted from *Ancient Indian Fables and Stories*, by permission of the publisher, John Murray. It has no title in the original.

THE DOVE AND THE CROW

(From the *Panchatantra*)

When Vishnu Sarma had finished telling and expounding these fables, his pupils were lost in admiration of their teacher, whose wisdom had been so clearly marked by his dexterous mingling of amusement with instruction. They rose and all three fell at his feet, thanking him for the wise lessons he had given them; they assured him that henceforth they would regard him as their guru and that they hoped with his help and advice to rise from the state of ignorance in which they had hitherto been. They prayed him to continue the work so happily begun and to give them more of his interesting lessons.

Vishnu Sarma was charmed to see that his pupils were well disposed and noticed with satisfaction that his plan had so far succeeded. He continued his task with enthusiasm and proceeded to tell them fresh fables.

"Now," said Vishnu Sarma, "listen, my young princes, to the fable I am going to tell you. In the complex nature of this life we must all help one another. It is by this mutual help that the weak escape the dangers to which they are exposed from the strong, as you shall now hear."

A certain dove, by name Chitrani, had built her nest on the top of the mountain Kanakachala and was living there comfortably with her family. At the foot of the mountain dwelt a crow. One day Vega-Varma (such was the crow's name) was flying round in search of food when he noticed a fowler spreading his nets in the way. He was frightened at sight of the danger and at once returned home.

The dove Chitrani passed by the same place with her family, but being off their guard, they all flew into the net and were captured. What was to be done? How could they escape from certain death? There was in fact no escape, no hope of obtaining their liberty. Already the fowler was running up to seize his prey, when all at once under the impulse of danger they took to flight together, carrying with them the net that enclosed them. So they succeeded in escaping, and the fowler, who had reckoned upon his capture, was not a little surprised when he saw them fly away with his nets. But they reached their home in safety still entangled in the nets into which they had flown.

When the crow saw them coming in this strange chariot, he hastened to meet them; and as soon as Chitrani saw him, she told him of their adventures and asked him to help them by disentangling the nets. The crow replied that he could not free them, but suggested a rat of the name of Hiranya Varma who lived close by and who could help them. Accordingly Chitrani called the rat, who came up at once, and when he saw the captives he began to scold Chitrani for her imprudence and folly which had brought them to this pass. Chitrani defended herself and quoted the maxim: "No one, be he never so wise or prudent, can escape his destiny." Then the rat, pitying the poor doves, called his fellows, and they all set to work to gnaw the knots of the nets, so that very soon they had freed Chitrani and her family.

The crow, who had seen the signal service performed by the rat for the doves, was anxious to make friends with him; he hoped also to obtain a useful ally should occasion arise. He accordingly made overtures to him; but the rat replied that they were of totally different species, the one living in the air and the other in the earth; he did not see the use of the close friendship of two creatures between whom Nature had fixed such a wide gulf.

But the crow insisted. Matters of personal interest and friendship, he said, are decided by our inclination. We do not consider distance or the difference of condition. So the rat yielded and they swore a close friendship. One day when they were out together they happened to meet a deer; they stopped him and asked his name and where he was going. The deer said he was called Chitranga, told them his story, and asked if he might join them. They readily consented, and so the three struck up a lasting friendship.

One day while they were out together and were very thirsty, in their search for water they found a well into which a tortoise had fallen. As soon as she saw the three friends she begged them to take her out of her prison and to put her somewhere where she could live in comfort. Pitying her plight, they rescued her and took her to a spring of clear water; and she, mindful of this service, also became their friend.

For a long time the four lived happily together, but one day when the deer had gone away to graze he fell into the snare of a hunter. But when the rat saw that his friend the deer was so long in returning, he guessed that he had met with an accident. So he called the crow and told him what he feared and advised him to fly up and try to discover their friend. This the crow did, and after looking about for some time, at last saw poor Chitranga in the snare struggling hard to get out, but in vain.

The crow at once told Hiranya Varma what had happened to their friend, and he, calling his fellow-rats, sallied out to help him. They soon set him free. Chitranga went home with his friends and the accident was soon forgotten. But later on, when the four friends were resting quietly in the shade of a tree, they were suddenly disturbed by the unexpected sight of a crowd of hunters. This alarmed them. The crow and the deer could easily avoid pursuit, but not so the rat, and least of all the tortoise. The other two would not leave them to the mercy of the hunters, who were coming on quickly, and so the deer undertook to attract attention to himself in order to save the life of his friends. He pretended to be lame. The hunters, seeing him limp and apparently hardly able to hold himself up, all ran to capture the easy prey. But the deer led them a long dance, sometimes quickening his pace, sometimes slowing down, until at last, having made them follow for a long time, he fairly used his four legs and was soon out of sight. Meanwhile the tortoise and the rat had found a place of safety out of reach of the hunters.

Once more the four friends were united and lived quietly together; these dangers had taught them the value of true unity and of sincere friendship, and by experience they learned how the weak need to support one another.

SOMADEVA

(Flourished about 1070 A.D.)

SOMADEVA (Soma with the Brahminical suffix *deva*) was a poet of Kashmir. His celebrated collection, the *Ocean of Streams of Stories*, based upon Buddhist stories, traditions, and an earlier collection of tales, is one of the most voluminous and interesting of its kind in Sanskrit literature.

The present story, translated by C. H. Tawney, appeared in *The Ocean of Story*, Vol. I, Book IV, Chap. 21, of the complete edition in ten volumes edited by M. M. Penzer, and published in 1924-25 by Chas. J. Sawyer, Ltd., by whose permission it is here included.

THE STORY OF DEVADATTA

(From the *Katha-Sarit-Sagara*)

IN old time there was a certain petty monarch of the name of Jayadatta, and there was born to him a son, named Devadatta. And that wise king, wishing to marry his son, who was grown up, thus reflected: "The prosperity of kings is very unstable, being like a courtesan to be enjoyed by force; but the prosperity of merchants is like a woman of good family; it is steady and does not fly to another man. Therefore I will take a wife to my son from a merchant's family, in order that misfortune may not overtake his throne, though it is surrounded with many relations." Having formed this resolve, that king sought for his son the daughter of a merchant in Pātaliputra named Vasudatta. Vasudatta for his part, eager for such a distinguished alliance, gave that daughter of his to the prince, though he dwelt in a remote foreign land.

And he loaded his son-in-law with wealth to such an extent that he no longer felt much respect for his father's magnificence. Then King Jayadatta dwelt happily with that son of his who had obtained the daughter of that rich merchant. Now one day the merchant Vasudatta came, full of desire to see his daughter, to the palace of his connection by marriage, and took away his daughter to his own home. Shortly after the King Jayadatta suddenly went to heaven, and that kingdom was seized by his relations, who rose in rebellion; through fear of them his son Devadatta was secretly taken away by his mother during the night to another country.

Then that mother, distressed in soul, said to the prince: "Our feudal lord is the emperor who rules the eastern region; repair to him, my son; he will procure you the kingdom."

When his mother said this to him, the prince answered her: "Who will respect me if I go there without attendants?" When she heard that, his mother went on to say: "Go to the house of your father-in-law, and get money there, and so procure followers; and then repair to the emperor." Being urged in these words by his mother, the prince, though full of shame, slowly plodded on and reached his father-in-law's house in the evening. But he could not bear to enter at such an unseasonable hour, for he was afraid of shedding tears, being bereaved of his father and having lost his worldly splendor; besides, shame withheld him.

So he remained in the veranda of an almshouse near, and at night he suddenly beheld a woman descending with a rope from his father-in-law's house, and immediately he recognized her as his wife, for she was so resplendent with jewels that she looked like a meteor fallen from the clouds; and he was much grieved thereat. But she, though she saw him, did not recognize him, as he was emaciated and begrimed, and asked him who he was. When he heard that, he answered: "I am a traveler." Then the merchant's daughter entered the almshouse, and the prince followed her secretly to watch her. There she advanced towards a certain man, and he towards her, and asking why she had come so late, he bestowed several kicks on her. Then the passion of the wicked woman was doubled, and she appeased him, and remained with him on the most affectionate terms.

When he saw that, the discreet prince reflected: "This is not the time for me to show anger, for I have other affairs in hand; and how could I employ against these two contemptible creatures, this wife of mine and the man who has done me this wrong, this sword which is to be used against my foes? Or what quarrel have I with this adulteress, for this is the work of malignant desire that showers calamities upon me, showing skill in the game of testing my firmness? It is my marriage with a woman below me in rank that is in fault, not the woman herself; how can a female crow leave the male crow to take pleasure in a cuckoo?"

Thus reflecting, he allowed that wife of his to remain in the society of her paramour; for in the minds of heroes possessed with an ardent desire of victory, of what importance is woman, valueless as a straw? But at the moment when his wife ardently embraced her paramour there fell from her ear an ornament thickly studded with valuable jewels. And she did not observe this, but at the end of her interview, taking leave of her paramour, returned hurriedly to her house as she came. And that unlawful lover also departed somewhere or other.

Then the prince saw that jeweled ornament, and took it up; it flashed with many jewel-gleams, dispelling the gathering darkness of despondency, and seemed like a hand-lamp obtained by him to assist him in searching for his lost prosperity. The prince immediately perceived that it was very valuable, and went off, having obtained all he required, to Kanyākubja; there he pledged that ornament for a hundred thousand gold pieces, and after buying horses and elephants went into the presence of the emperor. And with the troops which he gave him he marched, and slew his enemies in fight, and recovered his father's kingdom; and his mother applauded his success.

Then he redeemed from pawn that ornament, and sent it to his father-in-law to reveal that unsuspected secret; his father-in-law, when he saw that earring of his daughter's, which had come to him in such a way, was confounded, and showed it to her. She looked upon it, lost long ago like her own virtue; and when she heard that it had been sent by her husband she was distracted, and called to mind the whole circumstance: "This is the very ornament which I let fall in the almshouse the night I saw that unknown traveler standing there; so that must undoubtedly have been my husband come to test my virtue, but I did not recognize him, and he picked up this ornament."

While the merchant's daughter was going through this train of reflection, her heart, afflicted by the misfortune of her unchastity having been discovered, in its agony, broke. Then her father artfully questioned a maid of hers who knew all her secrets, and found out the truth, and so ceased to mourn for his daughter; as for the prince, after he recovered the kingdom, he obtained as wife the daughter of the emperor, won by his virtues, and enjoyed the highest prosperity.

THE JACKAL

(Anonymous: 14th Century, A.D., or earlier)

NOTHING is known of the author of the *Hitopadesa,* a manual of didactic fables composed—on the basis of the *Panchatantra*—before the year 1373 A.D.

The present story—which has no title in the original—is reprinted from Charles Wilkins' translation, London, 1787.

THE JACKAL

(From the *Hitopadesa*)

A CERTAIN jackal, as he was roaming about the borders of a town, just as his inclinations led him, fell into a dyer's vat; but being unable to get out, in the morning he feigned himself dead. At length, the master of the vat, which was filled with indigo, came, and seeing a jackal lying with his legs uppermost, his eyes closed, and his teeth bare, concluded that he was dead, and so, taking him out, he carried him a good way from the town, and there left him. The sly animal instantly got up, and ran into the woods; when, observing that his coat was turned blue, he meditated in this manner: "I am now of the finest color! what great exaltation may I not bring about for myself?" Saying this, he called a number of jackals together, and addressed them in the following words: "Know that I have lately been sprinkled king of the forests, by the hands of the goddess herself who presides over these woods, with a water drawn from a variety of choice herbs. Observe my color, and henceforward let every business be transacted according to my orders." The rest of the jackals, seeing him of such a fine complexion, prostrated themselves before him, and said: "According as Your Highness commands!" By this step he made himself honored by his own relations, and so gained the supreme power over those of his own species, as well as all the other inhabitants of the forests. But after a while, finding himself surrounded by a levee of the first quality, such as the tiger and the like, he began to look down upon his relations; and, at length, he kept them at a distance. A certain old jackal, perceiving that his brethren were very much cast down at this behavior, cried: "Do not despair! If it continue thus, this imprudent friend of ours will force us to be revenged. Let me alone to contrive his downfall. The lion, and the rest who pay him court, are taken by his outward appearance; and they obey him as their king, because they are not aware that he is nothing but a jackal: do something then by which he may be found out. Let this plan be pursued: Assemble all of you in a body about the close of the evening, and set up one general howl in his hearing; and I'll warrant you, the natural disposition of his species will incline him to join in the cry; for,

> Whatever may be the natural propensity of anyone is very hard to be overcome. If a dog were made king, would he not gnaw his shoe-straps?

And thus the tiger, discovering that he is nothing but a jackal, will presently put him to death." The plan was executed, and the event was just as it had been foretold.

Persia

INTRODUCTION

THE short story in Persia had its origin among the wandering story-tellers, who sometimes invented their plots (so far as any one ever invents a plot), but more commonly borrowed them from the extensive store of legends or folk-tales, Semitic or Mohammedan in origin. No story-teller's repertory was complete unless it included tales of treasure or of love. The motive of these characteristic stories was extremely simple: one set out to amass a fortune, either by cunning or outright theft; or else one pursued some woman who was acclaimed as the perfection of maidenly beauty. In any event, the hero almost invariably succeeded in his quest and lived happy ever after. The obstacles in the way of achievement, whether the quest was treasure or a beautiful woman, formed the basis of the story, and when these were of a supernatural character the teller excelled in the invention of particularly ingenious obstacles. The introduction of supernatural elements was to be expected among a people whose imaginations had been stimulated by long ages of wandering in the uninhabited spots of the earth, and the Persian story-teller delighted in mixing his facts with fancy.

The Golden Age of the Persian story was about the Eleventh Century A.D. Since that time there has been little activity on the part of the novelist or the short story writer.

The Persians added to the art they so zealously practised a decorative element that was wanting in the Sanscrit stories, from which they largely borrowed, but apart from this they would deserve enduring fame for having transmitted to the Arabians the celebrated *Arabian Nights*.

ABUL KASIM MANSUR FIRDAWSI

(935–1025 A.D.)

ABUL KASIM MANSUR FIRDAWSÍ was born in the city of Tus, in Persia, in 935. He left the city of his birth to join the famous court of Mahmud of Ghazna, but not before he had completed a rough draft of his justly famous *Shah-Nama*, or *Book of Kings*. About forty years he devoted to this wonderful epic, an account of the glories of Irán from its very beginnings and one of the great contributions to classic literature. It is related that Mahmud promised Firdawsí a fortune for his epic. When it was finally finished in 1010, the monarch failed of his word. Later, repenting of his misdeed, he sent the poet the promised gold, which arrived just as this ill-treated immortal was being buried.

The present version of *Jamshid and Zuhak*, a single episode from *The Book of the Kings*, is from the translation by Rueben Levy, M.A., copyrighted in 1923 by the Oxford University Press, by whose permission it is here reprinted.

JAMSHID AND ZUHAK

IN the days when the world was young, there was a king who, from his capital in Irán, ruled the earth for seven hundred years. His name was Jamshid, and he was indeed a mighty monarch, for men and divs and birds and peris all obeyed him. The world grew prosperous under him, for he said: "I will prevent evildoers from working ill, and will guide all men aright."

For fifty years he concerned himself with weapons of war, to open the path to glory for the valiant, and made helmets and lances and coats of mail. Then he turned to the making of garments for his people. He prepared stuffs of linen, of wool, of beaver skins and of rich brocade, and taught the people how to weave; and when the material was ready he showed them how to clean it and make it into garments. This being achieved, he devoted a space of time to seeking out the precious stones, and discovered such treasured things as ruby, yellow amber, silver, and gold. Then he invented perfumes, such as balm, camphor and pure musk, aloes, umber and rose-water. Thereafter he discovered medicine, remedies against every sickness, and the means of preserving health and of curing wounds. Thereby he made the world contented and was himself happy.

Three hundred years passed, and in that time death was unknown. There was neither pain nor sorrow, and the divs were kept in slavery, so that they never troubled men. But as time went on, the king became so powerful that he could see nothing in all the earth save himself, and by his arrogance incurred the anger of the gods.

Now there lived at this time in Arabia a king among the desert chieftains and the captain of many armed bands of horsemen. He possessed flocks and herds of goats, camels, and sheep, each a thousand strong, as well as cows and Arab horses. This generous king had a son Zuhak, who was brave, light-hearted, and care-free, and who was constantly engaged in wars against his enemies.

It happened one day that Iblis, the god of the divs, came to the palace disguised as a nobleman, and so pleased the young prince that he turned aside from his brave and noble way in order to follow the wicked div. Iblis rejoiced greatly, and said: "I know many things which none can learn except from me." "Teach me them," said the young man, "and do not delay." "First," said Iblis, "you must swear an oath not to reveal my secrets to any man." "I swear," said Zuhak, "and I will do everything you tell me." "Then," said Iblis to him, "why should there be any other man but you, illustrious prince, in the palace? Of what use is a father when he has a son like you? Take his throne, for it belongs to you, and if you follow my counsel, you will be a great king on the earth."

When Zuhak heard this he pondered long, for he loved his father. He said: "I cannot do it. Tell me something else, for that is not possible." Iblis replied in fury, "If you do not carry out my commands and if you break the oath you swore to me, my bonds will remain attached to your neck for ever." Zuhak submitted, and said: "How am I to bring this about?"

"I, Iblis, will prepare the means, and raise you to the sun. You have but to keep silence."

Now the king had around his palace a garden in which he took great delight, and here, often rising before dawn, he would walk, without even one slave to carry his torch. On the path the div dug a deep pit, covered it with brushwood, and spread earth on the top. Early the following morning, before the sun was up, the Arab king awoke and went out into the cold air of dawn. As he approached the fatal pit his star paled, but he disregarded its warning, and, falling into the chasm, was slain. Thus perished this pious man who had scarce ever spoken a harsh word to his son.

Iblis, his plan accomplished, then approached Zuhak again, and said: "When you have turned your heart towards me, you may obtain all that you desire. Renew but your oath, and the entire world will be your kingdom; the wild beasts, the birds, and the fishes will be your subjects." And with these words he vanished.

Soon afterwards Iblis assumed the guise of a young man of ready speech and agile form, and presented himself to Zuhak, saying that he was an excellent cook. The prince engaged him, and by his royal command delivered to him the keys of his kitchen. Now the design of Iblis was to make the prince abandon his eating of herbs and to persuade him to the eating of meat. He began by preparing yolk of egg for him, which in a short time gave him great vigor of body. Zuhak was pleased and commended his cook, who said, "To-morrow I will prepare for your Majesty a dish than which nought is more perfect." And the next day, when the blue dome of heaven was lighted by the red ruby of the sun, he prepared a dish of partridge and of silver pheasant, which the Arab ruler ate; and thus he abandoned his imprudent mind to the power of Iblis, who, on the third day, placed upon the table a mixture of birds and lambs' flesh. On the fourth day, when the meal was brought, the king feasted on the flesh of a young calf seasoned with rose-water, old wine, and pure musk. The meal filled him with delight at the skill of his cook, and, summoning him, he said, "Think what it is that you desire, and ask it of me." Iblis replied, "I have but one request to make of the king (may he live prosperous forever), but that is an honor too great for me; it is that I may be permitted to kiss his shoulders and to touch them with my eyes and face."

Zuhak suspected nothing of his intention, and said: "I grant your wish; it may be that some honor will thereby accrue to your name," and he bared his shoulders to him as to a friend. Iblis kissed them and vanished from the earth. But from each of Zuhak's shoulders appeared a black serpent, and Zuhak became sick at heart and sought on all sides for a remedy. Finally he bade that the serpents be cut off close to his shoulder, but they grew again. Every physician and wise man in the kingdom tried his remedies, but all in vain. The last to come was Iblis himself, who appeared as a physician before Zuhak. "It was inevitable," said he, "that this should happen. Leave the serpents and do not cut them off while there is life in them. To appease them you must feed them on the brains of men, which alone will at last slay them."

While these events were taking place at the court of Arabia, great tumults filled the land of Irán. The arrogance of Jamshid had set his subjects in revolt against him, and a great army marched towards Arabia from the highlands of Irán. They had heard that in Arabia there was a man with a serpent's face that inspired terror in men, and to him they went in order to elect him as their king. Zuhak eagerly returned with them and was crowned, and, turning his eyes towards the throne of Jamshid, began to treat the world familiarly as if it were the ring upon his finger. Jamshid fled before him, and for a hundred years was seen by no man, till Zuhak fell upon him without warning in the confines of China and put him to death. Thus perished his pride from the earth.

For a thousand years Zuhak occupied the throne and the world submitted to him, so that goodness died away and was replaced by evil. Every night during that long period two youths were slain to provide the serpents' food. Now in the king's country there remained two men of purity, of Persian race, the one Irmail the Pious, and the other Girmail the Clear-sighted. It happened that they met one day and talked of many matters great and small; of the unjust king, of his army, and of his horrible custom. The one said: "We ought, by the art of the kitchen, to introduce ourselves into the king's household and apply our wits to saving the unfortunates who lose their lives each day." Setting to work, they learned the art of cookery, and succeeded in entering the king's kitchen. There, after no long time, they were entrusted with the preparation of the king's meal, and they contrived to mix the brains of a sheep with those of one of the youths who was brought for slaughter. The other one they saved alive and dismissed secretly, saying to him: "Escape in secret, beware of visiting any inhabited town; your portion in the world must be the desert and the mountain."

In this manner they saved two hundred men, of whom is born the race of Kurds, who know not any fixed abode, whose houses are tents; and who have in their hearts no fear of God.

While Zuhak still had forty years to live, one night he dreamed a dream, and he saw three royal warriors emerge, two of them aged, and another, younger, who walked between them, and who had the form of a cypress and the visage of a king. His girth and his gait were those of a prince, and he carried a club with a bull's head. He advanced straight upon Zuhak, smote him upon the forehead with his club, tied him hand and foot with thongs, and overwhelmed him with shame and torments.

Zuhak awoke with a great cry of fear, that brought his wife, Arnawaz, and his attendants running to him in alarm. Arnawaz, as she approached, cried out to him: "O king, confide in me and tell me what has happened. You sleep in your palace securely; everything that is in the world obeys you; savage beasts, divs, and men are your guardians; the earth with its seven climes is your domain; all, from the firmament to the depths of the seas, is yours. Why then do you leap thus from your bed? Tell us." Zuhak replied: "My dream must be kept secret, for were I to reveal it, you would despair of my life." "Perhaps, if you reveal it," said Arnawaz, "we may find a remedy, for no ill exists that has not its remedy." The king was persuaded by this, and told what he had seen in his dream. "This is not a matter that you may neglect," exclaimed the queen on hearing it. "Summon from every country the sages that can read the stars, examine all sources, and seek thus to learn the secret. Discover what he is whose hand threatens you; man, div, or peri; and when you know, then immediately apply your remedy." And the king approved the counsel of this silver swan.

The world, plunged in night, was black as a raven's wing; suddenly light dawned upon the mountains as though the sun had scattered rubies upon the azure of the firmament. Wherever there were wise counselors the king sought them out and assembled them in his palace, where he told the whole company of his trouble, and sought their advice. The lips of the noblemen were dried with fear, their cheeks paled, and their hearts filled with anguish. "For," said each to himself, "if we disclose what must happen, he will die, and if we remain silent, then we must bid adieu to life." Thus they remained hesitating for three days. And on the fourth day, Zuhak assembled them again and in rage asked for their counsel, and menaced them with death if they withheld from him their knowledge of the future.

At length there stood out from among the noble counselors one who was their chief, whose conduct was upright and whose heart was filled with wisdom. He loosened his tongue before Zuhak, and spoke thus: "Empty thine heart of vain hope, for no one is born save to die. There have been many kings before you worthy of the throne of power, they saw much of grief and much of joy; and, when their long days had flowed past, they died. Were you a rampart of iron securely founded, the turn of the skies would break you too, and you would disappear. There will be some one who will inherit your throne and will overturn your fortunes. His name is Faridun, but he is not yet born, and the time to fear him is not yet. He will grow like a tree destined to bear fruit, and when he has reached manhood his head will touch the moon. Then he will demand your girdle and your crown, your throne and your diadem. He will carry upon his shoulder a club of steel, and with his bull-headed mace he will strike you and drag you from your palace."

"What reason has he for hating me?" cried out the impure Zuhak.

"Because his father will die at your hands."

The king heard and thought on this, fell from his throne, and swooned away. When his senses returned to him, he mounted again upon his throne and sent out searchers, both secret and public, to seek for traces of Faridun. He sought no rest or sleep or food, and bright day became gloomy to him.

Thus passed a long space of time, while the serpent-man remained prey to his terror. Faridun was born, and the lot of the whole world was thereby destined to change. The youth grew up like a cypress, and he was resplendent with all the glory of majesty. He was like the shining sun, as needful to the world as rain, an adornment to the mind like knowledge. Zuhak filled the earth with sound and fury, searching everywhere for Faridun son of Abtin. The earth became straitened for Abtin, who fled and struggled; but he was finally caught in the lion's net.

Meantime Faridun was well secured by his mother, and was safe. The king ceased not night or day to be in anguish concerning him. One day he seated himself on his ivory throne, and, putting his crown upon his head, summoned all his nobles. To them he spoke thus: "O you men of virtue, noble and prudent, I have a hidden enemy, as all men know. I despise no enemy however feeble, for I fear lest fortune betray me. I must increase my army, and will have it of men, divs, and peris. I desire you to aid me, for I cannot bear my torment alone. You must write for me a declaration that as king I have sown nought but the seed of good, that I have spoken nought save the words of truth, that I have never frustrated justice." All the noblemen, in fear of the king, consented to his demand, and all, old and young, declared what the serpent-man desired.

But suddenly at the gate of the palace was heard the voice of one crying out for justice. The complainant was brought before the king, who asked who had done him wrong. The man cried out, struck his head with his hands on seeing the monarch, and said: "I am Kawa, O king; I demand justice. Grant me justice. I have come in haste, and it is you whom I accuse in the bitterness of my heart. I had seventeen sons, and now there remains but one. Give me back this one, my only son; think how my heart will burn with grief, the whole length of my life. What crime have I committed? Even tyranny must have a pretext, and I am an innocent man, a blacksmith. You must render count to me for what you have done, and the world will be astonished thereby. It will see, by the account you will render to me, what my lot on earth has been, and how I have been compelled to give my sons to feed your serpents."

The king looked harshly upon him on hearing these words, gave back the man's son, and strove to soothe him with words. Lastly he asked Kawa to sign the declaration of the nobles, but he, trembling with rage, tore and trampled on it and emerged shouting with a mighty anger. The crowd in the market-place gathered round him, and to them and the whole world he appealed to aid him in obtaining justice. He took off the apron which blacksmiths wear, tied it to a lance and marched through the bazaars crying: "Illustrious men, you that adore God, who desire to be delivered from the clutches of Zuhak, let us go to Faridun and let us rest in the shadow of his sovereignty."

Having ascertained where Faridun lay hiding, he set out with a great troop of men, and after no long time reached his abode. The young prince saw the standard made of the blacksmith's apron, and accepted it as a good omen. Then, tarrying only while a suit of armor was made for him, he began his march at the head of his army, which moved as speedily as the wind. Soon they reached the Tigris River and the city of Baghdad. Arrived there, Faridun sent his greeting to the guardian of the crossing, and said: "Send me boats and ships, that I and my army may cross." But the guardian sent back answer: "The king has given me secret command that no man may cross without his sealed order."

Faridun heard the messenger with anger. The swift stream inspired him with no fear, and he with his warriors tightened girdle and plunged into it with their horses. Having crossed, they made their way to the royal city of Zuhak. On coming within a mile of it Faridun saw a palace whose walls were raised higher than Saturn, as if it had been built to tear the stars from the sky. It shone like Jupiter in the celestial sphere. From its vastness and magnificence Faridun knew it to be the palace of the monster-king, and, turning to his companions, he said: "I fear one that has been able from dust and stones to rear so mighty a structure. I fear some secret bond between fortune and him, but it is better to fling ourselves into battle than to delay here." Thus he spoke, and, giving rein to his spirited horse, he raised his club and rushed like a flame past the wardens of the gate and into the palace. He dashed to the ground a talisman which Zuhak had set up against him, and struck down all that offered resistance; he placed his foot upon the throne of Zuhak, seized the royal crown, and took his place.

A servant of Zuhak saw what had happened, and mounting a swift horse brought the tale to his master: "O king of a proud people, there are tokens that portend the fall of your fortunes. Three heroes have come from a strange land with an army. The youngest remains always between the two elder, his stature is that of a prince, his face that of a king. He carries a mighty club like a great rock, and he has seated himself upon the throne."

Zuhak, in great haste, prepared to return with an army of divs and men. By devious ways he flung his army against the terraces and gates of the palace, thinking of nought but vengeance. But the army of Faridun and the inhabitants of the town fought together in the battle, and their mass was like a mountain.

Meantime rage incited Zuhak to further enterprise. Covering himself from head to foot with armor, that none might know him, in the confusion he climbed unseen into the palace by means of a rope of sixty cubits. But he was recognized and pursued and, in his rage, leaped from the battlements to the ground. Faridun advanced, swift as the wind, and smote Zuhak with his club through his helmet to his head. But a faithful counselor held his hand, saying, "His time is not yet come. He is broken but not dead. Let him be placed to spend the rest of his days in the depths of the rocks, where neither his friends nor his vassals can find him."

So Faridun prepared thongs of lion skin, and bound Zuhak's hands and feet and body, in such manner that a wild elephant could not have broken the bonds. He bore the monster, thus tightly bound, to the height of the lofty mountain of Damawand, and there, in a narrow bottomless chasm, he chained him. And there Zuhak remains suspended until the ill he wrought shall have vanished from the earth.

THE SAILOR AND THE PEARL MERCHANT

THE author of the following story is unknown. It was gathered with others in Persia, brought to England and presented to the Bodleian Library.

The Story of the Sailor and the Pearl Merchant is a splendid example of the Persian story-teller's fantastic and magical art.

The present version is from a translation by Rueben Levy, M.A., of MS. Ouseley 231, Bodleian Library. Copyright, 1923, by Oxford University Press, by whose permission it is here reprinted.

THE SAILOR AND THE PEARL MERCHANT

IT is related that in the city of Basrah there was a man, Abu'l Fawaris, who was the chief of the sailors of the town, for in the great ocean there was no port at which he had not landed. One day, as he sat on the seashore, with his sailors round him, an old man arrived in a ship, landed where Abu'l Fawaris was sitting, and said: "Friend, I desire you to give me your ship for six months, and I will pay you whatever you desire." "I demand a thousand gold dinars," said the sailor, and at once received the gold from the old man, who, before departing, said that he would come again on the next day, and warned Abu'l Fawaris that there was to be no holding back.

The sailor took home his gold, made his ship ready, and then, taking leave of his wife and sons, he went down to the shore, where he found the old man waiting for him with a slave and twenty ass-loads of empty sacks. Abu'l Fawaris greeted him, and together they loaded the ship and set sail. Taking a particular star for their mark, they sailed for three months, when an island appeared to one side of them. For this the old man steered, and they soon landed upon it. Having loaded his slave with some sacks, the old man with his companions set out towards a mountain which they could see in the distance. This they reached after some hours of travel, and climbed to the summit, upon which they found a broad plain where more than two hundred pits had been dug. The old man then explained to the sailor that he was a merchant, and that he had, on that spot, found a mine of jewels. "Now that I have given you my confidence," he continued, "I expect faithfulness from you too. I desire you to go down into this pit and send up sufficient pearls to fill these sacks. Half I will give to you, and we shall be able to spend the rest of our lives in luxury." The sailor thereupon asked how the pearls had found their way into these pits, to which the old man replied that there was a passage connecting the pits with the sea. Along this passage oysters swam, and settled in the pits, where by chance he had come upon them. He explained further that he had only brought the sailor because he needed help; but he desired not to disclose the matter to any one else.

With great eagerness then the sailor descended into the pit, and there found oysters in great numbers. The old man let down a basket to him, which he filled again and again, until at last the merchant cried out that the oysters were useless, for they contained no pearls. Abu'l Fawaris therefore left that pit, and descended into another, where he found pearls in great number. By the time night fell he was utterly wearied, and called out to the old man to help him out of the pit. In reply the merchant shouted down that he intended to leave him in the pit, for he feared that Abu'l Fawaris might kill him for the sake of the jewels. With great vehemence the sailor protested that he was innocent of any such intention, but the old man was deaf to his entreaties, and, making his way back to the ship, sailed away.

For three days Abu'l Fawaris remained, hungry and thirsty. As he struggled to find a way out he came upon many human bones, and understood that the accursed old man had betrayed many others in the same fashion. In desperation he dug about, and at last he saw a small opening, which he enlarged with his hands. Soon it was big enough for him to crawl through, and he found himself in the darkness, standing upon mud. Along this he walked carefully, and then felt himself suddenly plunged to his neck in water, which was salt to the taste; and he knew that he was in the passage that led to the sea. He swam along in this for some way, till, in front of him, there appeared a faint light. Greatly heartened by the sight of it, he swam vigorously until he reached the mouth of the passage. On emerging, he found himself facing the sea, and threw himself on his face to give thanks for his delivery. Then he arose, and a little distance from him he found the cloak which he had left behind when he set out for the mountain; but of the old merchant there was no sign, and the ship had disappeared.

Full of trouble and despondency, he sat down at the water's brink, wondering what he was to do. As he gazed at the sea there came into view a ship, and he saw that it was filled with men. At sight of it the sailor leaped from his place; snatching his turban from his head, he waved it with all his might in the air, and shouted at the top of his voice. But as they approached he decided not to tell his rescuers the truth of his presence there; therefore when they landed and asked how he came to be on the island he told them that his ship had been wrecked at sea, that he had clung to a plank and been washed to the shore.

They praised his good fortune at his escape, and in reply to his questions with regard to the place of their origin, told him that they had sailed from Abyssinia, and were then on their way to Hindustan. At this, Abu'l Fawaris hesitated, saying that he had no business in Hindustan. They assured him, however, that they would meet ships going to Basrah, and would hand him over to one of them. He agreed then to go with them, and for forty days they sailed without seeing any inhabited spot. At last he asked them whether they had not mistaken their way, and they admitted that for five days they had been sailing without knowing whither they were going or what direction to follow. All together therefore set themselves to praying, and remained in prayer for some time.

Soon afterwards, as they sailed, something in appearance like a minaret emerged from the sea, and they seemed to behold the flash of a Chinese mirror. Also they perceived that their ship, without their rowing, and without any greater force of wind, began to move at great speed over the water. In great amazement the sailors ran to Abu'l Fawaris and asked him what had come to the ship that it moved so fast. He raised his eyes, and groaned deeply as in the distance he saw a mountain that rose out of the sea. In terror he clapped his hand to his eyes and shouted out: "We shall all perish! My father continually warned me that if ever I lost my way upon the sea I must steer to the East; for if I went to the West I would certainly fall into the Lion's Mouth. When I asked him what the Lion's Mouth was, he told me that the Almighty had created a great hole in the midst of the ocean, at the foot of a mountain. That is the Lion's Mouth. Over a hundred leagues of water it will attract a ship, and no vessel which encounters the mountain ever rises again. I believe that this is the place and that we are caught."

In great terror the sailors saw their ship being carried like the wind against the mountain. Soon it was caught in the whirlpool, where the wrecks of ten thousand ancient ships were being carried around in the swirling current. The sailors and merchants in the ship crowded to Abu'l Fawaris, begging him to tell them what they could do. He cried out to them to prepare all the ropes which they had in the ship; he would then swim out of the whirlpool and on to the shore at the foot of the mountain, where he would make fast to some stout tree. Then they were to cast their ropes to him and so he would rescue them from their peril. By great good fortune the current cast him out upon the shore, and he made the rope of his ship fast to a stout tree.

Then, as soon as was possible, the sailor climbed to the top of the mountain in search of food, for neither he nor his shipmates had eaten for some days. When he reached the summit he found a pleasant plain stretching away in front of him, and in the midst of it he saw a lofty arch, made of green stone. As he approached it and entered, he observed a tall pillar made of steel, from which there hung by a chain a great drum of Damascus bronze covered with a lion's skin. From the arch also hung a great tablet of bronze, upon which was engraved the following inscription: "O thou that dost reach this place, know that when Alexander voyaged round the world and reached the Lion's Mouth, he had been made aware of this place of calamity. He was therefore accompanied by four thousand wise men, whom he summoned and whom he commanded to provide a means of escape from this calamitous spot. For long the philosophers pondered on the matter, until at last Plato caused this drum to be made, whose quality is that if any one, being caught in the whirlpool, can come forth and strike the drum three times, he will bring out his ship to the surface."

When the sailor had read the inscription, he quickly made his way to the shore and told his fellows of it. After much debate he agreed to risk his life by staying on the island and striking the drum, on condition that they would return to Basrah on their escape, and give to his wife and sons one-half of what treasure they had in the ship. He bound them with an oath to do this, and then returned to the arch. Taking up a club he struck the drum three times, and as the mighty roar of it echoed from the hills, the ship, like an arrow shot from a bow, was flung out of the whirlpool. Then, with a cry of farewell to Abu'l Fawaris from the crew, they sailed to Basrah, where they gave one-half the treasure which they had to the sailor's family.

With great mourning the wife and family of Abu'l Fawaris celebrated his loss; but he, after sleeping soundly in the archway and giving thanks to his Maker for preserving him alive, made his way again to the summit of the mountain. As he advanced across the plain he saw black smoke arising from it, and also in the plain were rivers, of which he passed nine. He was like to die of hunger and weariness, when suddenly he perceived on one side a meadow, in which flocks of sheep were grazing. In great joy he thought that he was at last reaching human habitation, and as he came towards the sheep, he saw with them a youth, tall in stature as a mountain, and covered with a tattered cloak of red felt, though his head and body were clad in mail. The sailor greeted him, and received greeting in reply, and also the question "Whence come you?" Abu'l Fawaris answered that he was a man upon whom catastrophe had fallen, and so related his adventures to the shepherd. He heard it with a laugh, and said: "Count yourself fortunate to have escaped from that abyss. Do not fear now, I will bring you to a village." Saying this he set bread and milk before him and bade him eat. When he had eaten he said: "You cannot remain here all day, I will take you to my house, where you may rest for a time."

Together they descended to the foot of the mountain, where stood a gateway. Against it leaned a mighty stone, which a hundred men could not have lifted, but the shepherd, putting his hand into a hole in the stone, lifted it away from the gateway and admitted Abu'l Fawaris.

Then he restored the stone to its place, and continued on his way.

When the sailor had passed through the gateway he saw before him a beautiful garden in which were trees laden with fruit. In the midst of them was a kiosk, and this, the sailor thought, must be the shepherd's house. He entered and looked about from the roof, but though he saw many houses there was no person in sight. He descended therefore, and walked to the nearest house, which he entered. Upon crossing the threshold he beheld ten men, all naked and all so fat that their eyes were almost closed. With their heads down upon their knees, all were weeping bitterly. But at the sound of his footsteps they raised their heads and called out "Who are you?" He told them that the shepherd had brought him and offered him hospitality. A great cry arose from them as they heard this. "Here," they said, "is another unfortunate who has fallen, like ourselves, into the clutch of this monster. He is a vile creature, who in the guise of a shepherd goes about and seizes men and devours them. We are all merchants whom adverse winds have brought here. That div has seized us and keeps us in this fashion."

With a groan the sailor thought that now at last he was undone. At that moment he saw the shepherd coming, saw him let the sheep into the garden, and then close the gateway with the stone before entering the kiosk. He was carrying a bag full of almonds, dates, and pistachio nuts, with which he approached, and, giving it to the sailor, he told him to share it with the others. Abu'l Fawaris could say nothing, but sat down and ate the food with his companions. When they had finished their meal, the shepherd returned to them, took one of them by the hand, and then in sight of them all, slew, roasted, and devoured him. When he was sated, he brought out a skin of wine and drank until he fell into a drunken sleep.

Then the sailor turned to his companions and said: "Since I am to die, let me first destroy him; if you will give me your help, I will do so." They replied that they had no strength left; but he, seeing the two long spits on which the ogre had roasted his meat, put them into the fire until they were red hot, and then plunged them into the monster's eyes.

With a great cry the shepherd leaped up and tried to seize his tormentor, who sprang away and eluded him. Running to the stone, the shepherd moved it aside and began to let out the sheep one by one, in the hope that when the garden was emptier he could the more easily capture the sailor. Abu'l Fawaris understood his intention: without delay, he slew a sheep, put on the skin and tried to pass through. But the shepherd knew as soon as he felt him that this was not a sheep, and leaped after him in pursuit. Abu'l Fawaris flung off the pelt, and ran like the wind. Soon he came to the sea, and into this he plunged, while the shepherd after a few steps returned to the shore, for he could not swim.

Full of terror the sailor swam till he reached the other side of the mountain. There he met an old man who greeted him, and, after hearing his adventure, fed him and took him to his house. But soon, to his horror, Abu'l Fawaris found that this old man also was an ogre. With great cunning he told the ogre's wife that he could make many useful implements for her house, and she persuaded her husband to save him. After many days in the house, he was sent away to the care of a shepherd, and put to guard sheep. Day by day he planned to escape, but there was only one way across the mountain and that was guarded.

One day, as he wandered in a wood, he found in the hollow trunk of a tree a store of honey, of which he told the shepherd's wife when he went home. The next day, therefore, the woman sent her husband with Abu'l Fawaris, telling him to bring home some of the honey; but, on the way, the sailor leaped upon him and bound him to a tree. Then, taking the shepherd's ring, he returned and told the woman that her husband had given him leave to go, and that he sent his ring in token of this. But the woman was cunning and asked: "Why did not my husband come himself to tell me this?" Seizing him by the cloak, she told him that she would go with him and find out the truth. The sailor, however, tore himself free, and again fled to the sea, where he thought that he might escape death. In haste and terror he swam for many hours, until at last he espied a ship full of men, who steered towards him and took him on board. Full of wonder they asked how he came there, and he related to them all his adventures.

It happened by great good fortune that the ship's captain had business at one place only on the coast, and that from there he was sailing to Basrah. In the space of a month, therefore, Abu'l Fawaris was restored to his family, to the joy of them all.

The many dangers and sufferings of the sailor had turned his hair white. For many days he rested, and then, one day, as he walked by the seashore, that same old man who had before hired his ship again appeared. Without recognizing him, he asked if he would lend his ship on hire for six months. Abu'l Fawaris agreed to do so for a thousand dinars of gold, which the old man at once paid to him, saying that he would come in a boat on the morrow, ready to depart.

When the ancient departed, the sailor took home the money to his wife, who bade him beware not to cast himself again into danger. He replied that he must be avenged not only for himself, but also for the thousand Muslims whom the villainous old man had slain.

The next day, therefore, the sailor took on board the old man and a black slave, and for three months they sailed, until they once more reached the island of pearls. There they made fast the ship on the shore, and taking sacks, they ascended to the top of the mountain. Once arrived there, the old man made the same request to Abu'l Fawaris as before, namely, that he should go down into the pits and send up pearls. The sailor replied that he was unacquainted with the place, and preferred that the old man should go down first, in order to prove that there was no danger. He answered that there was surely no danger; he had never in his life harmed even an ant, and he would of a certainty never send Abu'l Fawaris down into the pits if he knew any peril lay there. But the sailor was obstinate, saying that until he knew how to carry it out, he could not undertake the task.

Very reluctantly, therefore, the old man allowed himself to be lowered into the first pit by a basket and a rope. He filled the basket with oysters and sent it up, crying out: "You see, there is nothing to do harm in this pit. Draw me up now, for I am an old man and have no more strength left." The sailor replied, "Now that you are there, it were better if you remained there to complete your task. To-morrow I myself will go into another pit and will send up so many pearls as to fill the ship." For a long time the old man worked, sending up pearls, and at last he cried out again, "O my brother, I am utterly wearied, draw me out now." Then the sailor turned upon him with fury, and cried out: "How is it that thou dost see ever thine own trouble and never that of others? Thou misbegotten dog, art thou blind that thou dost not know me? I am Abu'l Fawaris, the sailor, whom long ago you left in one of these pits. By the favor of Allah I was delivered, and now it is your turn. Open your eyes to the truth and remember what you have done to so many men." The old man cried aloud for mercy, but it availed him nothing, for Abu'l Fawaris brought a great stone and covered up the mouth of the pit. The slave too he overwhelmed with threats, and then together they carried down the pearls to the ship, in which they set sail. In three months they arrived at Basrah. There Abu'l Fawaris related his adventures, to the amazement of all. Thenceforward he abandoned the sea and adopted a life of ease. Finally he died, and this story remains in memory of him. And Allah knoweth best.

Arabia

INTRODUCTION

THE literature of the Arabs originated in the improvisations of stories and poems among the pre-Mohammedan inhabitants of Arabia. These were the oral recitations of the people, transmitted from generation to generation. It is improbable that anything was actually collected and reduced to writing before the Ninth or Tenth Century A.D., although some time during the Ninth Century Al-Asma'i brought together the elements that make up the *Romance of Antar*, one of the stories from which is here reprinted. This coloured and romantic accumulation of poetic stories and legends is the great epic of Arabian literature.

The Arabs are noted for their nomadic existence, but there were also town dwellers in Arabia who appreciated a less simple story than the recitations of the wandering inhabitants of the desert and therefore imported several cycles or collections of tales, of which the supreme masterpiece is the celebrated *Thousand Nights and One Night*, better known as the *Thousand and One Nights*, or simply the *Arabian Nights*. These famous tales had been translated from the Sanskrit (with certain elaborations) into the Persian, from which the Arabs borrowed them, though they added so much in the way of details and literary style that the collection may be considered an original contribution. These made their appearance in the Arabic somewhere between the Tenth and Fourteenth Centuries of our epoch.

It is hazardous to attribute to any one person the actual invention of a literary form, but it is customary to designate Hamadhani (968-1054) as the first writer of stories in Arabic. His art was practised and improved upon by Al-Hariri (1054-1122), whose *Lectures* constitute an imposing array of fanciful tales. The *Golden Meadows* of Mas'udi, composed during the Tenth Century, are interesting rather as commentaries upon contemporary life and manners than as tales.

After the appearance of the *Arabian Nights*, there was little more in Arabian literature in the way of short stories to be added. Modern literature is of relatively little importance.

The Arabian tale, although it was not altogether indigenous, has established itself, at least in the minds of Occidentals, as a sort of symbol of the romance of the Orient. There was a gorgeousness of local color, a riot of sensuous imagery in the best of the Arabian stories, that later writers have sought in vain to imitate.

AL-ASMA'I

(9th Century, A.D.)

PRACTICALLY nothing is known of the collector of the material that makes up the epical *Romance of Antar*. *Khaled and Djaida*, which is taken from that epic, is not so finished and skilful a narrative as the best of the tales in the *Arabian Nights:* it belongs rather to the type of episode which Homer introduced into the *Odyssey*, or the author of *Beowulf* into that work. Yet there is in it that element of wonder which the world's great story-tellers knew so well how to use, and a certain delicate art that spins out an incident to the delight of idle listeners.

The present text is based upon the translation by T. Hamilton: *A Bedoueen Romance*, London, 1820. There is no title to the original story.

KHALED AND DJAIDA

(From *The Romance of Antar*)

MOHARIB and Zahir were two brothers, by the same father and mother; the Arabians call them "germane." Both were eminent for their courage and daring. But Moharib was chief of the clan, and Zahir was his minister, subject to his authority, giving him counsel and advice. It happened that a violent dispute and quarrel arose between them. Zahir retired to his tent, sorrowing and not knowing what to do. "What is the matter with you?" demanded his wife. "Why are you troubled? What has happened? Has anyone displeased or insulted you—the greatest of Arabian chiefs?" "What am I to do?" said Zahir; "he who has injured me is one I cannot lay hands on, or wrong; my companion in private, my brother in the world. Oh, if it had been any other, I would have shown him what kind of man he was at odds with, and made an example of him before the chiefs of our people!" "Leave him in the enjoyment of his possessions," cried his wife, and, to persuade her husband to do this, she recited verses from a contemporary poet, dissuading a man from accepting an insult even from his parents.

Zahir accepted the advice of his wife. He made preparations for departure, took down his tents, loaded his camels, and started off towards the camp of the Saad clan, with whom he was allied. Nevertheless, he felt a pang at separating himself from his brother—and thus he spoke: "On starting a journey which takes me from you, I shall seem a thousand years on the way, each year carrying me a thousand leagues. . . . Even though the favors you heap upon me be worth a thousand Egypts, and each Egypt had a thousand Niles, they would all be despised. I shall be happy with little so long as I am far from you. In my absence, I shall recite this verse, which is worth more than a necklace of fine pearls: 'When a man is insulted on the soil of his clan, there is nothing to do but to leave it; you, who have so wickedly injured me, ere long shall feel the power of the beneficent divinity, for he is your judge and mine, unchangeable and everlasting.' "

Zahir proceeded on his journey, until he reached the Saad tribe, and dismounted from his horse. He was cordially welcomed and pressed to dwell among them. His wife was soon to become a mother, and he said to her: "If a son be given us, he will be welcome; but if it be a daughter, conceal her sex, and allow people to think we have a boy, so that my brother may have no reason to crow over us." When her time came Zahir's wife brought forth a daughter. They agreed that her name should be Djaida, but that in public she should be known as Djonder, that people might think her a boy. In order to promote this belief, they feasted and entertained early and late for many days.

About the same time Moharib, the other brother, had a son born to him, whom he called Khaled. He chose this name out of gratitude to God, because, since his brother's departure, his affairs had prospered.

The two children in time reached maturity, and their fame spread far and wide among the Arabians. Zahir had taught his daughter to ride horseback, and trained her in all the accomplishments fitting to a brave and daring warrior. He accustomed her to the severest labor, and the most perilous enterprises. When he went to war, he put her among the other Arabs of the clan, and among these horsemen she soon took her rank as one of the most valiant of them. And thus it came to pass that she outstripped all her comrades, and would even attack the lions in their dens. At last her name inspired the greatest terror; when she had conquered a champion she never failed to cry out: "I am Djonder, son of Zahir, horseman of the clans."

For his part, her cousin Khaled distinguished himself likewise by his brilliant courage. His father Moharib, a wise and prudent chieftain, had built places of entertainment for strangers; and horsemen found a welcome there. Khaled had grown up in the company of warriors. In this school his spirit had been moulded, here he had learned to ride, and had become at last an intrepid warrior, and a fear-inspiring hero. It was soon perceived by the army that his spirit and valor were unconquerable.

Now at last he heard news of his cousin Djonder, and his eagerness to see and know him and witness his skill in arms became extreme. But he was unable to satisfy this desire because of the dislike his father showed for his cousin, his uncle's son. Khaled's curiosity remained unsatisfied until the death of his father Moharib, which put him in possession of rank, riches and land. He followed the example of his father in entertaining strangers, protecting the weak and unfortunate, and giving clothing to the naked. He continued also to sweep the plains on horseback in company with his warriors, and thus became greater in bodily strength and courage. After some time, gathering together a number of precious gifts, he set out, in company with his mother, to visit his uncle. He did not draw rein until he reached the dwelling of Zahir, who was very glad to see him, and made magnificent preparations for his entertainment; for the uncle had heard news on several occasions of his nephew's worth and valor. Khaled also visited his cousin. He saluted her, pressed her to his bosom, and kissed her forehead, thinking that she was a young man. He felt the keenest pleasure when he was in her company, and remained for ten days with his uncle, taking part in the tournaments and contests of horsemen and warriors. As for his cousin, the moment she had seen how handsome and valiant Khaled was, she fell violently in love with him. She was unable to sleep; she could not eat; and her love drew to such a pitch that feeling her heart completely lost to him, she spoke to her mother, saying: "Oh, mother, if my cousin should leave without taking me with him, I shall die of grief at his absence." Then her mother was touched with pity for her, and spoke no reproaches, feeling that they would be in vain. "Djaida," she said, "conceal your feelings, and restrain yourself from grief. You have done nothing wrong, for your cousin is the man of your choice, and is of your own race and blood. Like him, you are beautiful and attractive; like him, brave and skilful in horsemanship. To-morrow morning, when his mother comes to us, I will lay before her the whole matter; we will soon afterwards give you to him in marriage, and at last we shall all return to our own country."

Zahir's wife waited patiently until the following morning, when Khaled's mother arrived. She then presented her daughter, whose head she uncovered so as to allow the hair to fall over her shoulders. At the sight of such charms Khaled's mother was immeasurably astonished, and exclaimed: "What! is not this your son Djonder?" "No! it is Djaida—behold, the moon of beauty! She at last has risen." She then went on to tell her all that had passed between herself and her husband, and how and why they had concealed the sex of their child. "Dear kinswoman," answered Khaled's mother, still quite surprised, "among all the daughters of Arabia who have been famed for their beauty I have never seen one more lovely than this one. What is her name?" "I have already told you that her name is Djaida, and my special purpose in telling you the secret is to offer you these charms, for I ardently wish to marry my daughter to your son, so that we may all be able to return to our own land." Khaled's mother at once assented to this proposal, and said: "The possession of Djaida will surely render my son very happy." She rose immediately and went to look for Khaled, and told him all that she had seen and learned, not failing to praise especially the charms of Djaida. "By the faith of an Arab," said she, "never, oh, son, have I seen in the desert, or in any city, a girl like your cousin; not even the most beautiful. Nothing is so perfect as she, nothing lovelier and more attractive. Hasten, my son, to see your uncle and ask him for his daughter in marriage. You will be happy indeed if he grants your prayer. Go, my son, and waste no time in winning her."

On hearing these words Khaled cast his eyes on the ground; and remained for some time thoughtful and gloomy. Then he answered: "Mother, I cannot remain here longer. I must return home in company with my horsemen and troops. I have no intention of saying more to my cousin; I am convinced that she is a girl whose temper and philosophy are uncertain; her character and mode of speech are destitute of stability and propriety. I have always been accustomed to live with warriors, on whom I spend my wealth, and with whom I win a soldier's fame. As for my cousin's love for me, it is the weakness of a woman, a young girl." He then put on his armor, mounted his horse, bade his uncle farewell, and announced his intention of leaving on the moment. "What means this haste?" cried Zahir. "I can remain here no longer," answered Khaled, and, putting his horse to a gallop, he plunged into the wilderness. His mother, after relating to Djaida the conversation she had had with her son, mounted a camel and proceeded on her way towards her own country.

The sensitive soul of Djaida felt keenly this indignity. She brooded over it—sleepless and without appetite. Some days afterwards, as her father was preparing to make a foray with his horsemen against his enemies, his glance fell on Djaida, and seeing how changed she was in face, and dejected in spirit, he refrained from saying anything, thinking and hoping that she would surely become herself again after a short time.

Scarcely was Zahir out of sight of his tents, when Djaida, who felt herself nigh unto death, and whose melancholy was quite insupportable, said to her mother: "Mother, I feel that I am dying, while this miserable Khaled is still in the vigor of life. I should like, if God grants me the power, to make him experience the fury of death, the bitterness of its pang and torture." So saying, she rose like a lioness, donned her armor, and mounted her horse, informing her mother she was going on a hunting expedition. Swiftly, and without stopping, she made her way over rocks and mountains, her excitement increasing as she approached the dwelling-place of her cousin. As she was disguised, she entered, without being recognized, into the tent where strangers were received. But her visor was lowered, like that of a horseman of Hijaz. Slaves and servants welcomed her, offered her hospitality, behaving towards her as to one of the guests, and the most noble personages of the country. That night Djaida took rest; but the following day she took part in the military exercises, challenged many warriors, and exhibited so much skill and bravery, that she called forth great astonishment among all the spectators. Long before midday the horsemen of her cousin were forced to acknowledge her superiority over themselves. Khaled wished to witness her prowess, and, astonished at the sight of such skill, he offered to match himself with her. Djaida entered the contest with him, and then both of them joining in combat tried, one after another, all the methods of attack and defense, until the shades of night came upon them. When they separated neither one was hurt, and none could say which was the victor. Thus Djaida, while rousing the admiration of the spectators, perceived the annoyance they felt on finding their chief equaled in fight by so skilful an opponent. Khaled ordered his antagonist to be treated with every care and honor, and then retired to his tent, his mind filled with thoughts of this conflict. Djaida remained for three days at her cousin's dwelling place. Every morning she presented herself on the field of combat and remained under arms until the fall of night. She enjoyed it greatly, still keeping her identity concealed, whilst Khaled, on the other hand, made no inquiries, and asked no questions of her, as to who she was and to what clan she might belong.

On the morning of the fourth day, while Khaled, according to his custom, rode out over the plain, and passed close to the tents reserved for strangers, he caught sight of Djaida mounting her horse. He saluted her, and she returned his salute. "Noble Arab," said Khaled, "I would ask you one question. Until this moment I have failed in courtesy towards you, but I now beg of you, in the name of that God who has given you such great dexterity in arms, tell me who you are, and to what noble princes are you allied? For I have never met your equal among brave warriors. Answer me, I beseech you, for I am most impatient to learn." Djaida smiled, and raising her visor, made answer: "Khaled, I am a woman, not a warrior. I am your own cousin Djaida, who offered herself to you, and desired to give herself to you; but you refused her—from the pride you felt in your passion for arms." As she spoke she turned her horse suddenly, pressed the spurs into him, and galloped off at full speed in the direction of her own country.

Khaled, covered with confusion, withdrew to his tent, not knowing what to do, and not knowing what would be the end of the passionate love which he suddenly felt surging within him. He was seized with a violent disgust for all his warlike habits and tastes, which had reduced him to the melancholy plight in which he now found himself. His distaste for women was suddenly changed into love. He sent for his mother and recounted to her all that had occurred. "My son," said she, "all these circumstances ought to render Djaida still dearer to you. Wait patiently a little, until I have been able to go and ask her hand of her mother." She thereupon mounted her camel at once, and started off through the desert on the tracks of Djaida, who immediately on her arrival home had told her mother everything that had happened. As soon as Khaled's mother had arrived, she threw herself into the arms of her relative and demanded Djaida in marriage for her son, for Zahir had not yet returned from his expedition. When Djaida heard from her mother the request of Khaled, she said, "This shall never be, even though I be forced to drink the cup of death. What occurred at his tents was brought about by me to quench the fire of my grief and unhappiness, and soothe the anguish of my soul."

On hearing these words Khaled's mother, disappointed, went back to her son, who was tortured by the cruelest anxiety. He rose suddenly to his feet, for his love had reached the point of despair, and asked uneasily what were the feelings of his cousin. When he learned the answer of Djaida his distress became overwhelming, for her refusal served only to increase his passion. "What can be done, my mother," he exclaimed. "I see no way of escaping from this predicament," she replied, "excepting that you assemble all your horsemen from among the Arabian sheiks, and among those with whom you are on friendly terms. Wait until your uncle returns from the campaign, and then, surrounded by all your followers, go to him, and in the presence of the assembled warriors, demand of him the hand of his daughter in marriage. If he denies that he has a daughter, tell him everything that has happened, and urge him until he gives in to your demand." This advice, and the plan that was proposed moderated the grief of Khaled. The moment he learned that his uncle had returned home, he assembled chiefs of his family and told his story to them. They were all much astonished, and Madi Kereb, one of Khaled's bravest companions, could not help saying: "This is a strange thing; we have always heard it said that your uncle had a son named Djonder, but now the truth is known. You are indeed the man who has the best right to the daughter of your uncle. It is therefore our best course to present ourselves in a body and prostrate ourselves before him, requesting him to return to his family and not give his daughter to any stranger." Khaled, without waiting to hear more, took with him a hundred of his bravest horsemen, those who had been brought up with Moharib and Zahir from their earliest childhood, and, having provided themselves with presents even more costly than those they had taken before, they started off on their journey, and marched until they came to the clan of Saad. Khaled began by complimenting his uncle on his fortunate return from war, but no one could be more astounded than Zahir at this second visit, particularly when he saw his nephew with all the chieftains of his family. It never occurred to him that his daughter Djaida had anything to do with Khaled's return; he thought that his nephew simply wished to persuade him to return to his native land. He offered them every hospitality, provided them with tents and entertained them in great magnificence. He ordered camels and sheep killed, and offered a banquet, furnishing his guests with all things needful and proper for a period of three days. On the fourth day Khaled arose, and after thanking his uncle for all his courtesy, asked him for his daughter's hand, and begged him to return to his own land. Zahir denied that he had any child except his son Djonder, but Khaled told him all that he had learned, and all that had passed between himself and Djaida. On hearing these words Zahir was overcome with shame and cast his eyes to the ground. He remained for some time plunged in thought, and after reflecting that the affair must needs proceed from bad to worse, he addressed those present in the following words: "Kinsmen, I can no longer delay acknowledging this secret; therefore, she shall be married to her cousin as soon as possible, for of all the men I know, he is most worthy of her." He offered his hand to Khaled, who at once clasped it in presence of the chiefs who were witnesses to the contract. The dowry was agreed upon at five hundred brown black-eyed camels, and a thousand camels loaded with the choicest products of Yemen. The clan of Saad, among which Zahir had lived, were excluded from all part in this matter.

When Zahir had asked his daughter's consent to this arrangement, Djaida was overwhelmed with confusion at the course her father had taken. Since he let the girl clearly understand that he did not wish her to remain unmarried, she at last replied: "Father, if my cousin desires to have me in marriage, I shall not enter into his tent until he undertakes to slaughter at my wedding a thousand camels, among those which belong to Gheshem, son of Malik, 'The Brandisher of Spears.' Khaled agreed to this; but the sheiks and warriors did not leave Zahir before he had collected his possessions for transportation to his own land. No sooner were these preparations finished than Khaled marched forth at the head of a thousand horsemen, with whose assistance he conquered the clan of Aamir. Having thrice wounded "The Brandisher of Spears," and slain a great number of his champions, he carried off their goods and brought back from their country a richer spoil even than Djaida had demanded. Loaded with booty he returned, and was intoxicated with his success. But when he asked that a day should be fixed for the wedding, Djaida begged him to approach, and spoke these words to him: "If you desire me to become your wife, fulfil first of all my wishes, and keep the engagement I make with you. This is my demand: that on the day of my marriage, some nobleman's daughter, a free-born woman, hold the bridle of my camel; she must be the daughter of a prince of the highest rank, in order that I may be most honored of all the daughters of Arabia." Khaled consented, and set about to carry out her wishes. That same day he started with his horsemen, and crossed plains and valleys, searching the land of Ymer, until he reached the country of Hijar and the hills of Sand. In that place he attacked the tribe-family of Moawich, son of Mizal. He fell upon them like a tempest, and cutting a way with his sword through the opposing horsemen, took prisoner Amima, daughter of Moawich, at the very moment when she was betaking herself to flight.

Having accomplished feats which rendered useless the resistance of the skilful heroes, after having scattered all the clans in flight, and carried off all the wealth of all the Arabs in that country, he returned home. But he did not wish to approach his tents until he had gathered in all the wealth he had left at various points and places in the desert.

The young girls marched before him sounding their cymbals and other musical instruments. All the clan rejoiced; and when Khaled appeared, he distributed clothing to widows and orphans, and invited his companions and friends to the banquet he was preparing for his wedding. All the Arabs of the country came in a vast assemblage to the marriage. He caused them to be regaled with abundance of flesh and wine. But while all the guests gave themselves up to feasting and pleasure, Khaled, accompanied by ten slaves, prepared to scour the wild and marshy places of the country, in order to attack in their lairs the lions and lionesses and their cubs, and carry them to the tents, in order to provide meat for all those who attended the festival.

But Djaida had been informed beforehand of this plan. She disguised herself in a coat of mail, mounted her horse, and left the tents; since three days of festivities still remained, she quickly followed Khaled into the desert, and met him face to face in a cavern. She flung herself upon him with the impetuosity of a wild animal, and attacked him furiously, crying aloud, "Arab! dismount from your horse, take off your coat of mail and your armor; if you hesitate, I will run this lance through your heart." Khaled was determined at once to resist her in this demand. They engaged in a furious combat. The struggle lasted for well over an hour, when the warrior saw in the eyes of his adversary an expression which frightened him. He mounted his horse again, and having wheeled round his steed from the place of combat, exclaimed: "By the faith of an Arab, I beg of you to tell me what horseman of the desert you are; for I feel that your attack and the violence of your blows are irresistible.

You have prevented me from accomplishing what I had intended, and everything that I had eagerly wished to do." On hearing these words Djaida raised her visor, allowing him to see her face. "Khaled," she cried, "is it necessary for the girl you love to attack wild beasts, in order that the daughters of Arabia may learn that this is not the sole privilege of a warrior?" At this stinging rebuke Khaled was overcome with shame. "By the faith of an Arab," he replied, "no one but you can conquer me; but is there any man in this country who has challenged you, or have you come here merely to prove to me the extent of your valor?" "By the faith of an Arab," replied Djaida, "I came into this desert solely for the purpose of helping you hunt wild beasts, that your warriors might not reproach you for choosing me as your wife." At these words Khaled was thrilled with astonishment and admiration, that such spirit and resolution should have been exhibited by Djaida.

Thereupon both of them dismounted from their horses annd entered into a cavern. Khaled seized two ferocious wild beasts, and Djaida attacked and carried off a lion and two lionesses. After these exploits they exchanged congratulations, and Djaida was happy to be with Khaled. "Meanwhile," she said, "I shall not allow you to leave our tents until after our marriage." She immediately left him in great haste and betook herself to her own dwelling.

Khaled then proceeded to rejoin the slaves he had left a little way off, and commanded them to carry to the tents the beasts he had slain. Trembling with fright at the view of what Khaled had done, they extolled him with admiration above all other champions.

Meanwhile the feasts went on, and all who came were welcomed with magnificence. The maidens clashed their cymbals; slaves waved their swords in the air, and young girls sang from morning till evening. In the midst of such rejoicings Djaida and Khaled were married. Amima, daughter of Moawich, held the reins of the young bride's camel, and both men and women exalted the name of Djaida.

ABOU HASSAN THE WAG

(Anonymous: 10th to 14th Century, A.D.)

The chief glory of Arabian prose literature is the celebrated collection known to us as *The Thousand and One Nights.* Out of this voluminous treasure store *Abou Hassan the Wag* has been chosen as an example of one of the numerous types of story to be found in it.

This tale is rich in Oriental color, furnishing as it does the humorous details of that craftiness which the Arab delights in—at least in the stories he tells and listens to. The story is among the best of the *Nights*.

The present version is translated by Edward William Lane, whose edition was first published in London in 1839. It is from the 271st to the 290th Night (Breslau ed.). The complete title is *The Story of Abou Hassan the Wag, or The Sleeper Awakened.*

THE STORY OF ABOU HASSAN THE WAG

OR THE SLEEPER AWAKENED

(From *The Thousand and One Nights*)

THERE was a merchant of Bagdad in the reign of the Caliph Haroun Alrashid, and he had a son named Abou Hassan the Wag. And this merchant died, leaving to his son his vast wealth; whereupon Abou Hassan divided his property into two equal portions, one of which he laid aside, and of the other he expended. He took as his familiar friends a number of the sons of the merchants, and others, and gave himself up to the delights of good drinking and good eating, until all the wealth that he had appropriated to this purpose was consumed. And upon this he repaired to his associates, and relations, and boon-companions, and exposed to them his case, showing them how little property remained in his possession; but none of them paid any regard to him, or uttered a word in reply. So he returned to his mother with a broken heart, and told her of the treatment that he had experienced from his associates, that they would neither do him justice nor even reply to him. But she said, O Abou Hassan, thus are the sons of this age: as long as thou hast anything, they draw thee near to them; and when thou hast nothing, they cast thee off. She was grieved for him, and he sighed and wept.

He then sprang up, and went to the place in which was deposited the other half of his wealth, and upon this he lived agreeably. He took an oath that he would not thenceforth associate with any one of those whom he knew, but only with the stranger, and that he would not associate with any person but for one night, and on the following morning would not recognize him. Accordingly, every night he went forth and seated himself on the bridge, and when a stranger passed by him, he invited him to an entertainment, and took him to his house, where he caroused with him that night, until the morning: he then dismissed him; and after that he would not salute him if he saw him.

Thus he continued to do for a whole year; after which, as he was sitting one day upon the bridge as usual, to see who might come toward him, Alrashid and certain of his domestics passed by in disguise; for the caliph had experienced a contraction of the bosom and had come forth to amuse himself among the people. So Abou Hassan laid hold upon him, and said to him, O my master, hast thou any desire for a repast and beverage? And Alrashid complied with his request, saying to him, Conduct us. And Abou Hassan knew not who was his guest. The caliph proceeded with him until they arrived at Abou Hassan's house: and when Alrashid entered, he found in it a saloon, such that if thou beheldest it, and lookedst towards its walls, thou wouldst behold wonders; and if thou observedst its conduits of water, thou wouldst see a fountain incased with gold. And after he had seated himself there, Abou Hassan called for a slave girl, like the twig of the Oriental willow, who took a lute and sang. And when Alrashid heard her, he said, Thou hast performed well. God bless thee! Her eloquence pleased him, and he wondered at Abou Hassan and his entertainment.

He then said to Abou Hassan, O young man, who art thou? Acquaint me with thy history, that I may requite thee for thy kindness. But Abou Hassan smiled, and replied, O my master, far be it from me that what hath happened should recur, and that I should be in thy company again after this time! And why so? said the caliph; and why wilt thou not acquaint me with thy case? So Abou Hassan told his story, and when the caliph heard it, he laughed violently, and said, By Allah, O my brother, thou art excusable in this matter. Then a dish of roast goose was placed before him, and a cake of fine bread; and Abou Hassan sat, and cut off the meat, and put morsels into the mouth of the caliph, and they continued eating until they were satisfied; when the basin and ewer were brought, with the kali; and they washed their hands. After this Abou Hassan lighted for his guests three candles and three lamps, spread the wine cloth, and brought clear, strained, old, perfumed wine, the odor of which was like fragrant musk, and, having filled the first cup, said, O my boon-companion, bashfulness is dismissed from us, with thy permission. Thy slave is by thee. May I never be afflicted by the loss of thee! And he drank the cup, and filled the second, which he handed to the caliph, waiting upon him as a servant. And the caliph was pleased with his actions, and the politeness of his words, and said within himself, By Allah, I will certainly requite him for this! Abou Hassan then, after he had kissed the cup, handed it to the caliph, who accepted it from his hand, kissed it and drank it, and handed it back to him. Abou Hassan still continued serving him, saying, Drink, and may it be attended with health and vigor. And they drank and caroused until midnight.

After this the caliph said to his host, O Abou Hassan, is there any service that thou wouldst have performed, or any desire that thou wouldst have accomplished? And Abou Hassan answered, In our neighborhood is a mosque to which belong an imam and four sheiks, and whenever they hear music or any sport, they incite the judge against me, and impose fines upon me, and trouble my life, so that I suffer torment from them. If I had them in my power, therefore, I would give each of them a thousand lashes, that I might be relieved from their excessive annoyance.

Alrashid replied, May Allah grant thee the accomplishment of thy wish! And without his being aware of it, he put into a cup a lozenge of bhang, and handed it to him; and as soon as it had settled in his stomach, he fell asleep immediately. Alrashid then arose and went to the door, where he found his young men waiting for him, and he ordered them to convey Abou Hassan upon a mule, and returned to the palace, Abou Hassan being intoxicated and insensible. And when the caliph had rested himself in the palace, he called for his vizier Giafar, and Abdallah the son of Tahir, the Judge of Bagdad, and certain of his chief attendants, and said to them all, In the morning when ye see this young man (pointing to Abou Hassan) seated on the royal couch, pay obedience to him, and salute him as caliph, and whatsoever he commandeth you, do it. Then going to his female slaves, he directed them to wait upon Abou Hassan, and to address him as Prince of the Faithful: after which he entered a private closet, and, having let down a curtain over the entrance, slept.

So when Abou Hassan awoke, he found himself upon the royal couch, with the attendants standing around, and kissing the ground before him; and a maid said to him, O our lord, it is the time for morning prayer. Upon which he laughed, and, looking round about him, he beheld a pavilion whose walls were adorned with gold and ultramarine, and the roof bespotted with red gold, surrounded by chambers with curtains of embroidered silk hanging before their doors; and he saw vessels of gold, and chinaware, and crystal, and furniture, and carpets spread, and lighted lamps, and female slaves, and eunuchs, and other attendants; whereat he was perplexed in his mind, and said, By Allah, either I am dreaming, or this is Paradise, and the Abode of Peace. And he closed his eyes. So a eunuch said to him, O my lord, this is not thy usual custom, O Prince of the Faithful. And he was perplexed at his case, and put his head into his bosom, and then began to open his eyes by little and little, laughing, and saying, What is this state in which I find myself? And he bit his finger; and when he found that the bite pained him, he cried, Ah! and was angry. Then raising his head, he called one of the female slaves, who answered him, At thy service, O Prince of the Faithful! And he said to her, What is thy name? She answered, Cluster of Pearls. And he said, Knowest thou in what place I am, and who I am? Thou art the Prince of the Faithful, she answered, sitting in thy palace, upon the royal couch. He replied, I am perplexed at my case; my reason hath departed, and it seemeth that I am asleep: but what shall I say of my yesterday's guest? I imagine nothing but that he is a devil, or an enchanter, who hath sported with my reason.

All this time the caliph was observing him from a place where Abou Hassan could not see him. And Abou Hassan looked toward the chief eunuch, and called to him. So he came, and kissed the ground before him, saying to him, Yes, O Prince of the Faithful. And Abou Hassan said to him, Who is the Prince of the Faithful? Thou, he answered. Abou Hassan replied, Thou liest. And addressing another eunuch, he said to him, O my chief, as thou hopest for Allah's protection, tell me, am I the Prince of the Faithful? Yea, by Allah, answered the eunuch; thou art at this present time the Prince of the Faithful, and the caliph of the Lord of all creatures. And Abou Hassan, perplexed at all that he beheld, said, In one night do I become Prince of the Faithful! Was I not yesterday Abou Hassan; and to-day am I Prince of the Faithful? He remained perplexed and confounded until the morning, when a eunuch advanced to him, and said to him, May Allah grant a happy morning to the Prince of the Faithful! And he handed to him a pair of shoes of gold stuff, reticulated with precious stones and rubies; and Abou Hassan took them, and after examining them a long time, put them into his sleeve. So the eunuch said to him, These are shoes to walk in. And Abou Hassan replied, Thou hast spoken truth. I put them not into my sleeve but in my fear lest they should be soiled. He therefore took them forth, and put them on his feet. And shortly after, the female slaves brought him a basin of gold and a ewer of silver, and poured the water upon his hands; and when he had performed the ablution, they spread for him a prayer carpet; and he prayed; but knew not how to do so. He continued his inclinations and prostrations until he had performed twenty rekahs; meditating and saying within himself, By Allah, I am none other than the Prince of the Faithful, in truth; or else this is a dream, and all these things occur not in a dream. He therefore convinced himself, and determined in his mind that he was the Prince of the Faithful; and he pronounced the salutations, and finished his prayers. They then brought him a magnificent dress, and, looking at himself as he sat upon the couch, he retracted, and said, All this is an illusion, and a machination of the Genii.

And while he was in this state, lo, one of the mamlouks came in and said to him, O Prince of the Faithful, the chamberlain is at the door, requesting permission to enter. Let him enter, replied Abou Hassan. So he came in, and, having kissed the ground before him, said, Peace be on thee, O Prince of the Faithful! And Abou Hassan rose, and descended from the couch to the floor; whereupon the chamberlain exclaimed, Allah! Allah! O Prince of the Faithful! Knowest thou not that all men are thy servants, and under thy authority, and that it is not proper for the Prince of the Faithful to rise to anyone? Abou Hassan was then told that Giafar the Barmecide, and Abdallah the son of Tahir, and the chiefs of the mamlouks, begged permission to enter. And he gave them permission. So they entered, and kissed the ground before him, each of them addressing him as Prince of the Faithful. And he was delighted at this, and returned their salutation; after which he called the judge, who approached him, and said, At thy service, O Prince of the Faithful! And Abou Hassan said to him, Repair immediately to such a street, and give a hundred pieces of gold to the mother of Abou Hassan the Wag, with my salutation; then take the imam of the mosque, and the four sheiks, inflict upon each of them a thousand lashes; and when thou hast done that, write a bond against them, confirmed by oath, that they shall not reside in the street, after thou shalt have paraded them through the city, mounted on beasts, with their faces to the tails, and hast proclaimed before them, This is the recompense of those who annoy their neighbors. And beware of neglecting that which I have commanded thee to do. So the judge did as he was ordered. And when Abou Hassan had exercised his authority until the close of the day, he looked toward the chamberlain and the rest of the attendants, and said to them, Depart.

He then called for a eunuch who was near at hand, and said to him, I am hungry, and desire something to eat. And he replied, I hear and obey; and led him by the hand into the eating chamber, where the attendants placed before him a table of rich viands; and ten slave girls, high-bosomed virgins, stood behind his head. Abou Hassan, looking at one of these, said to her, What is thy name? She answered, Branch of Willow. And he said to her, O Branch of Willow, who am I? Thou art the Prince of the Faithful, she answered. But he replied, Thou liest, by Allah, thou slut! Ye girls are laughing at me. So she said, Fear Allah, O Prince of the Faithful; this is thy palace, and the female slaves are thine. And upon this he said within himself, It is no great matter to be effected by God, to whom be ascribed might and glory! Then the slave girls led him by the hand to the drinking chamber, where he saw what astonished the mind; and he continued to say within himself, No doubt these are of the Genii, and this person who was my guest is one of the kings of the Genii, who saw no way of requiting and compensating me for my kindness to him but by ordering his slaves to address me as Prince of the Faithful. All these are of the Genii. May Allah then deliver me from them happily! And while he was thus talking to himself, lo, one of the slave girls filled for him a cup of wine; and he took it from her hand and drank it; after which, the slave girls plied him with wine in abundance; and one of them threw into his cup a lozenge of bhang; and when it had settled in his stomach, he fell down senseless.

Alrashid then gave orders to convey him to his house; and the servants did so, and laid him on his bed, still in a state of insensibility. So when he recovered from his intoxication, in the latter part of the night, he found himself in the dark; and he called out, Branch of Willow! Cluster of Pearls! But no one answered him. His mother, however, heard him shouting these names, and arose and came, and said to him, What hath happened to thee, O my son, and what hath befallen thee? Art thou mad? And when he heard the words of his mother, he said to her, Who art thou, O ill-omened old woman, that thou addressest the Prince of the Faithful with these expressions? She answered, I am thy mother, O my son. But he replied, Thou liest: I am the Prince of the Faithful, the lord of the countries and the people. Be silent, she said, or else thy life will be lost. And she began to pronounce spells, and to recite charms over him, and said to him, It seemeth, O my son, that thou hast seen this in a dream, and all this is one of the ideas suggested by the devil. She said to him, I give thee good news, at which thou wilt be rejoiced. And what is it? said he. She answered, The caliph gave orders yesterday to beat the imam and the four sheiks, and caused a bond to be written against them, confirmed by oath, that they shall not transgress henceforth against anyone by their impertinent meddling; and he sent me a hundred pieces of gold, with his salutation. And when Abou Hassan heard these words from his mother, he uttered a loud cry, with which his soul almost quitted the world; and he exclaimed, I am he who gave orders to beat the sheiks, and who sent thee the hundred pieces of gold, with my salutation, and I am the Prince of the Faithful.

Having said this, he rose up against his mother, and beat her with an almond stick, until she cried out, O ye faithful. And he beat her with increased violence, until the neighbors heard her cries and came to her relief. He was still beating her, and saying to her, O ill-omened old woman, am I not the Prince of the Faithful? Thou hast enchanted me! And when the people heard his words, they said, This man hath become mad. And not doubting his insanity, they came in and laid hold upon him, bound his hands behind him, and conveyed him to the madhouse. There every day they punished him, dosing him with abominable medicines, and flogging him with whips, making him a madman in spite of himself. Thus he continued, stripped of his clothing, and chained by the neck to a high window, for the space of ten days; after which his mother came to salute him. And he complained to her of his case. So she said to him, O my son, fear God in thy conduct: if thou wert Prince of the Faithful, thou wouldst not be in this predicament. And when he heard what his mother said, he replied, By Allah, thou hast spoken truth. It seemeth that I was only asleep, and dreamed that they made me caliph, and assigned me servants and female slaves. So his mother said to him, O my son, verily Satan doeth more than this. And he replied, Thou hast spoken truth, and I beg forgiveness of God for the actions committed by me.

They therefore took him forth from the madhouse, and conducted him into the bath; and when he recovered his health, he prepared food and drink, and began to eat. But eating by himself was not pleasant to him; and he said to his mother, O my mother, neither life nor eating by myself is pleasant to me. She replied, If thou desire to do according to thy will, thy return to the madhouse is most probable. Paying no attention, however, to her advice, he walked to the bridge to seek for himself a cup-companion. And while he was sitting there, lo, Alrashid came to him in the garb of a merchant; for, from the time of his parting with him he came every day to the bridge, but found him not till now. As soon as Abou Hassan saw him, he said to him, A friendly welcome to thee, O King of the Genii! So Alrashid said, What have I done to thee? What more couldst thou do, said Abou Hassan, than thou hast done to me, O filthiest of the Genii? I have suffered beating, and entered the madhouse, and they pronounced me a madman. All this was occasioned by thee. I brought thee to my abode, and fed thee with the best of my food; and after that thou gavest thy devils and thy slaves entire power over me, to make sport with my reason from morning to evening. Depart from me, therefore, and go thy way.

The caliph smiled at this, and, seating himself by his side, addressed him in courteous language, and said to him, O my brother, when I went forth from thee, I inadvertently left the door open, and probably the devil went in to thee. Abou Hassan replied, Inquire not respecting that which happened to me. And what possessed thee, he added, that thou leftest the door open, so that the devil came in to me, and that such and such things befell me? And he related to the caliph all that had happened to him from first to last, while Alrashid laughed, but concealed his laughter: after which the caliph said to him, Praise be to God that He hath dispelled from thee that which thou hatest, and that I have seen thee again in prosperity!

But Abou Hassan replied, I will not take thee again as my boon-companion, nor as an associate to sit with me; for the proverb saith, He who stumbleth against a stone and returneth to it, is to be blamed and reproached. and with thee, O my brother, I will not carouse, nor will I keep company with thee: since I have not found thy visit to be followed by good fortune to me. The caliph, however, said, I have been the means of the accomplishment of thy desire with regard to the imam and the sheiks. Yes, replied Abou Hassan. And Alrashid added, Perhaps something will happen to thee that will rejoice thy heart more than that. Then what dost thou desire of me? said Abou Hassan. My desire, answered Alrashid, is to be thy guest this night. And at length Abou Hassan said, On the condition that thou swear to me by the inscription on the seal of Solomon the son of David (on both of whom be peace!)

that thou wilt not suffer thy Afrites to make sport with me. And Alrashid replied, I hear and obey.

So Abou Hassan took him to his abode, and put the food before him and his attendants, and they ate as much as satisfied them; and when they had finished eating, the servants placed before them the wine and exhilarating beverages, and they continued drinking and carousing until the wine rose into their heads. Abou Hassan then said to the caliph, O my boon-companion, in truth I am perplexed respecting my case. It seemeth that I was Prince of the Faithful, and that I exercised authority, and gave and bestowed: and truly, O my brother, it was not a vision of sleep. But the caliph replied, This was the result of confused dreams. And having said this, he put a piece of bhang into the cup, and said, By my life, drink this cup. Verily I will drink it from thy hand, replied Abou Hassan. So he took the cup, and when he had drank it his head fell before his feet. The caliph then arose immediately, and ordered his young men to convey Abou Hassan to the palace, and to lay him upon his couch, and commanded the female slaves to stand around him; after which he concealed himself in a place where Abou Hassan could not see him, and ordered a slave girl to take her lute and strike its chords over Abou Hassan's head, and desired the other slave girls to play upon their instruments.

It was then the close of the night, and Abou Hassan, awaking, and hearing the sounds of the lutes, and tambourines, and flutes, and the singing of the slave girls, cried out, O my mother! Whereupon the slave girls answered, At thy service, O Prince of the Faithful! And when he heard this, he exclaimed, There is no strength nor power but in God, the High, the Great! Come to my help this night; for this night is more unlucky than the former! He reflected upon all that had happened to him with his mother, and how he had beaten her, and how he had been taken into the madhouse, and he saw the marks of the beating that he had suffered there. Then looking at the scene that surrounded him, he said, These are all of them of the Genii, in the shapes of human beings! I commit my affairs unto Allah! And looking toward a mamlouk by his side, he said to him, Bite my ear, that I may know if I be asleep or awake. The mamlouk said, How shall I bite thine ear, when thou art the Prince of the Faithful? But Abou Hassan answered, Do as I have commanded thee, or I will strike off thy head. So he bit it until his teeth met together, and Abou Hassan uttered a loud shriek. Alrashid (who was behind a curtain in a closet), and all who were present, fell down with laughter, and they said to the mamlouk, Art thou mad, that thou bitest the ear of the caliph? And Abou Hassan said to them, Is it not enough, O ye wretches of Genii, that hath befallen me? But ye are not in fault: the fault is your chief's, who transformed you from the shapes of Genii into the shapes of human beings. I implore help against you this night by the Verse of the Throne, and the Chapter of Sincerity, and the two Preventives! Upon this Alrashid exclaimed from behind the curtain, Thou hast killed us, O Abou Hassan! And Abou Hassan recognized him, and kissed the ground before him, greeting him with a prayer for the increase of his glory and the prolongation of his life. Alrashid then clad him in a rich dress, gave him a thousand pieces of gold, and made him one of his chief boon-companions.

Abou Hassan, after this, became a greater favorite with the caliph than all the other boon-companions, so that he sat with the caliph and his wife the Lady Zobeide, the daughter of Kasim, and he married her female treasurer, whose name was Nouzatalfuad. With this wife he resided, eating, and drinking, and enjoying a delightful life, until all the money that they possessed had gone; whereupon he said to her, O Nouzatalfuad! And she answered, At thy service. I desire, said he, to practise a trick upon the caliph, and thou shalt practise a trick upon the Lady Zobeide, and we will obtain from them immediately two hundred pieces of gold, and two pieces of silk. Do what thou desirest, replied she: and what, she asked, is it? He answered, We will feign ourselves dead. I will die before thee, and lay myself out: then do thou spread over me a napkin of silk, and unfold my turban over me, and tie my toes, and put upon my stomach a knife and a little salt: after which, dishevel thy hair, and go to thy Lady Zobeide, and tear thy vest, and slap thy face, and shriek. So she will say to thee, What is the matter with thee? And do thou answer her, May thy head long survive Abou Hassan the Wag; for he is dead! Whereupon she will mourn for me, and weep, and will order her female treasurer to give thee a hundred pieces of gold, and a piece of silk, and will say to thee, Go, prepare his corpse for burial, and convey it forth to the grave. So thou shalt receive from her the hundred pieces of gold, and the piece of silk, and come hither. And when thou comest to me, I will rise, and thou shalt lay thyself down in my place, and I will go to the caliph, and say to him, May thy head long survive Nouzatalfuad! And I will tear my vest and pluck my beard; upon which he will mourn for thee, and will say to his treasurer, Give to Abou Hassan a hundred pieces of gold, and a piece of silk: and he will say to me, Go, prepare her corpse for burial, and convey it forth to the grave. So I will come to thee. And Nouzatalfuad was delighted with this, and replied, Truly this is an excellent stratagem!

She forthwith closed his eyes, and tied his feet, covered him with the napkin, and did all that her master told her; after which she tore her vest, uncovered her head, and disheveled her hair, and went in to the Lady Zobeide, shrieking and weeping. When the Lady Zobeide, therefore, beheld her in this condition, she said to her, What is this state in which I see thee, and what hath happened unto thee, and what hath caused thee to weep? And Nouzatalfuad wept and shrieked, and said, O my mistress, may thy head long survive Abou Hassan the Wag; for he is dead! And the Lady Zobeide mourned for him, and said, Poor Abou Hassan the Wag! Then, after weeping for him a while, she ordered the female treasurer to give to Nouzatalfuad a hundred pieces of gold and a piece of silk, and said, O Nouzatalfuad, go, prepare his body for burial, and convey it forth. So she took the hundred pieces of gold and the piece of silk, and, returning to her abode full of joy, went in to Abou Hassan, and acquainted him with what had happened to her; upon which he arose and rejoiced, and girded his waist and danced, and took the hundred pieces of gold, with the piece of silk, and laid them up.

He then extended Nouzatalfuad, and did with her as she had done with him; after which he tore his vest, and plucked his beard, and disordered his turban, and ran without stopping until he went in to the caliph, who was in his hall of judgment; and in the condition above described, he beat his bosom. So the caliph said to him, What hath befallen thee, O Abou Hassan? and he wept, and said, Would that thy boon-companion had never been, nor his hour come to pass! The caliph therefore said to him, Tell me. He replied, May thy head long survive, O my lord, Nouzatalfuad! And the caliph exclaimed, There is no deity but God! and struck his hands together. He then consoled Abou Hassan, and said to him, Mourn not: I will give thee a slave in her stead. And he ordered his treasurer to give him a hundred pieces of gold, and a piece of silk. The treasurer therefore did as he was commanded, and the caliph said to Abou Hassan, Go, prepare her corpse for burial, and convey it forth, and make a handsome funeral for her. And he took what the caliph gave him, and went to his abode joyful, and going in to Nouzatalfuad, said to her, Arise; for our desire is accomplished. She therefore arose, and he put before her the hundred pieces of gold and the piece of silk. So she rejoiced; and they put these pieces of gold on the other pieces, and the piece of silk on the former one, and sat conversing and laughing at each other.

But as to the caliph, when Abou Hassan parted from him, and went with the pretense of preparing the corpse of Nouzatalfuad for burial, he mourned for her, and, having dismissed the council, arose and went in, leaning upon Mesrour his executioner, to console the Lady Zobeide for the loss of her slave girl. He found her, however, sitting weeping, and waiting for his arrival, that she might console him for the loss of Abou Hassan the Wag. The caliph said, May thy head long survive thy slave girl, Nouzatalfuad! But she replied, O my lord, Allah preserve my slave girl! Mayest thou long survive thy boon-companion Abou Hassan the Wag; for he is dead! And the caliph smiled, and said to his eunuch, O Mesrour, verily women are of little sense. By Allah, was not Abou Hassan just now with me? Upon this the Lady Zobeide said, after uttering a laugh from an angry bosom, Wilt thou not give over thy jesting? Is not the death of Abou Hassan enough, but thou must make my slave girl to be dead, as though we had lost them both, and thou must pronounce me of little sense? The caliph replied, Verily Nouzatalfuad is the person who is dead. And the Lady Zobeide rejoined, In truth he was not with thee, nor didst thou see him; and none was with me just now but Nouzatalfuad, who was mourning and weeping, with her clothes rent in pieces; and I exhorted her to have patience, and gave her a hundred pieces of gold, and a piece of silk; and I was waiting for thee, that I might console thee for the loss of thy boon-companion Abou Hassan the Wag; and I was going to send for thee. On hearing this the caliph laughed, and said, None is dead but Nouzatalfuad. And the Lady Zobeide said, No, no, O my lord; none is dead but Abou Hassan. But the caliph now became enraged; the vein between his eyes, which was remarkable in members of the family of Hashim, throbbed, and he called out to Mesrour the Executioner, saying to him, Go forth and repair to the house of Abou Hassan the Wag, and see which of the two is dead.

Mesrour, therefore, went forth running. And the caliph said to the Lady Zobeide, Wilt thou lay me a wager? She answered, Yes, I will, and I say that Abou Hassan is dead. And I, replied the caliph, lay a wager, and say that none is dead but Nouzatalfuad; and our wager shall be, that I stake the Garden of Delight against thy pavilion, the Pavilion of the Pictures. And they sat waiting for Mesrour to return with the information. Now as to Mesrour, he ran without ceasing until he entered the by-street in which was the house of Abou Hassan the Wag. Abou Hassan was sitting reclining against the window, and, turning his eyes, he saw Mesrour running along the street. So he said to Nouzatalfuad, It seemeth that the caliph, after I went forth from him, dismissed the court, and hath gone in to the Lady Zobeide to console her, and that she, on his arrival, hath arisen and consoled him, and said to him, May God largely compensate thee for the loss of Abou Hassan the Wag! whereupon the caliph hath said to her, None is dead but Nouzatalfuad. May thy head long survive her! And she hath replied, None is dead but Abou Hassan the Wag, thy boon-companion. And he hath said again to her, None is dead but Nouzatalfuad. So they have become obstinate, and the caliph hath been enraged, and they have laid a wager, in consequence of which Mesrour the Executioner hath been sent to see who is dead. It is therefore the more proper that *thou* lay thyself down, that he may see thee, and go and inform the caliph, who will thereupon believe my assertion.

Accordingly, Nouzatalfuad extended herself, and Abou Hassan covered her with her veil, and seated himself at her head, weeping. And lo, Mesrour the eunuch came up into the house of Abou Hassan, and saluted him, and saw Nouzatalfuad stretched out; upon which he uncovered her face, and exclaimed, There is no deity but God! Our sister Nouzatalfuad is dead! How speedy was the stroke of fate! May Allah have mercy upon her, and acquit thee of responsibility! He then returned, and related what had happened before the caliph and the Lady Zobeide, laughing as he spoke. So the caliph said to him, O thou accursed, this is not a time for laughing. Tell us which of them is dead. He therefore replied, By Allah, O my lord, verily Abou Hassan is well, and none is dead but Nouzatalfuad. And upon this the caliph said to Zobeide, Thou hast lost thy pavilion in thy play. And he laughed at her, and said, O Mesrour, relate to her what thou sawest. So Mesrour said to her, In truth, O my mistress, I ran incessantly until I went in to Abou Hassan in his house; whereupon I found Nouzatalfuad lying dead, and Abou Hassan sitting at her head, weeping; and I saluted him, and consoled him, and seated myself by his side; and, uncovering the face of Nouzatalfuad, I beheld her dead, with her face swollen: I therefore said to him, Convey her forth presently to the grave, that we may pray over her. And he replied, Yes. And I came, leaving him to prepare her corpse for burial, in order to inform you. Upon this the caliph laughed, and said, Tell it again and again to thy mistress, the person of little sense. But when the Lady Zobeide heard the words of Mesrour, she was enraged, and said, None is deficient in sense but he who believeth a slave. And she abused Mesrour, while the caliph continued laughing; and Mesrour was displeased, and said to the caliph, He spoke truth who said that women are deficient in sense and religion.

The Lady Zobeide then said, O Prince of the Faithful, thou sportest and jestest with me, and this slave deceiveth me for the purpose of pleasing thee; but I will send and see which of them is dead. The caliph replied, Do so. And she called to an old woman, a confidential slave, and said to her, Repair quickly to the house of Nouzatalfuad, and see who is dead, and delay not thy return. And she threw money to her. So the old woman went forth running, the caliph and Mesrour laughing. The old woman ran without ceasing until she entered the street, when Abou Hassan saw her and knew her; and he said to his wife, O Nouzatalfuad, it seemeth that the Lady Zobeide hath sent to us to see who is dead, and hath not believed what Mesrour hath said respecting thy death: wherefore she hath sent the old woman to ascertain the truth of the matter. It is therefore more proper now for *me* to be dead, that the Lady Zobeide may believe thee.

Then Abou Hassan laid himself along, and Nouzatalfuad covered him, and bound his eyes and his feet, and seated herself at his head, weeping. And the old woman came in to Nouzatalfuad, and saw her sitting at the head of Abou Hassan, weeping, and enumerating his merits; and when Nouzatalfuad saw the old woman, she shrieked, and said to her, See what hath befallen me! Abou Hassan hath died and left me single and solitary! Then she shrieked again, and tore her clothes in pieces, and said to the old woman, O my mother, how good he was! The old woman replied, Truly thou art excusable; for thou hadst become habituated to him, and he had become habituated to thee. And knowing how Mesrour had acted to the caliph and the Lady Zobeide, she said to Nouzatalfuad, Mesrour is about to cause a quarrel between the caliph and the Lady Zobeide. And what is this cause of quarrel, O my mother? said Nouzatalfuad. The old woman answered, O my daughter, Mesrour hath come to them and told them that thou wast dead, and that Abou Hassan was well. O my aunt, replied Nouzatalfuad, I was just now with my lady, and she gave me a hundred pieces of gold and a piece of silk; and see thou my condition, and what hath befallen me. I am perplexed; and what shall I do, single and solitary? Would that I had died, and that he had lived! Then she wept, and the old woman wept with her, and advancing, and uncovering the face of Abou Hassan, saw his eyes bound, and swollen from the bandage. And she covered him, and said, Truly, O Nouzatalfuad, thou hast been afflicted for Abou Hassan. And she consoled her, and went forth from her running until she went in to the Lady Zobeide, when she related to her the story; on hearing which, the Lady Zobeide laughed, and said, Tell it to the caliph who hath pronounced me of little sense, and caused this ill-omened, lying slave to behave arrogantly toward me. But Mesrour said, Verily this old woman lieth; for I saw Abou Hassan in good health, and it was Nouzatalfuad who was lying dead. The old woman replied, It is thou who liest, and thou desirest to excite a quarrel between the caliph and the Lady Zobeide. Mesrour rejoined, None lieth but thou, O ill-omened old woman, and thy lady believeth thee, for she is disordered in mind. And upon this the Lady Zobeide cried out at him, enraged at him and at his words; and she wept.

At length the caliph said to her, I lie, and my eunuch lieth, and thou liest, and thy female slave lieth. The right course, in my opinion, is this, that we four go together to see who among us speaketh truth. So Mesrour said, Arise with us, that I may bring misfortunes upon this ill-omened old woman, and bastinade her for her lying. O thou imbecile in mind! exclaimed the old woman: is thy sense like mine? Nay, thy sense is like that of the hen. And Mesrour was enraged at her words, and would have laid violent hands upon her; but the Lady Zobeide, having pushed him away from her, said to him, Immediately will her veracity be distinguished from thine, and her lying from thine. They all four arose, laying wagers with each other, and went forth and walked from the gate of the palace until they entered the gate of the street in which dwelt Abou Hassan the Wag: when Abou Hassan saw them, and said to his wife Nouzatalfuad, In truth, everything that is slippery is not a pancake, and not every time the jar is struck doth it escape unbroken. It seemeth that the old woman hath gone and related the story to her lady, and acquainted her with our case, and that she hath contended with Mesrour the eunuch, and they have laid wagers respecting our death: so the caliph, and the eunuch, and the Lady Zobeide, and the old woman have all four come to us. And upon this Nouzatalfuad arose from her extended position, and said, What is to be done? Abou Hassan answered her, We will both feign ourselves dead, and lay ourselves out and hold in our breath. And she assented to his proposal.

They both stretched themselves along, bound their feet, closed their eyes, and held in their breath, lying with their heads in the direction of the kebla, and covered themselves with the veil. Then the caliph, and Zobeide, and Mesrour, and the old woman entered the house of Abou Hassan the Wag, and found him and his wife extended as if they were dead. And when the Lady Zobeide saw them, she wept, and said, They continued to assert the death of my female slave until she actually died; but I imagine that the death of Abou Hassan so grieved her that she died after him in consequence of it. The caliph, however, said, Do not prevent me with thy talk and assertions; for she died before Abou Hassan, because Abou Hassan came to me with his clothes torn in pieces, and with his beard plucked, and striking his bosom with two clods; and I gave him a hundred pieces of gold, with a piece of silk, and said to him, Go, prepare her body for burial, and I will give thee a concubine better than her, and she shall serve in her stead: and it appears that her loss was insupportable to him; so he died after her. I have therefore overcome thee, and gained thy stake. But the Lady Zobeide replied in many words, and a long dispute ensued between them.

The caliph then seated himself at the heads of the two pretended corpses, and said, By the tomb of the Apostle of Allah (God favor and preserve him!), and by the tombs of my ancestors, if anyone would acquaint me which of them died before the other, I would give him a thousand pieces of gold. And when Abou Hassan heard these words of the caliph, he quickly rose and sprang up, and said, It was I who died first, O Prince of the Faithful. Give me the thousand pieces of gold, and so acquit thyself of the oath that thou hast sworn. Then Nouzatalfuad arose and sat up before the caliph and the Lady Zobeide, who rejoiced at their safety. But Zobeide chid her female slave. The caliph and the Lady Zobeide congratulated them both on their safety, and knew this pretended death was a stratagem for the purpose of obtaining the gold: so the Lady Zobeide said to Nouzatalfuad, Thou shouldst have asked of me what thou desiredst without this proceeding, and not have tortured my heart on thine account. I was ashamed, O my mistress, replied Nouzatalfuad. But as to the caliph, he was almost senseless from laughing, and said, O Abou Hassan, thou hast not ceased to be a wag, and to do wonders and strange acts. Abou Hassan replied, O Prince of the Faithful, this stratagem I practised in consequence of the dissipation of the wealth that I received from thy hand; for I was ashamed to ask of thee a second time. When I was alone, I was not tenacious of wealth; but since thou hast married me to this female slave who is with me, if I possessed all thy wealth I should make an end of it. And when all that was in my possession was exhausted, I practised this stratagem, by means of which I obtained from thee these hundred pieces of gold and the piece of silk, all of which are an alms of our lord. And now make haste in giving me the thousand pieces of gold, and acquit thyself of thine oath.

At this the caliph and the Lady Zobeide both laughed; and after they had returned to the palace, the caliph gave to Abou Hassan the thousand pieces of gold, saying to him, Receive them as a gratuity on account of thy safety from death. In like manner, also, the Lady Zobeide gave to Nouzatalfuad a thousand pieces of gold, saying to her the same words. Then the caliph allotted to Abou Hassan an ample salary and ample supplies, and he ceased not to live with his wife in joy and happiness, until they were visited by the terminator of delights and the separator of companions, the devastator of palaces and houses, and the replenisher of the graves.

Great Britain

INTRODUCTION

THE history of the short story in Great Britain can be traced back to the very earliest epoch, before even the formation of the language itself. By varying one's definition of the term "short story," it is possible to fix a date as early as the Seventh or the Eighth Century A.D., or as late as the days of Addison, a thousand years after. The first example chosen for this collection is a brief episode from the Anglo-Saxon epic tale of *Beowulf*. When "our own branch of the Teutonic race migrated from the Continent, among the furniture it deemed too precious to be left behind was, apparently, the group of legends from which sprang *Beowulf*." (Walker.) Apart from such largely mythological works, we find in the ecclesiastical literature (particularly in the writings of Bede and Alfred) little stories which were used in sermons. These were popular for centuries, and in the form of apologues and fables were in later times collected into such books as the Thirteenth Century *South English Legendary*.

To trace the many and diverse influences—French, German, Scandinavian and Celtic—that operated to produce the tales and poetical romances of the Middle Ages, is here out of the question. It is sufficient to state that tales and traditional lore from all these sources were told and retold by poets and singers, priests and kings, each adapting the old material to his own ends. Of the writers who flourished in England before the time of Malory, only a few are represented in this volume: the authors of the stories in *The Mabinogion* and the *Gesta Romanorum*, and Geoffrey of Monmouth.

Chaucer's contribution to English literature is, of course, of the first importance, but his original prose tales are neither very short nor very interesting. His contemporaries, Langland and Gower, were somewhat better equipped, bringing as they did a sense of proportion into their otherwise inferior work. In the period between Chaucer and the end of the Fifteenth Century, when the *Morte d'Arthur* appeared, there is, except for the *Gesta Romanorum*, very little to detain us in our rapid survey of the development of the short story.

When the ideas of the Italian Renaissance were at last introduced into England, there were several writers ready to translate, adapt, and imitate the stories of Boccaccio and his followers. Among the first of the English collections of tales was Painter's famous *Palace of Pleasure* (1566-67), to which Shakespeare was indebted for more than one of his plots. Though the Elizabethans never altogether assimilated the Italian tale, men like Greene occasionally produced clever imitations. Thomas Deloney was an exceptional figure: his homely and realistic stories of middle- and lower-class life are still worth reading. The other fiction writers—Lyly and Lodge and the rest—were preoccupied rather with evolving a literary style than with the telling of effective stories.

Between the age of Elizabeth and that of Anne there is little to record. With the advent of Addison and Defoe a new epoch opened. Addison has so long been praised as a stylist that it is time we remembered him as a story writer. His narratives in *The Spectator* are among the very best specimens of their kind in English literature. And to Defoe is due the credit not only for his epoch-making *Robinson Crusoe*, but for his remarkable realistic tales, *The Cock-Lane Ghost* and *The Apparition of Mrs. Veal.*

The little moral tale, as told by Addison and Steele, was taken up by Hawkesworth, Johnson, and Goldsmith, while even the novelists (in particular Laurence Sterne) delighted to break the thread of their long narratives in order to introduce episodes that are true short stories. By the end of the Eighteenth Century there were comparatively few writers who did anything with the story, and although Scott and Dickens wrote brief narratives, and an occasional Lover or Carleton devoted his life to the exploitation of character in the briefer narrative form, it was not until after the middle of the Nineteenth Century that the short story came into its own. The second half of the last century, not only in England, but throughout Europe and America, was an age of great fiction—both in the novel and the short story.

There is no use in repeating the names of the great story writers of modern times; it is enough to say that nearly all the novelists of Victorian and later days wrote short tales as well as long ones.

In more recent times we have seen the development of the short story in the hands of specialists, like Kipling and Morrison, Jacobs and Merrick, writers who regard the story as an independent literary form deserving a life-time of application and care.

GRENDEL'S RAID

(Anonymous: About 7th Century, A.D.)

The poet who wrote the first important extant specimen of Anglo-Saxon literature was probably an inhabitant of Anglia, and except that he wrote *Beowulf* late in the Seventh Century or early in the Eighth (not later than 752), we know nothing of him. Apart from its intrinsic merits, *Beowulf* is the "oldest surviving epic of any Teutonic people." It is partly mythological, but it does contain a certain amount of historical fact. The grim tale here offered is a crude but stirring narrative.

The present version, translated from the Anglo-Saxon by J. R. C. Hall, is from *Beowulf and the Finnsburg Fragment*, published in London in 1911 by George Allen and Unwin, by whose permission it is here reprinted. There is no title in the original.

GRENDEL'S RAID

(From *Beowulf*)

THEN came Grendel, advancing from the moor, under the misty slopes; God's anger rested on him. The deadly foe thought to entrap one of the human race in the high Hall: he strode beneath the clouds in such wise that he might best discern the wine-building, the gold chamber of men, resplendent with adornment. Nor was that the first time that he had visited Hrothgar's home. Never in the days of his life, before or since, did he discover a braver warrior and hall-guards.

So this creature, deprived of joys, came journeying to the hall. The door, fastened by four bands, opened straightway, when he touched it with his hand. Thus, bent on destruction, for he was swollen with rage, he tore away the entrance of the building.

Quickly, after that, the fiend stepped onto the fair-paved floor, advanced in angry mood; out of his eyes there started a weird light, most like a flame. He saw many men in the hall, a troop of kinsmen, a band of warriors, sleeping all together. Then his spirit exulted; he, the cruel monster, resolved that he would sever the soul of every one of them from his body before day came; for the hope of feasting full had come to him. That was no longer his fortune, that he should devour more of human kind after that night. Hygelac's mighty kinsman kept watching how the murderous foe would set to work with his sudden snatchings. The monster was not minded to put it off, but quickly seized a sleeping warrior as a first start, rent him undisturbed, bit his sinews, drank the blood from his veins, swallowed bite after bite, and soon he had eaten up all of the dead man, even his feet and hands.

Forward and nearer he advanced, and then seized with his hands the doughty warrior on his bed—the fiend reached out towards him with his claw. He (Beowulf) at once took in his evil plans, and pressed heavily on his (Grendel's) arm. Instantly the master of crimes realized that never in this middle-world, these regions of earth, had he met with a mightier hand-grip in any other man. He became affrighted in soul and spirit, but he could get away no faster for all that. His mind was bent on getting off,—he wished to flee into the darkness and go back to the herd of devils. His case was unlike anything he had met with in his life-time there before. Then Hygelac's brave kinsman was mindful of his evening speech: he stood erect and grasped him tight,—his fingers burst. The monster was moving out; the chief stepped forward too. The infamous creature thought to slip further off, wheresoever he could, and to flee away thence to his fen-refuge; he knew the power of his fingers was in the foeman's grip. That was a sorry journey which the baleful fiend had made to Heorot!

The warriors' hall resounded, there was panic among all the Danes, the castle-dwellers, the nobles and the heroes every one. Both the raging wardens of the house were furious; the building rang again. Then was it a great wonder that the wine-hall was proof against the savage fighters,—that the fair earthly dwelling did not fall to the ground; yet it was (made) firm enough for it, inside and out, by means of iron clamps, forged with curious art. There, where the foemen fought, many a mead-bench adorned with gilding, started from the sill, as I have heard. Before that, veterans of the Scyldings weened that no man could shatter it, splendid and horn-bedecked, in any wise, or ruin it by craft, although the embrace of fire might swallow it in smoke.

A sound arose, startling enough; a horrible fear clung to the North Danes, to everyone who heard the shrieking from the wall—(heard) the adversary of God chant his grisly lay, his song of non-success,—the prisoner of hell wailing over his wound. He held him fast who was strongest of men in might in this life's day!

The defender of nobles would not by any means let the murderous visitor escape alive,—he did not count his (Grendel's) life (-days) of use to any of the people. There many a noble of Beowulf's company brandished an old ancestral weapon—they wished to protect the life of their lord, of their famous chief, if so be they might. They did not know, brave-minded men of war, when they took part in the contest, and thought to hew at him on every side, and to hunt out his life, that no war-bill on earth, no best of sabers, could touch the cursed foe, for that he used enchantment against conquering weapons, every sort of blades.

In this life's day his breaking-up was to be pitiable—the alien spirit was to journey far into the power of fiends. Then he who of yore had accomplished much of the joy of his heart, of crime against mankind, he, the rebel against God, discovered this—that his bodily frame was no help to him, but that the bold kinsman of Hygelac had him by the hands. While he lived, each was abhorrent to the other. The horrible wretch suffered deadly hurt, on his shoulder gaped a wound past remedy, the sinews sprang asunder, the tendons burst. Glory in fight was granted to Beowulf; Grendel, sick to death, must needs flee thence under the fen-fastnesses—seek out his joyless dwelling;—he knew too well that the end of his life had come, the (daily-) number of his days. After that bloody contest, the desire of all the Danes had come to pass!

GEOFFREY OF MONMOUTH

(1100?–1154?)

Our information about Geoffrey of Monmouth is very limited. He was probably of Welsh origin, and lived in the Welsh Marches, not far from the scenes of the most famous exploits of Arthur and his knights. His *Chronicle* has been aptly called a "romance-history." The twelve books or chapters of which it is composed are stories of the early (actual or imaginary) rulers of Britain. Among the finest of these are the stories of King Lear, King Arthur, and the one here reprinted. *Esyllt and Sabrina* is one of the loveliest of all the early English tales.

The present version, translated from the original Latin by Louisa J. Menzies, is reprinted from *Legendary Tales of the Ancient Britons,* London, 1864.

ESYLLT AND SABRINA

(From the *Chronicle of Geoffrey of Monmouth*)

It was about three thousand years ago that there lived a fierce warrior, named Hymyr, the Hun, whose chief delight it was to voyage about over the mighty sea, and to make descents upon fruitful lands and take to himself by rapine and violence the produce of the long toil of the husbandman and the artisan; nor was he always content with stores of corn, treasure of gold, of silver, and apparel; many fair children did he carry off from burning homesteads, young maidens, and even wives, who sorrowed in vain for slaughtered husbands and brothers, and bore in pale resignation the stern rule of the tyrant and his haughty queen.

Once Hymyr fitted out a great armament, and voyaging up the river Albis, carried off from its banks the fair daughter of a German King, whom he found playing with her maidens in a flowery meadow; then he coasted along the shore of Frisia, a terror to the husbandmen, and, forasmuch as he had heard that there was much and singular wealth in the island of Albion, newly named Britain, from its King Brutus, he turned the heads of his ships northward, and came to the part of the island that lies towards the Great Bear, and which was then called Albany. Landing here with his fierce sea-robbers, he easily defeated Albanactus, the king, who came hastily to meet him with raw levies, for he was but newly come to his throne, and was thinking of nothing less than invasion.

Then Hymyr had a joyous time of it, he reveled and feasted in the halls of Albanactus, and so pleasant did the country seem in his eyes, with its great rows of purple mountains, its gleaming lakes abounding in fish, and its forests teeming with game, that he was in no hurry to take to the sea again: so he hunted and feasted till the summer was past its prime, eating the good fruits of the earth, and making the land desolate of men. Then news came to him that Albanactus, the king, was marching up from the south with an army of tried warriors, the warriors of Locrinus, his brother, King of Loegria, for so the southern part of Britain was named, and that Locrinus himself was with them.

Then Hymyr might have got on board his ships and sailed away as he had been wont to do, but the gods had maddened him with long good fortune, and nothing seemed good to him but to go and meet the brothers; for he thought in his heart that he would slay them both, and possess their lands; but the gods had willed it otherwise. The armies met at a great river, half way down the island, and, because the brothers were afraid to cross in the face of the enemy, they remained in their camp on the right bank of the river till they could construct rafts to cross in safety; but Hymyr had brought his ships round the coast, and impatient of delay, he went on board of them, and crossed the arm of the sea at the river's mouth, and his men came down on the compact lines of the brothers with shouting and boasting more like a rabble of revelers than tried soldiers going into battle.

Then there was fierce fighting on both sides, and the Huns knew at last what was the manliness of the Britons, and repented them in blood and agony of their rash boasting; and Hymyr, their chief, flying to his ships, was carried away by the current of the river, and drowned; and the river perpetuates the memory of his defeat and death, even to this day; for the men of the country call it the Humber, as it was called at that time from Hymyr, the Hun.

When Hymyr was dead, his men, such, at least, as remained of them, laid down their arms, and gave themselves up to the Kings Locrinus and Albanactus, who received them kindly, and gave them waste lands to till, and ordered that they should be supplied with corn till their own crops were grown. Then all the treasure stored up in the ships was brought to the kings, and they were amazed at the costly garments, at the precious vessels plundered from the glowing west, at the armor, and at the rich furniture, spoil of palaces; and while they were admiring these things, lo! there came to them from the ships the fair princess Esyllt, led in triumph by the soldiers who had found her cowering among the sails, for she knew not whether the defeat of Hymyr were a cause of sorrow or rejoicing to her.

The warlike bearing of the sturdy Britons tended little to reassure her, and she came slowly and fearfully to the tent where the princes were inspecting the spoil; but when the eyes of Locrinus lighted on her, albeit her looks were bent on the ground, and her long hair almost hid her features, love suddenly flooded his soul, and he stood like one smitten by the powerful wand of a magician; but when at length he gathered power to speak, and bade her be of good cheer, the sound of his noble voice and his kind words made the damsel lift her eyes with a touch of hope; and when she beheld the broad brow of the king, and all his presence radiant with youth and love, the color came into her cheeks and she stood revealed in all her beauty.

Then King Locrinus knew what is the bliss of the gods who live forever, but because he would not have the princess stand as a captive and unattended in a place so public, he caused her to be conducted in all honor to his own tent, and spoke to his brother in this wise:—

"Brother, take the goodly ships, the armor, and the spoil; haply thou wilt find thy palace but an empty barn, and all thy costly things wasted by the riot of the slain sea-robber; but leave to me the fair Princess Esyllt, for my soul cleaveth to her, that I may make her my wife; she is of noble parentage and deserveth well to be a queen."

"Alas! my brother," replied Albanactus, "what frenzy hath seized thy mind? The captive is passing fair, and doubtless of noble lineage, but art not thou affianced to the Lady Guendolen, the only child of Corineus, our father's trusty comrade? How, think you, will the haughty chieftain brook it, if he hears that his daughter is set at naught for a captive?"

The face of Locrinus darkened, and he answered from a heavy heart:—

"I never loved the proud Guendolen; who could love her? but because Corineus wished it, and because I thought it well to have him for a friend rather than a foe, I consented to take her. But, brother, then I had seen no damsel whom I desired to call my wife; now the gods hold out to me a joy which is like their own; I will grasp it if I die for it."

Seeing him so set upon the matter, Albanactus said no more, but gathered his spoil together, and having made costly presents to his brother for his timely help, marched homewards where affairs were eagerly calling for him to restore law and order to his lands.

Then Locrinus straightway took the Princess Esyllt for his wife, and delighted in her more and more: for she was as prudent as she was beautiful, and she loved the king, her deliverer, with the love of a true wife, and of a noble princess.

But when Corineus, the giant-slayer, heard that Locrinus had taken a foreign princess to be his wife, and that she sat beside him on his throne to the open scorn of Guendolen, his daughter, he arose in great wrath, and swore a mighty oath, that he would either make him put away his wife and marry the Lady Guendolen, to whom he was affianced, or that one of the two should never eat bread more; and gathering together a band of Cornish men, sons of the giants, and taking with him Guendolen, his daughter, he marched eastward, passing like an angry meteor through town and hamlet, for wrath drove him like a scourge.

King Locrinus, hearing of his coming, and boding ill of the issue, hid his wife privily in a shepherd's cottage, and caused a rumor to be spread that at the terror of the coming of the Giant-slayer, his queen had fallen into the pangs of premature labor, and that she and her infant had both perished; and to add greater faith to the tale, he had funeral rites performed, and went heavily as one who mourneth, and put on mourning garments.

These tidings, meeting Corineus on the way, somewhat slaked the fury of his wrath, and halting, he sent forward a messenger to Locrinus, to demand of him that he would fulfil his contract with the Lady Guendolen.

The King with a sad heart assented, but would that the marriage should be deferred for the present that he might furnish himself with fitting ceremony to do honor to his bride; but Corineus would hear nothing of delay, and resuming his onward course burst furiously into the city of Trinovant, where Locrinus abode, and breaking unannounced into the presence of the King bade him keep to his covenant, and take the Lady Guendolen at once to his throne.

The fierce countenance of Corineus was not less terrible because it was furrowed by age, and set round with strong white hair, and a beard like a trail of autumn cloud; the muscles stood out like serpents from his bare arms, and his loose garment of Tyrian purple left to view a broad patch of the shaggy breast against which, as in a vise, he had crushed the ribs of the monster Gogmagog. Such as Corineus was, such were his followers; shaggy-browed, iron-sinewed, ample in stature, resolute in purpose, and ruthless in action, they waited but a sign from their chief to dash like wolves upon the homesteads of the peaceful subjects of the King, or to tear him to pieces in his own halls. Then Locrinus sadly gave way, priests whom Corineus had brought with him performed the rites that united a frowning bride to a bridegroom in a mourning habit, and the haughty Guendolen sat in the place of Esyllt.

Little love was there between Locrinus and his new queen, as you may well guess; for the daughter of Corineus was not one to win love; but the more she saw that the heart of her husband was turned away from her, the more did she exult in the submission that her father had forced upon him, and triumph in the power that her high place gave her.

Esyllt, meanwhile, tarried sadly in the shepherd's cottage, wearying for the coming of her lord; the daily pain of his absence left her little thought for her changed fortunes, or for the lost throne; if she could only see him she thought she could be content to die, and day by day she sat upon the lonely shore looking out on the immeasurable waters, or climbed to the trackless downs, if perchance he might be coming by sea or by land; and when she came back weary and faint to the cottage, she could find little comfort in the talk of the shepherd and his wife, who told such tales of the wrath and of the strength of the great Prince Corineus, that the poor lady trembled to think of her dear lord, and lay awake half the night weeping and praying to the gods to protect him.

At length, however, King Locrinus, on pretense of hunting, contrived to steal away from Guendolen, and to visit the lonely Esyllt, and the hearts of both were refreshed, and the spark of life which was dying out in Esyllt's bosom shot up again into a bright flame, like a waning lamp newly fed with oil; and they dared even to think of a time when their troubles might be at an end, and the gods, to whom all things are possible, might give them back something of their old happiness. But because the King loved Esyllt better than his life, and because he feared everything from the jealousy of Guendolen if she should in any way discover that Esyllt lived, he fitted up a secret chamber, curiously contrived years ago by his father Brutus, for the deposit of treasure or for other need; and thither he conveyed the princess in the night, and hid her there for seven weary years. She had not been there many days, when a daughter was born to her, and care for the new life that had opened in the grave as it were, caused the princess herself to take fresh hold on life, and gave her strength to bear the privation of the blessed gifts of the sun for all those years.

The little Sabrina, it was so Esyllt named her daughter, pined not for what she knew not of; the pale light of the lamp which burnt day and night in the chamber could not ripen the color in her cheeks or the laughter on her lips as the goodly sun does; but she grew ever more sweet and fair, her one pleasure to watch the motion of her mother's hands as she busily plied the loom, counting the threads and marking with great joy the pattern as it sprung into shape under her creative fingers; and so for seven long years they lived, companions only to each other, and looking fondly for the short visit which Locrinus from time to time was able to pay them. But when the seven years were ended, news came from Cornwall that a sudden sickness had seized Corineus, and that he was dead. And Locrinus straightway resolved to divorce his Queen Guendolen, whose haughty and cruel temper made the lives of all about her bitter to them, and to bring the imprisoned Esyllt to light again, and place her once more on the throne. When Guendolen heard the purpose of the King, and that Esyllt was still alive, her anger was very fierce; but, forasmuch, as there were none who loved her in Loegria, as Cornwall was far away, and in great confusion at the death of Corineus, she dissembled her wrath, and taking with her her son Madoc; she went back to her own Duchy of Cornwall, thinking of nothing but how she might revenge herself.

But Locrinus fetched home his Queen Esyllt and his little daughter Sabrina in great state, and brought them to his palace in Trinovant; and the whole land rejoiced, as the earth rejoices and covers herself with beauty, when the east wind is driven back to his caverns, and the genial western breeze dimples the lakes and calls forth the lingering flowers. But those who were near enough to see her marveled much at the pale countenance of the Queen, and at the face of the little princess, who sat like one dazzled and sorely perplexed by the side of her mother.

In truth the glory of the upper world was well nigh too much for the child, she hid herself from the light and from the sounds, and languished for the still chamber which had been her home; the crowding faces, the gay dresses, and the obsequious manners of the many attendants about the court bewildered her, and she glided about like a silent shadow after her mother, weary and faint in spirit; but as months passed on, the strangeness of things wore off, and she grew to endure, and finally to love the open air; but it was ever the paths of shady forests that pleased her most, where the sunlight came tempered through countless leaves, and pale primroses and lurking violets formed a chaplet that pleased her better than roses and lilies. Her sweet nature made her very courteous to those about her, and she learned with aptitude the arts that were taught her, so that men praised her beauty and her princely carriage; but her cheeks remained ever colorless, and the smile that played on her features like moonlight on the waters was never broken up into laughter.

And so it was, that when she was grown to be a fair damsel, and the King her father was thinking to which of the foreign princes whom the fame of her beauty had drawn to his court, he should give her in marriage, so as to strengthen his own hands and secure the throne to her, tidings came that the Lady Guendolen and Madoc her son were making ready to march eastward, and boasted that they would slay Locrinus and take Esyllt and her daughter alive.

Then the King bestirred himself, and gathering his troops marched to meet them, taking with him the Queen and the Princess, for he thought them safe nowhere but with him, neither would they let him go alone, for they saw that his soul foreboded evil, and that his heart was heavy within him. And so it was that the armies met together at a river just on the frontiers of Cambria, and a great battle was fought in which King Locrinus was slain by an arrow, and Esyllt and her daughter fell into the hands of Guendolen.

When they were brought before the daughter of Corineus, the stern

Princess gazed unmoved on the sorrow-stricken pair, no touch of pity stirring her bosom, but with fierce and angry words she reviled them, heaping insults on the head of the slain King, and triumphing savagely in her victory. To all this Esyllt said not a word, she only embraced her daughter, who clung to her in silent terror. Then Guendolen gave orders that both should be taken and flung without more ado into the river that was flowing by, and six fierce Cornish men, sons of the giants, sprung forward to seize them; but Esyllt lifted her head, and looking straight into the eyes of Guendolen, spoke to her in this wise:—

"Princess, if I have wronged thee, the gods have richly avenged thee, seeing that I did it unwillingly, yea even unwittingly. The fate thou adjudgest to me and to this child is a merciful one; I seek not to change it—it is better to fall into the power of the gods; add to it yet this favor—let not the hands of thy warriors come upon the maiden, seeing she is a Princess, and the daughter of Locrinus. Behold we go whither thou biddest us. May the gods receive us!"

So saying, she walked down the green meadow to the amber river leading her daughter by the hand, and when they came to the brink, and the murmuring water kissed their feet, the Queen Esyllt turned her face to the setting sun, silently saluting it, then folding her daughter in her arms, she plunged with her into the bosom of the stream, and no one saw them more; but the name of the Princess clung to the river, and men as they wander by the Glassy Severn dream even yet of the gentle Sabrina, dwelling in the halls of the River Gods, and ready to hearken to the cry of the innocent, and to lend her help to the oppressed.

THE HUMBLING OF JOVINIAN

(Anonymous: 13th Century)

The famous collection of mediæval tales gathered together under the title *Deeds of the Romans* (*Gesta Romanorum*) was compiled in Latin by an unidentified preacher some time between the Twelfth and the Fourteenth Centuries in England. The collection comprises two hundred and fifteen stories, that "might be used to enforce and enliven lessons from the pulpit." Each tale is written round some actual or imaginary Roman emperor. The writer was indebted for his material to the floating legends and traditions of the Middle Ages, to actual history, and to the fables and tales of the Arabs and other Oriental peoples. First printed in 1473, the tales of the *Gesta Romanorum* have been utilized time and again by Shakespeare and other writers of succeeding ages.

The present version is reprinted from the translation by C. Swan, published in London in 1824.

THE HUMBLING OF JOVINIAN

(From the *Gesta Romanorum*)

WHEN Jovinian was emperor, he had very great power, and as he lay in bed reflecting upon the extent of his dominions, his heart was elated.

"Is there," he impiously asked, "is there any other god than me?" Amid such thoughts he fell asleep.

In the morning, he reviewed his troops, and said, "My friends, after breakfast we will hunt."

Preparations being made accordingly, he set out with a large retinue. During the chase, the emperor felt such extreme oppression from the heat, that he believed his very existence depended upon a cold bath. As he anxiously looked around, he discovered a sheet of water at no great distance. "Remain here," said he to his guard, "until I have refreshed myself in yonder stream." Then spurring his steed, he rode hastily to the edge of the water. Alighting, he stripped off his clothes, and experienced the greatest pleasure from its invigorating freshness and coolness. But whilst he was thus employed, a person similar to him in every respect—in countenance and gesture—arrayed himself unperceived in the emperor's dress, and then mounting his horse, rode off to the attendants. The resemblance to the sovereign was such that no doubt was entertained of the reality; and straightway command was issued for their return to the palace.

Jovinian, however, having quitted the water, sought in every possible direction for his horse and clothes, and to his utter astonishment, could find neither. Vexed beyond measure at the circumstance (for he was completely naked, and saw no one near to assist him), he began to reflect upon what course he should pursue. "Miserable man that I am," said he, "to what a strait am I reduced! There is, I remember, a knight who lives close by; I will go to him, and command his attendance and service. I will then ride on to the palace and strictly investigate the cause of this extraordinary conduct. Some shall smart for it."

Jovinian proceeded, naked and ashamed, to the castle of the aforesaid knight, and beat loudly at the gate. The porter, without unclosing the wicket, inquired the cause of the knocking. "Open the gate," said the enraged emperor, "and you will see who I am." The gate was opened; and the porter, struck with the strange appearance he exhibited, replied, "In the name of all that is marvelous, what are you?" "I am," said he, "Jovinian, your emperor; go to your lord, and command him from me to supply the wants of his sovereign. I have lost both horse and clothes."

"Infamous ribald!" shouted the porter, "just before thy approach, the

Emperor Jovinian, accompanied by the officers of his household, entered the palace. My lord both went and returned with him; and but even now sat with him at meat. But because thou hast called thyself the emperor, however madly, my lord shall know of thy presumption." The porter entered, and related what had passed. Jovinian was introduced, but the knight retained not the slightest recollection of his master, although the emperor remembered him. "Who are you?" said the knight, "and what is your name?" "I am the Emperor Jovinian," rejoined he; "canst thou have forgotten me? At such a time I promoted thee to a military command." "Why, thou most audacious scoundrel," said the knight, "darest thou call thyself the emperor? I rode with him myself to the palace, from whence I am this moment returned. But thy impudence shall not go without its reward. Flog him," said he, turning to his servants. "Flog him soundly, and drive him away."

This sentence was immediately executed, and the poor emperor, bursting into a convulsion of tears, exclaimed, "Oh, my God, is it possible that one whom I have so much honored and exalted should do this? Not content with pretending ignorance of my person, he orders these merciless villains to abuse me! However, it will not be long unavenged. There is a certain duke, one of my privy councilors, to whom I will make known my calamity. At least, he will enable me to return decently to the palace." To him, therefore, Jovinian proceeded, and the gate was opened at his knock. But the porter, beholding a naked man, exclaimed in the greatest amaze, "Friend, who are you, and why come you here in such a guise?" He replied, "I am your emporor; I have accidentally lost my clothes and my horse, and I have come for succor to your lord. Inform the duke, therefore, that I have business with him." The porter, more and more astonished, entered the hall, and told of the man outside. "Bring him in," said the duke. He was brought in, but neither did he recognize the person of the emperor. "What art thou?" was again asked, and answered as before. "Poor mad wretch," said the duke, "a short time since, I returned from the palace, where I left the very emperor thou assumest to be. But ignorant whether thou art more fool or knave, we will administer such remedy as may suit both. Carry him to prison, and feed him with bread and water." The command was no sooner delivered, than obeyed; and the following day his naked body was submitted to the lash, and again cast into the dungeon.

Thus afflicted, he gave himself up to the wretchedness of his untoward condition. In the agony of his heart, he said: "What shall I do? Oh! what will be my destiny? I am loaded with the coarsest contumely, and exposed to the malicious observation of my people. It were better to hasten immediately to my palace, and there discover myself—my wife will know me; surely, my wife will know me!" Escaping, therefore, from his confinement, he approached the palace and beat upon the gate.

The same questions were repeated, and the same answers returned. "Who art thou?" said the porter. "It is strange," replied the aggrieved emperor, "it is strange that thou shouldst not know me; thou, who hast served me so long!" "Served *thee!*" returned the porter indignantly; "thou liest abominably. I have served none but the emperor." "Why," said the other, "thou knowest that I am he. Yet, though you disregard my words, go, I implore you, to the empress; communicate what I will tell thee, and by these signs, bid her send the imperial robes, of which some rogue has deprived me. The signs I tell thee of are known to none but to ourselves." "In verity," said the porter, "thou art specially mad; at this very moment my lord sits at table with the empress herself. Nevertheless, out of regard for thy singular merits, I will intimate thy declaration within; and rest assured thou wilt presently find thyself most royally beaten." The porter went accordingly, and related what he had heard. But the empress became very sorrowful, and said: "Oh, my lord, what am I to think? The most hidden passages of our lives are revealed by an obscene fellow at the gate, and repeated to me by the porter, on the strength of which he declares himself the emperor, and my espoused lord!" When the fictitious monarch was apprised of this, he commanded him to be brought in. He had no sooner entered, than a large dog, which crouched upon the hearth, and had been much cherished by him, flew at his throat, and, but for timely prevention, would have killed him. A falcon also, seated upon her perch, no sooner beheld him than she broke her jesses and flew out of the hall. Then the pretended emperor, addressing those who stood about him, said: "My friends, hear what I will ask of yon ribald. Who are you? and what do you want?" "These questions," said the suffering man, "are very strange. You know I am the emperor and master of this place." The other, turning to the nobles who sat or stood at the table, continued: "Tell me, on your allegiance, which of us two is your lord and master?" "Your majesty asks us an easy thing," replied they, "and need not to remind us of our allegiance. That obscene wretch cannot be our sovereign. You alone are he, whom we have known from childhood; and we intreat that this fellow may be severely punished as a warning to others how they give scope to their mad presumption." Then turning to the empress, the usurper said: "Tell me, my lady, on the faith you have sworn, do you know this man who calls himself thy lord and emperor?" She answered: "My lord, how can you ask such a question? Have I not known thee more than thirty years, and borne thee many children? Yet, at one thing I do admire. How can this fellow have acquired so intimate a knowledge of what has passed between us?"

The pretended emperor made no reply, but addressing the real one, said: "Friend, how darest thou to call thyself emperor? We sentence thee, for this unexampled impudence, to be drawn, without loss of time, at the tail of a horse. And if thou utterest the same words again, thou shalt be doomed to an ignominious death." He then commanded his guards to see the sentence put in force, but to preserve his life. The unfortunate emperor was now almost distracted; and urged by his despair, wished vehemently for death. "Why was I born?" he exclaimed. "My friends shun me, and my wife and children will not acknowledge me. But there is my confessor, still. To him will I go; perhaps he will recollect me, because he has often received my confessions." He went accordingly, and knocked at the window of his cell. "Who is there?" said the confessor. "The Emperor Jovinian," was the reply; "open the window and I will speak to thee." The window was opened; but no sooner had he looked out than he closed it again in great haste. "Depart from me," said he, "accursed thing: thou art not the emperor, but the devil incarnate." This completed the miseries of the persecuted man; and he tore his hair, and plucked up his beard by the roots. "Woe is me," he cried, "for what strange doom am I reserved?" At this crisis, the impious words which, in the arrogance of his heart, he had uttered crossed his recollection. Immediately he beat again at the window of the confessor's cell, and exclaimed: "For the love of Him who was suspended from the cross, hear my confession." The recluse opened the window, and said, "I will do this with pleasure"; and then Jovinian acquainted him with every particular of his past life; and principally how he had lifted himself up against his Maker.

The confession made, and absolution given, the recluse looked out of his window, and directly knew him. "Blessed be the most high God," said he, "now I do know thee. I have here a few garments: clothe thyself, and go to the palace. I trust that they also will recognize thee." The emperor did as the confessor directed. The porter opened the gate, and made a low obeisance to him. "Dost thou know me?" said he. "Very well, my lord!" replied the menial; "but I marvel that I did not observe you go out." Entering the hall of his mansion, Jovinian was received by all with a profound reverence. The strange emperor was at that time in another apartment with the queen; and a certain knight going to him, said, "My lord, there is one in the hall to whom everybody bends; he so much resembles you, that we know not which is the emperor." Hearing this, the usurper said to the empress, "Go and see if you know him." She went, and returned greatly surprised at what she saw. "Oh, my lord," said she, "I declare to you that I know not whom to trust." "Then," returned he, "I will go and determine you." And taking her hand he led her into the hall and placed her on the throne beside him. Addressing the assembly, he said, "By the oaths you have taken, declare which of us is your emperor." The empress answered: "It is incumbent on me to speak first; but heaven is my witness, that I am unable to determine which is he." And so said all. Then the feigned emperor spoke thus: "My friends, hearken! That man is your king and your lord. He exalted himself to the disparagement of his Maker; and God, therefore, scourged and hid him from your knowledge. But his repentance removes the rod; he has now made ample satisfaction, and again let your obedience wait upon him. Commend yourselves to the protection of heaven." So saying, he disappeared. The emperor gave thanks to God, and surrendering to Him all his soul, lived happily and finished his days in peace.

LLUDD AND LLEVELYS

(Anonymous: Some Time Before 14th Century)

Not only is nothing known of the author of this story, but it is hardly possible to make a good guess within several centuries of the date of its composition. *The Mabinogion*, from which it is taken, is the title given to a collection of translations made from the Welsh by Lady Charlotte Guest some eighty years ago, in which she included twelve old Welsh romances. The literature of early Wales was extremely rich; from it sprang a host of stories, of which the most important were those treating of King Arthur and his court. In the words of Lady Guest, Welsh literature has "strong claims to be considered the cradle of European romance."

The present tale, translated by Lady Guest, is reprinted from *The Mabinogion*, Everyman's Library, by permission of the publisher, J. M. Dent and Sons.

LLUDD AND LLEVELYS

(From *The Mabinogion*)

BELI the great, the son of Manogan, had three sons, Lludd and Caswallawn, and Nynyaw; and according to the story he had a fourth son called Llevelys. And after the death of Beli, the kingdom of the Island of Britain fell into the hands of Lludd, his eldest son; and Lludd ruled prosperously, and rebuilt the walls of London, and encompassed it about with numberless towers. And after that he bade the citizens build houses therein, such as no houses in the kingdoms could equal. And moreover he was a mighty warrior, and generous and liberal in giving meat and drink to all that sought them. And though he had many castles and cities this one loved he more than any. And he dwelt therein most part of the year, and therefore was it called Caer Lludd, and at last Caer London. And after the stranger-race came there, it was called London, or Lwndrys.

Lludd loved Llevelys best of all his brothers, because he was a wise and discreet man. Having heard that the king of France had died, leaving no heir except a daughter, and that he had left all his possessions in her hands, he came to Lludd his brother, to beseech his counsel and aid. And that not so much for his own welfare, as to seek to add to the glory and honor and dignity of his kindred, if he might go to France to woo the maiden for his wife. And forthwith his brother conferred with him, and this counsel was pleasing unto him.

So he prepared ships and filled them with armed knights, and set forth towards France. And as soon as they had landed, they sent messengers to show the nobles of France the cause of the embassy. And by the joint counsel of the nobles of France and of the princes, the maiden was given to Llevelys, and the crown of the kingdom with her. And thenceforth he ruled the land discreetly, and wisely, and happily, as long as his life lasted.

After a space of time had passed, three plagues fell on the Island of Britain, such as none in the islands had ever seen the like of. The first was a certain race that came, and was called the Coranians; and so great was their knowledge, that there was no discourse upon the face of the Island, however low it might be spoken, but what, if the wind met it, it was known to them. And through this they could not be injured.

The second plague was a shriek which came on every May-eve, over every hearth in the Island of Britain. And this went through people's hearts, and so scared them that the men lost their hue and their strength, and the women their children, and the young men and the maidens lost their senses, and all the animals and trees and the earth and the waters were left barren.

The third plague was, that however much of provisions and food might be prepared in the king's courts, were there even so much as a year's provision of meat and drink, none of it could ever be found, except what was consumed in the first night. And two of these plagues, no one ever knew their cause, therefore was there better hope of being freed from the first than from the second and third.

And thereupon King Lludd felt great sorrow and care, because that he knew not how he might be freed from these plagues. And he called to him all the nobles of his kingdom, and asked counsel of them what they should do against these afflictions. And by the common counsel of the nobles, Lludd the son of Beli went to Llevelys his brother, king of France, for he was a man great of counsel and wisdom, to seek his advice.

And they made ready a fleet, and that in secret and in silence, lest that race should know the cause of their errand, or any besides the king and his counselors. And when they were made ready, they went into their ships, Lludd and those whom he chose with him. And they began to cleave the seas towards France.

And when these tidings came to Llevelys, seeing that he knew not the cause of his brother's ships, he came on the other side to meet him, and with him was a fleet vast of size. And when Lludd saw this, he left all the ships out upon the sea except one only; and in that one he came to meet his brother, and he likewise with a single ship came to meet him. And when they were come together, each put his arms about the other's neck, and they welcomed each other with brotherly love.

After that Lludd had shown his brother the cause of his errand, Llevelys said that he himself knew the cause of the coming to those lands. And they took counsel together to discourse on the matter otherwise than thus, in order that the wind might not catch their words, nor the Coranians know what they might say. Then Llevelys caused a long horn to be made of brass, and through this horn they discoursed. But whatsoever words they spoke through this horn, one to the other, neither of them could hear any other but harsh and hostile words. And when Llevelys saw this, and that there was a demon thwarting them and disturbing through this horn, he caused wine to be put therein to wash it. And through the virtue of the wine the demon was driven out of the horn. And when their discourse was unobstructed, Llevelys told his brother that he would give him some insects whereof he should keep some to breed, lest by chance the like affliction might come a second time. And other of these insects he should take and bruise in water. And he assured him that it would have power to destroy the race of the Coranians. That is to say, that when he came home to his kingdom he should call together all the people both of his own race and of the race of the Coranians for a conference, as though with the intent of making peace between them; and that when they were all together, he should take this charmed water, and cast it over all alike. And he assured him that the water would poison the race of the Coranians, but that it would not slay or harm those of his own race.

"And the second plague," said he, "that is in thy dominion, behold it is a dragon. And another dragon of a foreign race is fighting with it, and striving to overcome it. And therefore does your dragon make a fearful outcry. And on this wise mayest thou come to know this. After thou hast returned home, cause the Island to be measured in its length and breadth, and in the place where thou dost find the exact central point, there cause a pit to be dug, and cause a cauldron full of the best mead that can be made to be put in the pit, with a covering of satin over the face of the cauldron. And then, in thine own person do thou remain there watching, and thou wilt see the dragon fighting in the form of terrific animals. And at length they will take the form of dragons in the air. And last of all, after wearying themselves with fierce and furious fighting, they will fall in the form of two pigs upon the covering, and they will sink in, and the covering with them, and they will draw it down to the very bottom of the cauldron. And they will drink up the whole of the mead; and after that they will sleep. Thereupon do thou immediately fold the covering around them, and bury them in a kistvaen, in the strongest place thou hast in thy dominions, and hide them in the earth. And as long as they shall bide in that strong place no plague shall come to the Island of Britain from elsewhere.

"The cause of the third plague," said he, "is a mighty man of magic, who takes thy meat and thy drink and thy store. And he through illusions and charms causes every one to sleep. Therefore it is needful for thee in thy own person to watch thy food and thy provisions. And lest he should overcome thee with sleep, be there a cauldron of cold water by thy side, and when thou art oppressed with sleep, plunge into the cauldron."

Then Lludd returned back unto his land. And immediately he summoned to him the whole of his own race and of the Coranians. And as Llevelys had taught him, he bruised the insects in water, the which he cast over them all together, and forthwith it destroyed the whole tribe of the Coranians, without hurt to any of the Britons.

And some time after this, Lludd caused the Island to be measured in its length and in its breadth. And in Oxford he found the central point, and in that place he caused the earth to be dug, and in that pit a cauldron to be set, full of the best mead that could be made, and a covering of satin over the face of it. And he himself watched that night. And while he was there, he beheld the dragons fighting. And when they were weary they fell, and came down upon the top of the satin, and drew it with them to the bottom of the cauldron. And when they had drunk the mead they slept. And in their sleep, Lludd folded the covering around them, and in the securest place he had in Snowdon, he hid them in a kistvaen. Now after that this spot was called Dinas Emreis, but before that, Dinas Ffaraon. And thus the fierce outcry ceased in his dominions.

And when this was ended, King Lludd caused an exceeding great banquet to be prepared. And when it was ready, he placed a vessel of cold water by his side, and he in his own proper person watched it. And as he abode thus clad with arms, about the third watch of the night, lo, he heard many surpassing fascinations and various songs. And drowsiness urged him to sleep. Upon this, lest he should be hindered from his purpose and be overcome by sleep, he went often into the water. And at last, behold, a man of vast size, clad in strong, heavy armor, came in, bearing a hamper. And, as he was wont, he put all the food and provisions of meat and drink into the hamper, and proceeded to go with it forth. And nothing was ever more wonderful to Lludd, than that the hamper should hold so much.

And thereupon King Lludd went after him and spoke unto him thus. "Stop, stop," said he, "though thou hast done many insults and much spoil erewhile, thou shalt not do so any more, unless thy skill in arms and thy prowess be greater than mine."

Then he instantly put down the hamper on the floor, and awaited him. And a fierce encounter was between them, so that the glittering fire flew out from their arms. And at last Lludd grappled with him, and fate bestowed the victory on Lludd. And he threw the plague to the earth. And after he had overcome him by strength and might, he besought his mercy. "How can I grant thee mercy," said the king, "after all the many injuries and wrongs that thou hast done me?" "All the losses that ever I have caused thee," said he, "I will make thee atonement for equal to what I have taken. And I will never do the like from this time forth. But thy faithful vassal will I be." And the king accepted this from him.

And thus Lludd freed the Island of Britain from the three plagues. And from thenceforth until the end of his life, in prosperous peace did Lludd the son of Beli rule the Island of Britain. And this Tale is called the Story of Lludd and Llevelys. And thus it ends.

SIR THOMAS MALORY

(Flourished Late 15th Century)

PRACTICALLY nothing is known of this first great writer of English prose romance. Malory's significance in the development of the English language is, for our purposes, not so vital a matter as his contribution to the art of story-telling. His vast compilation, which is a rewritten version of the outstanding episodes in the Arthurian cycle, was printed by Caxton in 1485, and, due to the rapid spread of books through the recently invented printing-press, Malory's influence was far greater than it would otherwise have been. "Malory," says Edmund Gosse, "tinges the whole English character; he is the primal fount of our passion for adventure, and of our love for active chivalry."

The present version is reprinted from *Malory's History of King Arthur and the Quest of the Holy Grail*, London, 1886. There is no title in the original text.

LAUNCELOT'S TOURNEY

(From the *Morte d'Arthur*)

AND then the Queen let make a privy dinner in the city of London, unto the knights of the Round Table; and all was to show outward that she had a great joy in all other knights of the Round Table, as she had in Sir Launcelot. All only at that dinner she had Sir Gawaine and his brethren; that is to say, Sir Agravaine, Sir Gaheris, Sir Gareth, and Sir Mordred. Also there was Sir Bors de Ganis, Sir Blamor de Ganis, Sir Bleoberis de Ganis, Sir Galihud, Sir Galihodin, Sir Ector de Maris, Sir Lionel, Sir Palomides, and his brother, Sir Safre; la Cote mal Tail, Sir Persuant, Sir Ironside, Sir Brandiles, Sir Kaye the seneschal, Sir Mador de la Port, Sir Patrice a knight of Ireland, Sir Aliducke, Sir Astomore, and Sir Pinell le Savage, the which was cousin unto Sir Lamoracke de Galis, the good knight, the which Sir Gawaine and brethren slew by treason. And so these knights should dine with the Queen in a privy place by themselves; and there was made a great feast of all manner of dainty meats and drinks. But Sir Gawaine had a custom that he used daily at dinner and at supper, that he loved well all manner of fruits, and in especial apples and pears; and, therefore, whosoever dined or feasted, Sir Gawaine would commonly purvey for good fruit for him: and so did the Queen; for, to please Sir Gawaine, she let purvey for him of all manner of fruits. For Sir Gawaine was a passing hot knight of nature; and this Sir Pinell hated Sir Gawaine, because of his kinsman, Sir Lamoracke de Galis: and, therefore, for pure envy and hate, Sir Pinell poisoned certain apples for to poison Sir Gawaine withal. And so this was well unto the end of the meat; and so it befell, by misfortune, that a good knight, named Sir Patrice, cousin unto Sir Mador de la Port, took one of the poisoned apples: and, when he had eaten it, he swelled till he burst; and there Sir Patrice fell down dead suddenly among them. Then every knight leaped from the board, ashamed, and enraged for wrath nigh out of their wits; for they wist not what to say, considering that Queen Guenever made the feast and dinner, they all had suspicion upon her. "My lady, the Queen," said Sir Gawaine, "wit ye well, madam, that this dinner was made for me: for all folks, that know my conditions, understand well that I love fruit; and now I see well I had been near slain: therefore, madam, I dread me least ye will be shamed." Then the Queen stood still, and was right sore abashed, that she wist not what to say. "This shall not be ended so," said Sir Mador de la Port; "for here have I lost a full noble knight of my blood: and, therefore, upon this shame and despite I will be revenged to the uttermost." And thereupon Sir Mador appealed Queen Guenever of the death of his cousin, Sir Patrice. Then stood they all still, that none of them would speak a word against him; for they had a great suspection unto Queen Guenever, because she let make the dinner. And the Queen was so sore abashed, that she could none otherwise do, but wept so heartily, that she fell in a swoon. With this noise and sudden cry came unto them King Arthur, and marveled greatly what it might be; and, when he wist of their trouble, and the sudden death of that good knight, Sir Patrice, he was a passing heavy man.

And ever Sir Mador stood still before King Arthur, and ever he appealed Queen Guenever of treason. For the custom was such at that time, that all manner of shameful death was called treason. "Fair lords," said King Arthur, "me repenteth sore of this trouble, but the cause is so, we may not have to do in this matter; for I must be a rightful judge, and that repenteth me that I may not do battle for my wife; for, as I deem, this deed came never of her, and therefore I suppose we shall not be all destitute, but that some good knight shall put his body in jeopardy, rather than she should be burnt in a wrong quarrel. And, therefore, Sir Mador, be not so hasty; for it may happen she shall not be all friendless: and, therefore, desire thou the day of battle, and she shall purvey her of some good knight, which shall answer you, or else it were to me great shame, and unto all my court." "My gracious lord," said Sir Mador, "ye must hold me excused: for, though ye be our King in that degree, ye are but a knight as we are, and ye are sworn unto knighthood as we are: and, therefore, I pray you, that ye will not be displeased; for there is none of the twenty knights that were bidden for to come unto this dinner, but all they have great suspection unto the Queen. What say ye all, my lords?" said Sir Mador. Then they answered by and by, and said, that they "could not excuse the Queen; for why she made the dinner: and either it must come by her, or by her servants." "Alas!" said the Queen, "I made this dinner for a good intent, and never for any evil (so God help me in my right!) as I was never purposed to do such evil deeds, and that I report me unto God." "My lord, the King," said Sir Mador, "I require you heartily, as ye be a righteous king, give me a day that I may have justice." "Well," said King Arthur, "I give you a day this day fifteen days, that ye be ready armed on horseback in the meadow beside Westminster; and, if it so fall that there be any knight to encounter with you, there may ye do your best, and God speed the right: and, if it so fall that there be no knight at that day, then must my Queen be burnt, and there shall ye be ready to have her judgment." "Well I am answered," said Sir Mador; and every knight went where it liked him. So, when the King and the Queen were together, the King asked the Queen how this case befell. Then answered the Queen, "So God me help, I wot not how, or in what manner." "Where is Sir Launcelot?" said King Arthur. "An he were here, he would not grudge to do battle for you." "Sir," said the Queen, "I cannot tell you where he is; but his brother, and all his kinsmen, deem that he is not within this realm." "That sore repenteth me," said King Arthur; "for an he were here, he would full soon stint this strife. Then I will counsel you," said the King, "that ye go unto Sir Bors, and pray him to do that battle for you for Sir Launcelot's sake: and, upon my life, he will not refuse you. For right well I perceive," said King Arthur, "that none of all those twenty knights, without more, that were with you in fellowship together at your dinner, where Sir Patrice was so traitorously slain, that will do battle for you, nor none of them will say well of you; and that shall be great slander for you in this court." "Alas!" said the Queen, "I cannot do withal: but now I miss Sir Launcelot; for, an he were here, he would put me full soon unto my heart's ease." "What aileth you," said King Arthur, "that ye cannot keep Sir Launcelot on your side? For wit ye well," said King Arthur, "whosoever hath the noble knight, Sir Launcelot, on his part, hath the most man of worship in the world on his side. Now, go your way," said the King unto the Queen, "and require Sir Bors to do battle for you for Sir Launcelot's sake."

So the Queen departed from the King, and sent for Sir Bors into her chamber; and when he was come, she besought him of succor. "Madam," said he, "what would ye that I do? for I may not with my worship have to do in this matter, because I was at the same dinner, for dread that any of those knights would have me in suspection. Also, madam," said Sir Bors, "now miss ye Sir Launcelot; for he would not have failed you, neither in right, nor yet in wrong, as ye have well proved when ye have been in danger; and now have ye driven him out of this country, by whom ye and we all were daily worshiped. Therefore, madam, I greatly marvel me how ye dare for shame require me to do any thing for you, insomuch as ye have chased him out of your country, by whom I was borne up and honored." "Alas! fair knight," said the Queen, "I put me wholly in your grace; and all that is done amiss I will amend, as ye will counsel me." And therewith she kneeled down upon both her knees, and besought Sir Bors to have mercy upon her, "for I shall have a shameful death, and thereto I never offended." Right so came King Arthur, and found the Queen kneeling before Sir Bors. Then Sir Bors took her up, and said, "Madam, ye do to me great dishonor." "Ah! gentle knight," said King Arthur, "have mercy upon my Queen, for I am now in a certain that she is now untruly defamed; and, therefore, courteous knight," said the King, "promise her to do battle for her: I require you for the love of Sir Launcelot." "My lord," said Sir Bors, "ye require me of the greatest thing that any man may require me; and wit ye well if I grant to do battle for the Queen, I shall wrath many of my fellowship of the Round Table; but, as for that," said Sir Bors, "I will grant my lord, for my lord Sir Launcelot's sake, and for your sake, I will at that day be the Queen's champion, unless that there come by adventure a better knight than I am to do battle for her." "Will ye promise this," said the King, "by your faith?" "Yes, sir," said Sir Bors, "of that will I not fail you, nor her both: but if that there come a better knight than I am, then shall he have the battle." Then were the King and the Queen passing glad, thanked him heartily, and so departed.

So then Sir Bors departed secretly upon a day, and rode unto Sir Launcelot there as he was with the hermit by Sir Brastias, and told him of all his adventures. "Ah! Jesu," said Sir Launcelot, "this is happily come as I would have it, and therefore I pray you make you ready to do battle; but look that ye tarry till ye see me come as long as ye may, for I am sure Sir Mador is a hot knight, if he be chafed, for the more ye suffer him, the hastier will he be to do battle." "Sir," said Sir Bors, "let me deal with him; doubt ye not ye shall have all your will." Then departed Sir Bors from him, and came unto the court again. Then was it noised in all the court that Sir Bors should do battle for the Queen; wherefore many knights were greatly displeased with him, that he should take upon him to do battle in the Queen's quarrel; for there were but few knights in the court but that they deemed the Queen was in the wrong, and that she had done that treason. So Sir Bors answered thus unto his fellows of the Round Table, "Wit ye well, my fair lords, it were shame unto us all, and we suffered to see the most noble queen of the world for to be shamed openly, considering that her lord and our lord is the man of most worship of the world, and the most christened; and he hath always worshiped us all in all places." Many knights answered him again, and said, "As for our most noble King Arthur, we love him and honor him as well as ye do; but as for Queen Guenever, we love her not, for because she is a destroyer of good knights." "Fair lords," said Sir Bors, "me seemeth, ye say, not as ye should say, for never yet in all my days knew I, nor heard say, that ever she was a destroyer of any good knight; but at all times as far as I ever could know, she was always a maintainer of good knights; and always she hath been large and free of her goods to all good knights, and the most bounteous lady of her gifts and her good grace that ever I saw, or heard speak of; and therefore it were great shame (said Sir Bors) unto us all to our most noble King's wife, if we suffer her to be shamefully slain: and wit ye well (said Sir Bors) I will not suffer it; for I dare say so much the Queen is not guilty of Sir Patrice's death, for she ought him never none evil will, nor none of the twenty knights that were at that dinner; for I dare well say that it was for good love she had us to dinner, and not for no malice, and that I doubt not shall be proved hereafter; for howsoever the game goeth, there was treason among some of us." Then some said to Sir Bors, "We may well believe your words." And so some of them were well pleased, and some were not pleased.

The day came on fast until the even that the battle should be. Then the Queen sent for Sir Bors, and asked him "how he was disposed." "Truly, madam," said he, "I am disposed in likewise as I promised you; that is to say, I shall not fail you, unless by adventure there come a better knight than I to do battle for you; then, madam, am I discharged of my promise." "Will ye," said the Queen, "that I tell my lord, King Arthur, thus?" "Do as it shall please you, madam," said Sir Bors. Then the Queen went unto the King, and told him the answer of Sir Bors.

"Have ye no doubt," said the King, "of Sir Bors, for I call him now one of the best knights of the world, and the most profitablest man; and this is past forth until the morrow." And the King and the Queen, and all the knights that were there at that time, drew them to the meadow beside Winchester, whereas the battle should be. And so when the King was come with the Queen, and many knights of the Round Table, then the Queen was put there in the constable's ward, and there was made a great fire about the iron stake, that an Sir Mador de la Port had the better she should be burnt; such a custom was used in those days, that neither for favor, nor for love, nor for affinity, there should be none other but right wise judgment as well upon a King as upon a knight, as well upon a Queen as upon another poor lady.

So in the meanwhile came in Sir Mador de la Port, and took the oath before the King, that Queen Guenever did this treason unto his cousin, Sir Patrice, and unto his oath he would prove it with his body, hand for hand, who that would say the contrary thereto. Right so came Sir Bors de Ganis, and said "that as for Queen Guenever she is in the right, and that will I make good with my hands, that she is not culpable of this treason that is put upon her." "Then make thee ready," said Sir Mador, "and we shall soon prove whether thou be in the right or I." "Sir," said Sir Bors, "wit ye well I know thee for a good knight, not for then I shall not fear thee so greatly, but I trust unto Almighty God, my Maker, I shall be able enough to withstand thy malice; but thus much have I promised my lord, King Arthur, and my lady, the Queen, that I shall do battle for her in this case to the uttermost, only that there came a better knight than I am, and discharged me." "Is that all?" said Sir Mador. "Either come thou off and do battle with me, or else say nay." "Take your horse," said Sir Bors, "and as I suppose ye shall not tarry long, but that ye shall be answered." Then either departed to their tents, and made them ready to mount upon horseback as they thought best. And anon Sir Mador de la Port came into the field with his shield on his shoulder, and a spear in his hand, and so rode about the place, crying unto King Arthur, "Bid your champion come forth an he dare." Then was Sir Bors ashamed, and took his horse, and came to the list end; and then was he ware whereas came out of a wood there fast by, a knight, all armed at all points, upon a white horse, with a strong shield and of strange arms; and he came riding all that he might run. And so he came to Sir Bors, and said, "Fair knight, I pray you, be not displeased, for here must a better knight than ye are have this battle; therefore I pray you to withdraw you; for I would ye knew I have had this day a right great journey, and this battle ought to be mine, and so I promised you when I spake with you last, and with all my heart I thank you for your good will." Then Sir Bors rode unto King Arthur, and told him how there was a knight come that would have the battle for to fight for the Queen.

"What knight is he?" said King Arthur. "I cannot show you," said Sir Bors, "but such a covenant made he with me for to be here this day. Now, my lord," said Sir Bors, "here am I discharged."

Then the King called unto the knight, and asked him "if he would fight for the Queen?" Then he answered unto the King, "Therefore came I hither; and, therefore, Sir King," he said, "tarry me no longer, for I may not tarry; for anon as I have finished this battle, I must depart hence, for I have to do many matters elsewhere: for wit ye well," said that knight, "this is dishonor unto you, all knights of the Round Table, to see and know so noble a lady and so courteous a Queen, as Queen Guenever is, thus to be rebuked and shamed among you." Then marveled they all what knight that might be, that so took the battle upon him; but there was not one that knew him but if it were Sir Bors. "Then," said Sir Mador de la Port unto the King, "now let me wit with whom I shall have to do withal." And then they rode to the list's end, and there they couched their spears, and ran the one against the other with all their mights: and Sir Mador's spear brake all to pieces: but Sir Launcelot's spear held, and bare Sir Mador's horse and all backward to the ground, and had a great fall; but mightily and suddenly he avoided his horse, and dressed his shield before him, and then drew his sword, and bade that other knight alight and do battle with him on foot. Then that knight descended lightly from his horse like a valiant man, and put his shield afore him, and drew out his sword. And so they came eagerly to battle, and either gave other many sad strokes, tracing and traversing, racing and foyning, and hurtling together with their swords, as they had been two wild boars.

Thus were they fighting nigh an hour; for this Sir Mador was a full strong knight, and mightily proved in many strong battles. But, at the last, the knight smote Sir Mador groveling upon the ground, and the knight stepped near him for to have pulled Sir Mador flat-long upon the ground. And therewith, all suddenly, Sir Mador arose; and, in his arising, he smote that knight through the thigh, that the blood ran out right fiercely. And when he felt himself so wounded, and saw his blood, he let him arise upon his feet, and then he gave him such a buffet upon the helm that he fell flat-long to the ground. And therewith he strode to him, for to have pulled off his helm from his head: and then Sir Mador prayed that knight to save his life; and so he yielded him as an overcome knight, and released the Queen of his quarrel. "I will not grant thee life," said the knight, "but only that you freely release the Queen forever, and that no manner of mention be made upon Sir Patrice's tomb that ever Queen Guenever consented to that treason." "All this shall be done," said Sir Mador; "and clearly I discharge my quarrel forever." Then the knights' porters of the list took up Sir Mador, and led him to his tent; and the other knight went straight to the stairfoot, whereas King Arthur sat. And by that time was the Queen come unto the King, and either kissed other lovingly. And, when the King saw that knight, he stooped unto him, and thanked him; and in likewise did the Queen: and then the King prayed him to pull off his helm, and to rest him, and to take a sup of wine. And then he put off his helm to drink, and then every knight knew that he was the noble knight, Sir Launcelot.

ROBERT GREENE

(1560?–1592)

GREENE was born at Norwich about 1560. He attended both Cambridge and Oxford Universities. He seems to have lived a wild and irregular life in London. He wrote plays, pamphlets, novels and stories and despite his popularity he died in poverty at an early age. Greene was one of the few Elizabethan writers who turned his hand to the composition of short tales. Two of his romances contain several examples, and here and there in his other writings, he has introduced a story in the style of *Roberto's Tale*. In an age that had not learned to copy the technical finish of the Italians, Greene managed in this story, none the less, to surpass most of his predecessors in the art of elimination.

ROBERTO'S TALE

(From *Greene's Groatsworth of Wit Bought with a Million of Repentance*)

IN the North parts there dwelt an old squire that had a young daughter his heir, who had (as I know, Madam Lamilia, you have had) many youthful gentlemen that long time sued to obtain her love. But she, knowing her own perfection (as women are by nature proud), would not to any of them vouchsafe favor, insomuch that they, perceiving her relentless, showed themselves not altogether witless, but left her to her fortune when they found her frowardness. At last it fortuned, among other strangers, a farmer's son visited her father's house, on whom, at the first sight, she was enamored; he likewise on her. Tokens of love passed between them; either acquainted other's parents of their choice, and they kindly gave their consent. Short tale to make, married they were, and great solemnity was at the wedding feast.

A young gentleman that had been long a suitor to her, vexing that the son of a farmer should be so preferred, cast in his mind by what means, to mar their merriment, he might steal away the bride. Hereupon he confers with an old beldam called Mother Gunby dwelling thereby, whose counsel being taken, he fell to his practise and drift, and proceeded thus. In the afternoon, when dancers were very busy, he takes the bride by the hand and after a turn or two tells her in her ear he has a secret to impart unto her, appointing her in any wise, in the evening, to find a time to confer with him. She promised she would, and so they parted. Then goes he to the bridegroom and with protestations of entire affection, protests the great sorrow he takes at that which he must utter, whereon depended his especial credit, if it were known the matter by him should be discovered. After the bridegroom's promise of secrecy, the gentleman tells him that a friend of his received that morning from the bride a letter, wherein she willed him with some sixteen horse to await her coming at a park side; for that she detested him in her heart as a base country hind, whom her father compelled her to marry. The bridegroom, almost out of his wits, began to bite his lip. "Nay," said the gentleman, "if you will by me be advised, you shall save her credit, win her by kindness, and yet prevent her wanton complot." "As how?" said the bridegroom. "Marry, thus," said the gentleman: "In the evening (for till the guests be gone she intends not to gad) get you on horseback, and seem to be of the company that attends her coming. I am appointed to bring her from the house to the park, and from thence fetch a winding compass of a mile about, but to turn unto old Mother Gunby's house, where her lover (my friend) abides. When she alights, I will conduct her to a chamber far from his lodging, but when the lights are out and she expecting her adulterous copes-mate, yourself (as reason is) shall prove her bedfellow, where privately you may reprove her, and in the morning early return home without trouble. As for the gentleman my friend, I will excuse her absence to him by saying, She mocked thee with her maid instead of herself, whom, when I knew at her lighting, I disdained to bring her unto his presence." The bridegroom gave his hand it should be so.

Now by the way we must understand this Mother Gunby had a daughter who all that day sat heavily at home with a willow garland, for that the bridegroom (if he had dealt faithfully) should have wedded her before any other. But men, Lamilia, are inconstant: money nowadays makes the match, or else the match is marred. But to the matter: the bridegroom and the gentleman thus agreed. He took his time, conferred with the bride, persuaded her that her husband notwithstanding his fair show at the marriage had sworn to his old sweetheart, neighbor Gunby's daughter, to be that night her bedfellow, and if she would bring her father, his father and her friends to the house at midnight, they should find it so. At this the young gentlewoman, inwardly vexed to be by a peasant so abused, promised, if she saw likelihood of his slipping away, that then she would do as he directed.

All this thus sorting, the old woman's daughter was trickly attired, ready to furnish this pageant, for her old mother provided all things necessary. Well, supper past, dancing ended, all the guests would home, and the bridegroom pretending to bring some friend of his home, got his horse and to the park side he rode, and stayed with the horsemen that attended the gentleman. Anon came Marian like mistress bride, and, mounted behind the gentleman, away they passed, fetched their compass, and at last alighted at an old wife's house, where suddenly she is conveyed to her chamber, and the bridegroom sent to keep her company; where he had scarce devised how to begin his exhortation, but the father of his bride knocked at the chamber door. At which being somewhat amazed yet thinking to turn it to a jest, sith his wife (as he thought) was in bed with him, he opened the door saying, "Father, you are heartily welcome. I wonder how you found us out here. This device to remove ourselves was with my wife's consent, that we might rest quietly, without the maids and bachelors disturbing us."

"But where is your wife?" said the gentleman.

"Why, here in bed," quoth the other.

"My daughter had been your wife, for sure I am to-day she was given you in marriage."

"You are merrily disposed," said the bridegroom. "What! Think you I have another wife?"

"I think but as you speak," quoth the gentleman, "for my daughter is below, and you say your wife is in the bed."

"Below!" said he. "You are a merry man." And with that, casting on a night-gown, he went down where, when he saw his wife, the gentleman his father, and a number of his friends assembled, he was so confounded that how to behave himself he knew not, only he cried out that he was deceived. At this the old woman arrived, and making herself ignorant of all the whole matter, inquires the cause of that sudden tumult. When she was told the new bridegroom was found in bed with her daughter, she exclaimed against so great an injury. Marian was called *in quorum;* she justified it was by his allurement. He, being condemned by all their consents, was judged unworthy to have the gentlewoman unto his wife, and compelled (for escaping of punishment) to marry Marian; and the young gentleman (for his care in discovering the farmer's lewdness) was recompensed with the gentlewoman's ever-during love.

DANIEL DEFOE

(1659?–1731)

DANIEL FOE—later changed to Defoe—was born in London, probably in 1659, of a lower middle-class family of Dissenters. He lived an active life as a hack-writer, earning a livelihood for the most part by writing political pamphlets, satires—in a word paid propaganda—for one or other of the powerful parties. He was also engaged in business, and edited a periodical for nine years. He was once imprisoned for two years because of his bitter satire, *The Shortest Way with Dissenters*. It has not yet been possible to identify all his very numerous writings. It was not until he reached the age of sixty that he began to write the works by which he is best known. The first of these was *Robinson Crusoe*, celebrated as one of the world's favorite books. But some years earlier he had written a few sketches, the best of which appears in the following pages. It is a most convincing bit of realistic writing. It was first published in 1706 in pamphlet form, and later revised.

The present is a reprint from the latest revised edition, in which spelling and punctuation have been modernized.

TRUE RELATION OF THE APPARITION OF ONE MRS. VEAL

THIS thing is so rare in all its circumstances, and on so good authority, that my reading and conversation have not given me anything like it. It is fit to gratify the most ingenious and serious inquirer. Mrs. Bargrave is the person to whom Mrs. Veal appeared after her death; she is my intimate friend, and I can avouch for her reputation for these fifteen or sixteen years, on my own knowledge; and I can affirm the good character she had from her youth to the time of my acquaintance. Though, since this relation, she is calumniated by some people that are friends to the brother of Mrs. Veal who appeared to think the relation of this appearance to be a reflection, and endeavor what they can to blast Mrs. Bargrave's reputation and to laugh the story out of countenance. But by the circumstances thereof, and the cheerful disposition of Mrs. Bargrave, notwithstanding the ill usage of a very wicked husband, there is not yet the least sign of dejection in her face; nor did I ever hear her let fall a desponding or murmuring expression; nay, not when actually under her husband's barbarity, which I have been a witness to, and several other persons of undoubted repu-

Now you must know Mrs. Veal was a maiden gentlewoman of about thirty years of age, and for some years past had been troubled with fits, which were perceived coming on her by her going off from her discourse very abruptly to some impertinence. She was maintained by an only brother, and kept his house in Dover. She was a very pious woman, and her brother a very sober man, to all appearance; but now he does all he can to null and quash the story. Mrs. Veal was intimately acquainted with Mrs. Bargrave from her childhood. Mrs. Veal's circumstances were then mean; her father did not take care of his children as he ought, so that they were exposed to hardships. And Mrs. Bargrave in those days had as unkind a father, though she wanted neither for food nor clothing; while Mrs. Veal wanted for both, insomuch that she would often say, "Mrs. Bargrave, you are not only the best, but the only friend I have in the world; and no circumstance of life shall ever dissolve my friendship." They would often condole each other's adverse fortunes, and read together *Drelincourt upon Death*, and other books; and so, like two Christian friends, they comforted each other under their sorrow.

Some time after, Mr. Veal's friends got him a place in the custom-house at Dover, which occasioned Mrs. Veal, by little and little, to fall off from her intimacy with Mrs. Bargrave, though there was never any such thing as a quarrel; but an indifferency came on by degrees, till at last Mrs. Bargrave had not seen her in two years and a half, though above a twelvemonth of the time Mrs. Bargrave hath been absent from Dover, and this last half-year has been in Canterbury about two months of the time, dwelling in a house of her own.

In this house, on the eighth of September, one thousand seven hundred and five, she was sitting alone in the forenoon, thinking over her unfortunate life, and arguing herself into a due resignation to Providence, though her condition seemed hard: "And," said she, "I have been provided for hitherto, and doubt not but I shall be still, and am well satisfied that my afflictions shall end when it is most fit for me." And then took up her sewing work, which she had no sooner done but she hears a knocking at the door; she went to see who was there, and this proved to be Mrs. Veal, her old friend, who was in a riding habit. At that moment of time the clock struck twelve at noon.

"Madam," says Mrs. Bargrave, "I am surprised to see you, you who have been so long a stranger"; but told her she was glad to see her, and offered to salute her, which Mrs. Veal complied with, till their lips almost touched, and then Mrs. Veal drew her hand across her own eyes, and said, "I am not very well," and so waived it. She told Mrs. Bargrave she was going a journey, and had a great mind to see her first. "But," says Mrs. Bargrave, "how can you take a journey alone? I am amazed at it, because I know you have a fond brother." "Oh," says

Mrs. Veal, "I gave my brother the slip, and came away, because I had so great a desire to see you before I took my journey." So Mrs. Bargrave went in with her into another room within the first, and Mrs. Veal sat her down in an elbow-chair, in which Mrs. Bargrave was sitting when she heard Mrs. Veal knock. "Then," says Mrs. Veal, "my dear friend, I am come to renew our old friendship again, and beg your pardon for my breach of it; and if you can forgive me, you are the best of women." "Oh," says Mrs. Bargrave, "do not mention such a thing; I have not had an uneasy thought about it." "What did you think of me?" says Mrs. Veal. Says Mrs. Bargrave, "I thought you were like the rest of the world, and that prosperity had made you forget yourself and me." Then Mrs. Veal reminded Mrs. Bargrave of the many friendly offices she did her in former days, and much of the conversation they had with each other in the times of their adversity; what books they read, and what comfort in particular they received from Drelincourt's *Book of Death*, which was the best, she said, on the subject ever wrote. She also mentioned Dr. Sherlock, and two Dutch books, which were translated, wrote upon death, and several others. But Drelincourt, she said, had the clearest notions of death and of the future state of any who had handled that subject. Then she asked Mrs. Bargrave whether she had Drelincourt. She said, "Yes." Says Mrs. Veal, "Fetch it." And so Mrs. Bargrave goes upstairs and brings it down. Says Mrs. Veal, "Dear Mrs. Bargrave, if the eyes of our faith were as open as the eyes of our body, we should see numbers of angels about us for our guard. The notions we have of Heaven now are nothing like what it is, as Drelincourt says; therefore be comforted under your afflictions, and believe that the Almighty has a particular regard to you, and that your afflictions are marks of God's favor; and when they have done the business they are sent for, they shall be removed from you. And believe me, my dear friend, believe what I say to you, one minute of future happiness will infinitely reward you for all your sufferings. For I can never believe" (and claps her hand upon her knee with great earnestness, which, indeed, ran through most of her discourse) "that ever God will suffer you to spend all your days in this afflicted state. But be assured that your afflictions shall leave you, or you them, in a short time." She spake in that pathetical and heavenly manner that Mrs. Bargrave wept several times, she was so deeply affected with it.

Then Mrs. Veal mentioned Doctor Kendrick's *Ascetic*, at the end of which he gives an account of the lives of the primitive Christians. Their pattern she recommended to our imitation, and said, "Their conversation was not like this of our age. For now," says she, "there is nothing but vain, frothy discourse, which is far different from theirs. Theirs was to edification, and to build one another up in faith, so that they were not as we are, nor are we as they were. But," said she, "we ought to do as they did; there was a hearty friendship among them; but where is it now to be found?" Says Mrs. Bargrave, "It is hard indeed to find a true friend in these days." Says Mrs. Veal, "Mr. Norris has a fine copy of verses, called *Friendship in Perfection,* which I wonderfully admire. Have you seen the book?" says Mrs. Veal. "No," says Mrs. Bargrave, "but I have the verses of my own writing out." "Have you?" says Mrs. Veal; "then fetch them"; which she did from above stairs, and offered them to Mrs. Veal to read, who refused, and waived the thing, saying, "holding down her head would make it ache"; and then desiring Mrs. Bargrave to read them to her, which she did. As they were admiring *Friendship,* Mrs. Veal said, "Dear Mrs. Bargrave, I shall love you forever." In these verses there is twice used the word Elysian. "Ah!" says Mrs. Veal, "these poets have such names for Heaven." She would often draw her hand across her own eyes, and say, "Mrs. Bargrave, do not you think I am mightily impaired by my fits?" "No," says Mrs. Bargrave; "I think you look as well as ever I knew you."

After this discourse, which the apparition put in much finer words than Mrs. Bargrave said she could pretend to, and as much more as she can remember—for it cannot be thought that an hour and three quarters' conversation could all be retained, though the main of it she thinks she does—she said to Mrs. Bargrave she would have her write a letter to her brother, and tell him she would have him give rings to such and such; and that there was a purse of gold in her cabinet, and that she would have two broad pieces given to her cousin Watson.

Talking at this rate, Mrs. Bargrave thought that a fit was coming upon her, and so placed herself on a chair just before her knees, to keep her from falling to the ground, if her fits should occasion it; for the elbow-chair, she thought, would keep her from falling on either side. And to divert Mrs. Veal, as she thought, took hold of her gown-sleeve several times, and commended it. Mrs. Veal told her it was a scoured silk, and newly made up. But, for all this, Mrs. Veal persisted in her request, and told Mrs. Bargrave she must not deny her. And she would have her tell her brother all their conversation when she had the opportunity. "Dear Mrs. Veal," says Mrs. Bargrave, "it is much better, methinks, to do it yourself." "No," says Mrs. Veal, "though it seems impertinent to you now, you will see more reasons for it hereafter." Mrs. Bargrave, then, to satisfy her importunity, was going to fetch a pen and ink, but Mrs. Veal said, "Let it alone now, but do it when I am gone; but you must be sure to do it"; which was one of the last things she enjoined her at parting, and so she promised her.

Then Mrs. Veal asked for Mrs. Bargrave's daughter. She said she was not at home. "But if you have a mind to see her," says Mrs. Bargrave, "I'll send for her." "Do," says Mrs. Veal; on which she left her, and went to a neighbor's to see her; and by the time Mrs. Bargrave was returning, Mrs. Veal was without the door in the street, in the face of the beast-market, on a Saturday (which is market-day), and stood ready to part as soon as Mrs. Bargrave came to her. She asked her why she was in such haste. She said she must be going, though perhaps she might not go her journey till Monday; and told Mrs. Bargrave she hoped she should see her again at her cousin Watson's before she went whither she was going. Then she said she would take her leave of her, and walked from Mrs. Bargrave, in her view, till a turning interrupted the sight of her, which was three-quarters after one in the afternoon.

Mrs. Veal died the seventh of September, at twelve o'clock at noon, of her fits, and had not above four hours' senses before her death, in which time she received the sacrament. The next day after Mrs. Veal's appearance, being Sunday, Mrs. Bargrave was mightily indisposed with a cold and sore throat, that she could not go out that day; but on Monday morning she sends a person to Captain Watson's to know if Mrs. Veal was there. They wondered at Mrs. Bargrave's inquiry, and sent her word she was not there, nor was expected. At this answer, Mrs. Bargrave told the maid she had certainly mistook the name or made some blunder. And though she was ill, she put on her hood and went herself to Captain Watson's, though she knew none of the family, to see if Mrs. Veal was there or not. They said they wondered at her asking, for that she had not been in town; they were sure, if she had, she would have been there. Says Mrs. Bargrave, "I am sure she was with me on Saturday almost two hours." They said it was impossible, for they must have seen her if she had. In comes Captain Watson, while they were in dispute, and said that Mrs. Veal was certainly dead, and the escutcheons were making. This strangely surprised Mrs. Bargrave, when she sent to the person immediately who had the care of them, and found it true. Then she related the whole story to Captain Watson's family; and what gown she had on, and how striped; and that Mrs. Veal told her that it was scoured. Then Mrs. Watson cried out, "You have seen her indeed, for none knew but Mrs. Veal and myself that the gown was scoured." And Mrs. Watson owned that she described the gown exactly; "for," said she, "I helped her to make it up." This Mrs. Watson blazed all about the town, and avouched the demonstration of truth of Mrs. Bargrave's seeing Mrs. Veal's apparition. And Captain Watson carried two gentlemen immediately to Mrs. Bargrave's house to hear the relation from her own mouth. And when it spread so fast that gentlemen and persons of quality, the judicious and skeptical part of the world, flocked in upon her, it at last became such a task that she was forced to go out of the way; for they were in general extremely satisfied of the truth of the thing, and plainly saw that Mrs. Bargrave was no hypochondriac, for she always appears with such a cheerful air and pleasing mien that she has gained the favor and esteem of all the gentry, and it is thought a great favor if they can but get the relation from her own mouth. I should have told you before that Mrs. Veal told Mrs. Bargrave that her sister and brother-in-law were just come down from London to see her. Says Mrs. Bargrave, "How came you to order matters so strangely?" "It could not be helped," said Mrs. Veal. And her brother and sister did come to see her, and entered the town of Dover just as Mrs. Veal was expiring. Mrs. Bargrave asked her whether she would drink some tea. Says Mrs. Veal, "I do not care if I do; but I'll warrant you this mad fellow"—meaning Mrs. Bargrave's husband—"has broke all your trinkets." "But," says Mrs. Bargrave, "I'll get something to drink in for all that"; but Mrs. Veal waived it, and said, "It is no matter; let it alone," and so it passed.

All the time I sat with Mrs. Bargrave, which was some hours, she recollected fresh sayings of Mrs. Veal. And one material thing more she told Mrs. Bargrave, that old Mr. Bretton allowed Mrs. Veal ten pounds a year, which was a secret, and unknown to Mrs. Bargrave till Mrs. Veal told her.

Mrs. Bargrave never varies in her story, which puzzles those who doubt of the truth, or are unwilling to believe it. A servant in the neighbor's yard adjoining to Mrs. Bargrave's house heard her talking to somebody an hour of the time Mrs. Veal was with her. Mrs. Bargrave went out to her next neighbor's the very moment she parted with Mrs. Veal, and told her what ravishing conversation she had had with an old friend, and told the whole of it. Drelincourt's *Book of Death* is, since this happened, bought up strangely. And it is to be observed that, notwithstanding all the trouble and fatigue Mrs. Bargrave has undergone upon this account, she never took the value of a farthing, nor suffered her daughter to take anything of anybody, and therefore can have no interest in telling the story.

But Mr. Veal does what he can to stifle the matter, and said he would see Mrs. Bargrave; but yet it is certain matter of fact that he has been at Captain Watson's since the death of his sister, and yet never went near Mrs. Bargrave; and some of his friends report her to be a liar, and that she knew of Mr. Bretton's ten pounds a year. But the person who pretends to say so has the reputation to be a notorious liar among persons whom I know to be of undoubted credit. Now, Mr. Veal is more of a gentleman than to say she lies, but says a bad husband has crazed her; but she needs only present herself, and it will effectually confute that pretense. Mr. Veal says he asked his sister on her death-bed whether she had a mind to dispose of anything. And she said no. Now the things which Mrs. Veal's apparition would have disposed of were so trifling, and nothing of justice aimed at in her disposal, that the design of it appears to me to be only in order to make Mrs. Bargrave satisfy the world of the reality thereof as to what she had seen and heard, and to secure her reputation among the reasonable and understanding part of mankind. And then again, Mr. Veal owns that there was a purse of gold; but it was not found in her cabinet, but in a comb-box. This looks improbable; for that Mrs. Watson owned that Mrs. Veal was so very careful of the key of her cabinet that she would trust nobody with it; and if so, no doubt she would not trust her gold out of it. And Mrs. Veal's often drawing her hands over her eyes, and asking Mrs. Bargrave whether her fits had not impaired her, looks to me as if she did it on purpose to remind Mrs. Bargrave of her fits, to prepare her not to think it strange that she should put her upon writing to her brother, to dispose of rings and gold, which looks so much like a dying person's bequest; and it took accordingly with Mrs. Bargrave as the effect of her fits coming upon her, and was one of the many instances of her wonderful love to her and care of her, that she should not be affrighted, which, indeed, appears in her whole management, particularly in her coming to her in the daytime, waiving the salutation, and when she was alone; and then the manner of her parting, to prevent a second attempt to salute her.

Now, why Mr. Veal should think this relation a reflection—as it is plain he does, by his endeavoring to stifle it—I cannot imagine; because the generality believe her to be a good spirit, her discourse was so heavenly. Her two great errands were, to comfort Mrs. Bargrave in her affliction, and to ask her forgiveness for her breach of friendship, and with a pious discourse to encourage her. So that, after all, to suppose that Mrs. Bargrave could hatch such an invention as this, from Friday noon to Saturday noon—supposing that she knew of Mrs. Veal's death the very first moment—without jumbling circumstances, and without any interest, too, she must be more witty, fortunate, and wicked, too, than any indifferent person, I dare say, will allow. I asked Mrs. Bargrave several times if she was sure she felt the gown. She answered, modestly, "If my senses be to be relied on, I am sure of it." I asked her if she heard a sound when she clapped her hand upon her knee. She said she did not remember she did, but said she appeared to be as much a substance as I did who talked with her. "And I may," said she, "be as soon persuaded that your apparition is talking to me now as that I did not really see her; for I was under no manner of fear, and received her as a friend, and parted with her as such. I would not," says she, "give one farthing to make any one believe it; I have no interest in it; nothing but trouble is entailed upon me for a long time, for aught I know; and, had it not come to light by accident, it would never have been made public." But now she says she will make her own private use of it, and keep herself out of the way as much as she can; and so she has done since. She says she had a gentleman who came thirty miles to her to hear the relation; and that she had told it to a roomful of people at the time. Several particular gentlemen have had the story from Mrs. Bargrave's own mouth.

This thing has very much affected me, and I am as well satisfied as I am of the best-grounded matter of fact. And why we should dispute matter of fact, because we cannot solve things of which we can have no certain or demonstrative notions, seems strange to me; Mrs. Bargrave's authority and sincerity alone would have been undoubted in any other case.

JOSEPH ADDISON

(1672–1719)

Born in Wiltshire in 1672, of a respected and cultured family, Joseph Addison went to Oxford, and began his literary life by writing Latin verses. In 1699 he travelled on the Continent by way of preparation for a political career. But on the death of the King in 1703 his hopes of advancement were shattered. The next year, however, he celebrated Marlborough's victory at Blenheim in his poem *The Campaign*, which attracted considerable notice. In 1709 he collaborated with his friend Richard Steele in the recently founded periodical, *The Tatler*, and later in the better-known *Spectator*, contributing essays and sketches and several charmingly written tales which are among the most finished and neatly turned stories in the language.

THE STORY OF AN HEIR

(From *The Spectator*)

As I was yesterday taking the air with my friend Sir Roger, we were met by a fresh-colored ruddy young man who rid by us full speed, with a couple of servants behind him. Upon my inquiry who he was, Sir Roger told me that he was a young gentleman of a considerable estate, who had been educated by a tender mother that lived not many miles from the place where we were. She is a very good lady, says my friend, but took so much care of her son's health that she has made him good for nothing. She quickly found that reading was bad for his eyes, and that writing made his head ache. He was let loose among the woods as soon as he was able to ride on horseback, or to carry a gun upon his shoulder. To be brief, I found, by my friend's account of him, that he had got a great stock of health, but nothing else; and that if it were a man's business only to live, there would not be a more accomplished young fellow in the whole country.

The truth of it is, since my residing in these parts I have seen and heard innumerable instances of young heirs and elder brothers who either from their own reflecting upon the estates they are born to, and therefore thinking all other accomplishments unnecessary, or from hearing these notions frequently inculcated to them by the flattery of their servants and domestics, or from the same foolish thought prevailing in those who have the care of their education, are of no manner of use but to keep up their families, and transmit their lands and houses in a line to posterity.

This makes me often think on a story I have heard of two friends, which I shall give my reader at large, under feigned names. The moral of it may, I hope, be useful, though there are some circumstances which make it rather appear like a novel, than a true story.

Eudoxus and Leontine began the world with small estates. They were both of them men of good sense and great virtue. They prosecuted their studies together in their earlier years, and entered into such a friendship as lasted to the end of their lives. Eudoxus, at his first setting out in the world, threw himself into a court, where by his natural endowments and his acquired abilities he made his way from one post to another, till at length he had raised a very considerable fortune. Leontine on the contrary sought all opportunities of improving his mind by study, conversation and travel. He was not only acquainted with all the sciences, but with the most eminent professors of them throughout Europe. He knew perfectly well the interests of its princes, with the customs and fashions of their courts, and could scarce meet with the name of an extraordinary person in the *Gazette* whom he had not either talked to or seen. In short, he had so well mixed and digested his knowledge of men and books, that he made one of the most accomplished persons of his age. During the whole course of his studies and travels he kept up a punctual correspondence with Eudoxus, who often made himself acceptable to the principal men about court by the intelligence which he received from Leontine. When they were both turned of forty (an age in which, according to Mr. Cowley, *there is no dallying with life*) they determined, pursuant to the resolution they had taken in the beginning of their lives, to retire, and pass the remainder of their days in the country. In order to this, they both of them married much about the same time. Leontine, with his own and his wife's fortune, bought a farm of three hundred a year, which lay within the neighborhood of his friend Eudoxus, who had purchased an estate of as many thousands. They were both of them fathers about the same time, Eudoxus having a son born to him, and Leontine a daughter; but to the unspeakable grief of the latter, his young wife (in whom all his happiness was wrapped up) died in a few days after the birth of her daughter. His affliction would have been insupportable, had not he been comforted by the daily visits and conversations of his friend. As they were one day talking together with their usual intimacy, Leontine, considering how incapable he was of giving his daughter a proper education in his own house, and Eudoxus, reflecting on the ordinary behavior of a son who knows himself to be the heir of a great estate, they both agreed upon an exchange of children, namely that the boy should be bred up with Leontine as his son, and that the girl should live with Eudoxus as his daughter, till they were each of them arrived at years of discretion. The wife of Eudoxus, knowing that her son could not be so advantageously brought up as under the care of Leontine, and considering at the same time that he would be perpetually under her own eye, was by degrees prevailed upon to fall in with the project. She therefore took Leonilla, for that was the name of the girl, and educated her as her own daughter. The two friends on each side had wrought themselves to such an habitual tenderness for the children who were under their direction, that each of them had the real passion of a father, where the title was but imaginary. Florio, the name of the young heir that lived with Leontine, though he had all the duty and affection imaginable for his supposed parent, was taught to rejoice at the sight of Eudoxus, who visited his friend very frequently, and was dictated by his natural affection, as well as by the rules of prudence, to make himself esteemed and beloved by Florio. The boy was now old enough to know his supposed father's circumstances, and that therefore he was to make his way in the world by his own industry. This consideration grew stronger in him every day, and produced so good an effect, that he applied himself with more than ordinary attention to the pursuit of everything which Leontine recommended to him. His natural abilities, which were very good, assisted by the directions of so excellent a counselor, enabled him to make a quicker progress than ordinary through all the parts of his education. Before he was twenty years of age, having finished his studies and exercises with great applause, he was removed from the university to the Inns of Court, where there are very few that make themselves considerable proficients in the studies of the place, who know they shall arrive at great estates without them. This was not Florio's case; he found that three hundred a year was but a poor estate for Leontine and himself to live upon, so that he studied without intermission till he gained a very good insight into the constitution and laws of his country.

I should have told my reader, that whilst Florio lived at the house of his foster-father he was always an acceptable guest in the family of

Eudoxus, where he became acquainted with Leonilla from her infancy. His acquaintance with her by degrees grew into love, which in a mind trained up in all the sentiments of honor and virtue became a very uneasy passion. He despaired of gaining an heiress of so great a fortune, and would rather have died than attempted it by any indirect methods. Leonilla, who was a woman of the greatest beauty joined with the greatest modesty, entertained at the same time a secret passion for Florio, but conducted herself with so much prudence that she never gave him the least intimation of it. Florio was now engaged in all those arts and improvements that are proper to raise a man's private fortune, and give him a figure in his country, but secretly tormented with that passion which burns with the greatest fury in a virtuous and noble heart, when he received a sudden summons from Leontine to repair to him in the country the next day. For it seems Eudoxus was so filled with the report of his son's reputation that he could no longer withhold making himself known to him. The morning after his arrival at the house of his supposed father, Leontine told him that Eudoxus had something of great importance to communicate to him; upon which the good man embraced him and wept. Florio was no sooner arrived at the great house that stood in his neighborhood, but Eudoxus took him by the hand, after the first salutes were over, and conducted him into his closet. He there opened to him the whole secret of his parentage and education, concluding after this manner: *I have no other way left of acknowledging my gratitude to Leontine, than by marrying you to his daughter. He shall not lose the pleasure of being your father by the discovery I have made to you. Leonilla too shall be still my daughter; her filial piety, though misplaced, has been so exemplary that it deserves the greatest reward I can confer upon it. You shall have the pleasure of seeing a great estate fall to you, which you would have lost the relish of had you known yourself born to it. Continue only to deserve it in the same manner you did before you were possessed of it. I have left your mother in the next room. Her heart yearns towards you. She is making the same discoveries to Leonilla which I have made to yourself.* Florio was so overwhelmed with this profusion of happiness, that he was not able to make a reply, but threw himself down at his father's feet, and amidst a flood of tears, kissed and embraced his knees, asking his blessing, and expressing in dumb show those sentiments of love, duty, and gratitude that were too big for utterance. To conclude, the happy pair were married, and half Eudoxus' estate settled upon them. Leontine and Eudoxus passed the remainder of their lives together; and received in the dutiful and affectionate behavior of Florio and Leonilla the just recompense, as well as the natural effects, of that care which they had bestowed upon them in their education.

OLIVER GOLDSMITH

(1728–1774)

GOLDSMITH'S family were Irish people of English descent. Oliver Goldsmith was born in County Longford, Ireland. He went to Trinity College, Dublin, and after his graduation in 1749, began the study of medicine at Edinburgh. After a short period in Scotland he left for the Continent, where he wandered from country to country. After his return to London in 1756 his early essays and verses attracted the attention of Dr. Johnson, and he became a member of the illustrious group that gathered round that literary monarch. The years between 1759 and 1773 were the most productive of his entire career. *The Vicar of Wakefield*, which is a landmark in the development of prose fiction, appeared in 1766. Like Addison and Steele and other of the periodical essayists, Goldsmith wrote several short stories of high merit. *The Disabled Soldier* was first printed in the *Citizen of the World*, in 1760.

THE DISABLED SOLDIER

(From the *Citizen of the World*)

NO observation is more common, and at the same time more true, than that one half of the world are ignorant how the other half lives. The misfortunes of the great are held up to engage our attention; are enlarged upon in tones of declamation; and the world is called upon to gaze at the noble sufferers: the great, under the pressure of calamity, are conscious of several others sympathizing with their distress; and have, at once, the comfort of admiration and pity.

There is nothing magnanimous in bearing misfortunes with fortitude, when the whole world is looking on: men in such circumstances will act bravely even from motives of vanity: but he who, in the vale of obscurity, can brave adversity; who without friends to encourage, acquaintances to pity, or even without hope to alleviate his misfortunes, can behave with tranquillity and indifference, is truly great: whether peasant or courtier, he deserves admiration, and should be held up for our imitation and respect.

While the slightest inconveniences of the great are magnified into calamities; while tragedy mouths out their sufferings in all the strains of eloquence, the miseries of the poor are entirely disregarded; and yet some of the lower ranks of people undergo more real hardships in one day, than those of a more exalted station suffer in their whole lives. It is inconceivable what difficulties the meanest of our common sailors and soldiers endure without murmuring or regret; without passionately declaiming against providence, or calling their fellows to be gazers on their intrepidity. Every day is to them a day of misery, and yet they entertain their hard fate without repining.

With what indignation do I hear an Ovid, a Cicero, or a Rabutin complain of their misfortunes and hardships, whose greatest calamity was that of being unable to visit a certain spot of earth, to which they had foolishly attached an idea of happiness. Their distresses were pleasures, compared to what many of the adventuring poor every day endure without murmuring. They ate, drank, and slept; they had slaves to attend them, and were sure of subsistence for life; while many of their fellow creatures are obliged to wander without a friend to comfort or assist them, and even without shelter from the severity of the season.

I have been led into these reflections from accidentally meeting, some days ago, a poor fellow, whom I knew when a boy, dressed in a sailor's jacket, and begging at one of the outlets of the town, with a wooden leg. I knew him to have been honest and industrious when in the country, and was curious to learn what had reduced him to his present situation. Wherefore, after giving him what I thought proper, I desired to know the history of his life and misfortunes, and the manner in which he was reduced to his present distress. The disabled soldier, for such he was, though dressed in a sailor's habit, scratching his head, and leaning on his crutch, put himself into an attitude to comply with my request, and gave me his history as follows:

"As for my misfortunes, master, I can't pretend to have gone through any more than other folks; for, except the loss of my limb, and my being obliged to beg, I don't know any reason, thank Heaven, that I have to complain. There is Bill Tibbs, of our regiment, he has lost both his legs, and an eye to boot; but, thank Heaven, it is not so bad with me yet.

"I was born in Shropshire; my father was a laborer, and died when I was five years old, so I was put upon the parish. As he had been a wandering sort of a man, the parishioners were not able to tell to what parish I belonged, or where I was born, so they sent me to another parish, and that parish sent me to a third. I thought in my heart, they kept sending me about so long, that they would not let me be born in any parish at all; but at last, however, they fixed me. I had some disposition to be a scholar, and was resolved at least to know my letters: but the master of the workhouse put me to business as soon as I was able to handle a mallet; and here I lived an easy kind of life for five years. I only wrought ten hours in the day, and had my meat and drink provided for my labor. It is true, I was not suffered to stir out of the house, for fear, as they said, I should run away; but what of that? I had the liberty of the whole house, and the yard before the door, and that was enough for me. I was then bound out to a farmer, where I was up both early and late; but I ate and drank well; and liked my business well enough, till he died, when I was obliged to provide for myself; so I resolved to go seek my fortune.

"In this manner I went from town to town, worked when I could get employment, and starved when I could get none; when, happening one day to go through a field belonging to a justice of peace, I spied a hare crossing the path just before me; and I believe the devil put it into my head to fling my stick at it. Well, what will you have on't? I killed the hare, and was bringing it away, when the justice himself met me; he called me a poacher and a villain, and collaring me, desired I would give an account of myself. I fell upon my knees, begged his worship's pardon, and began to give a full account of all that I knew of my breed, seed, and generation; but though I gave a very true account, the justice said I could give no account; so I was indicted at the sessions, found guilty of being poor, and sent up to London to Newgate, in order to be transported as a vagabond.

"People may say this and that of being in jail, but, for my part, I found Newgate as agreeable a place as ever I was in in all my life. I had my belly full to eat and drink, and did no work at all. This kind of life was too good to last forever; so I was taken out of prison, after five months, put on board of ship, and sent off, with two hundred more, to the plantations. We had but an indifferent passage, for being all confined in the hold, more than a hundred of our people died for want of sweet air; and those that remained were sickly enough, God knows. When we came ashore we were sold to the planters, and I was bound for seven years more. As I was no scholar, for I did not know my letters, I was obliged to work among the negroes; and I served out my time, as in duty bound to do.

"When my time was expired, I worked my passage home, and glad I was to see old England again, because I loved my country. I was afraid, however, that I should be indicted for a vagabond once more, so did not much care to go down into the country, but kept about the town, and did little jobs when I could get them.

"I was very happy in this manner for some time till one evening, coming home from work, two men knocked me down, and then desired me to stand. They belonged to a press-gang. I was carried before the justice, and as I could give no account of myself, I had my choice left, whether to go on board a man-of-war, or list for a soldier. I chose the latter, and in this post of a gentleman, I served two campaigns in Flanders, was at the battles of Val and Fontenoy, and received but one wound through the breast here; but the doctor of our regiment soon made me well again.

"When the peace came on I was discharged; and as I could not work, because my wound was sometimes troublesome, I listed for a landman in the East India Company's service. I have fought the French in six pitched battles; and I verily believe that if I could read or write, our captain would have made me a corporal. But it was not my good fortune to have any promotion, for I soon fell sick, and so got leave to return home again with forty pounds in my pocket. This was at the beginning of the present war, and I hoped to be set on shore, and to have the pleasure of spending my money; but the Government wanted men, and so I was pressed for a sailor, before ever I could set a foot on shore.

"The boatswain found me, as he said, an obstinate fellow: he swore he knew that I understood my business well, but that I shammed Abraham, to be idle; but God knows, I knew nothing of sea-business, and he beat me without considering what he was about. I had still, however, my forty pounds, and that was some comfort to me under every beating; and the money I might have had to this day, but that our ship was taken by the French, and so I lost all.

"Our crew was carried into Brest, and many of them died, because they were not used to live in a jail; but, for my part, it was nothing to me, for I was seasoned. One night, as I was asleep on the bed of boards, with a warm blanket about me, for I always loved to lie well, I was awakened by the boatswain, who had a dark lantern in his hand. 'Jack,' says he to me, 'will you knock out the French sentry's brains?' 'I don't care,' says I, striving to keep myself awake, 'if I lend a hand.' 'Then, follow me,' says he, 'and I hope we shall do business.' So up I got, and tied my blanket, which was all the clothes I had, about my middle, and went with him to fight the Frenchman. I hate the French, because they are all slaves, and wear wooden shoes.

"Though we had no arms, one Englishman is able to beat five French at any time; so we went down to the door where both the sentries were posted, and rushing upon them, seized their arms in a moment, and knocked them down. From thence nine of us ran together to the quay, and seizing the first boat we met, got out of the harbor and put to sea. We had not been here three days before we were taken up by the Dorset privateer, who were glad of so many good hands; and we consented to run our chance. However, we had not as much luck as we expected. In three days we fell in with the *Pompadour* privateer of forty guns, while we had but twenty-three, so to it we went, yard-arm and yard-arm. The fight lasted three hours, and I verily believe we should have taken the Frenchman, had we but had some more men left behind; but unfortunately we lost all our men just as we were going to get the victory.

"I was once more in the power of the French, and I believe it would have gone hard with me had I been brought back to Brest; but by good fortune we were retaken by the *Viper*. I had almost forgotten to tell you that in that engagement I was wounded in two places: I lost four fingers off the left hand, and my leg was shot off. If I had had the good fortune to have lost my leg and use of my hand on board a king's ship, and not aboard a privateer, I should have been entitled to clothing and maintenance during the rest of my life; but that was not my chance: one man is born with a silver spoon in his mouth, and another with a wooden ladle. However, blessed be God, I enjoy good health, and will forever love liberty and old England. Liberty, property, and old England, forever, huzza!"

Thus saying, he limped off, leaving me in admiration at his intrepidity and content; nor could I avoid acknowledging that an habitual acquaintance with misery serves better than philosophy to teach us to despise it.

SIR WALTER SCOTT

(1771–1832)

WALTER SCOTT, founder of the romantic historical novel, was born at Edinburgh in 1771. He entered his father's law office, but before long gave up law for literature. His first works were ballads and long narrative poems. In 1814 he published the novel *Waverley*, which established his position as a writer. At the very height of his brilliant career he found himself morally obliged to pay off an enormous debt, and spent the rest of his life trying to do so. Scott wrote several short stories. *The Bridal of Janet Dalrymple,* not so well known as the far longer *Wandering Willie's Tale* from *Redgauntlet,* is a well-written and (for Scott) surprisingly short and closely-woven narrative.

The present edition is reprinted from the volume, *Scottish Love Tales,* London, no date.

THE BRIDAL OF JANET DALRYMPLE

MISS JANET DALRYMPLE, daughter of the first Lord Stair, and Dame Margaret Ross, had engaged herself without the knowledge of her parents to the Lord Rutherford, who was not acceptable to them either on account of his political principles, or his want of fortune. The young couple broke a piece of gold together, and pledged their troth in the most solemn manner; and it is said the young lady imprecated dreadful evils on herself should she break her plighted faith. Shortly after, a suitor who was favored by Lord Stair, and still more so by his lady, paid his addresses to Miss Dalrymple. The young lady refused the proposal, and being pressed on the subject, confessed her secret engagement. Lady Stair, a woman accustomed to universal submission (for even her husband did not dare to contradict her), treated this objection as a trifle, and insisted upon her daughter yielding her consent to marry the new suitor, David Dunbar, son and heir to David Dunbar of Baldoon, in Wigtonshire. The first lover, a man of very high spirit, then interfered by letter, and insisted on the right he had acquired by his troth plighted with the young lady. Lady Stair sent him for answer, that her daughter, sensible of her undutiful behavior in entering into a contract unsanctioned by her parents, had retracted her unlawful vow, and now refused to fulfil her engagement with him.

The lover in return declined positively to receive such an answer from anyone but his mistress in person; and as she had to deal with a man who was both of a most determined character, and of too high condition to be trifled with, Lady Stair was obliged to consent to an interview between Lord Rutherford and her daughter. But she took care to be present in person, and argued the point with the disappointed and incensed lover with pertinacity equal to his own. She particularly insisted on the Levitical law, which declares, that a woman shall be free of a vow which her parents dissent from. This is the passage of Scripture she founded on:

"If a man vow a vow unto the Lord, or swear an oath to bind his soul with a bond; he shall not break his word, he shall do according to all that proceedeth out of his mouth.

"If a woman also vow a vow unto the Lord, and bind herself by a bond, being in her father's house in her youth;

"And her father hear her vow, and her bond wherewith she hath bound her soul, and her father shall hold his peace at her: then all her vows shall stand, and every bond wherewith she hath bound her soul shall stand.

"But if her father disallow her in the day that he heareth; not any of her vows, or of her bonds wherewith she hath bound her soul, shall stand: and the Lord shall forgive her, because her father disallowed her."—Numbers xxx. 2, 3, 4, 5.

While the mother insisted on these topics, the lover in vain conjured the daughter to declare her own opinion and feelings. She remained totally overwhelmed, as it seemed—mute, pale, and motionless as a statue. Only at her mother's command, sternly uttered, she summoned strength enough to restore to her plighted suitor the piece of broken gold, which was the emblem of her troth. On this he burst forth into a tremendous passion, took leave of the mother with maledictions, and as he left the apartment, turned back to say to his weak, if not fickle, mistress, "For you, madam, you will be a world's wonder"; a phrase by which some remarkable degree of calamity is usually implied. He went abroad, and returned not again. If the last Lord Rutherford was the unfortunate party, he must have been the third who bore that title, and who died in 1685.

The marriage betwixt Janet Dalrymple and David Dunbar of Baldoon now went forward, the bride showing no repugnance, but being absolutely passive in everything her mother commanded or advised. On the day of the marriage, which, as was then usual, was celebrated by a great assemblage of friends and relations, she was the same—sad, silent, and resigned, as it seemed, to her destiny. A lady, very nearly connected with the family, told the author that she had conversed on the subject with one of the brothers of the bride, a mere lad at the time, who had ridden before his sister to church. He said her hand, which lay on his as she held her arm round his waist, was as cold and damp as marble. But, full of his new dress, and the part he acted in the procession, the circumstance, which he long afterwards remembered with bitter sorrow and compunction, made no impression on him at the time.

The bridal feast was followed by dancing; the bride and bridegroom retired as usual, when of a sudden the most wild and piercing cries were heard from the nuptial chamber. It was then the custom, to prevent any coarse pleasantry which old times perhaps admitted, that the key of the nuptial chamber should be intrusted to the brideman. He was called upon, but refused at first to give it up, till the shrieks became so hideous that he was compelled to hasten with others to learn the cause. On opening the door, they found the bridegroom lying across the threshold, dreadfully wounded, and streaming with blood. The bride was then sought for. She was found in the corner of the large chimney, having no covering save her shift, and that dabbled in gore. There she sat grinning at them, mopping and mowing, as I heard the expression used; in a word, absolutely insane. The only words she spoke were, "Tak up your bonny bridegroom." She survived this horrible scene little more than a fortnight, having been married on the 24th of August, and dying on the 12th of September, 1669.

The unfortunate Baldoon recovered from his wounds, but sternly prohibited all inquiries respecting the manner in which he had received them. If a lady, he said, asked him any question upon the subject, he would neither answer her nor speak to her again while he lived; if a gentleman, he would consider it as a mortal affront, and demand satisfaction as having received such. He did not very long survive the dreadful catastrophe, having met with a fatal injury by a fall from his horse, as he rode between Leith and Holyrood House, of which he died the next day, 28th March, 1682. Thus a few years removed all the principal actors in this frightful tragedy.

Various reports went abroad on this mysterious affair, many of them very inaccurate, though they could hardly be said to be exaggerated. It was difficult at that time to become acquainted with the history of a Scottish family above the lower rank; and strange things sometimes took place there, into which even the law did not scrupulously inquire.

The credulous Mr. Law says, generally, that the Lord President Stair had a daughter, who "being married, the night she was *bride in* [that is, bedded bride], was taken from her bridegroom and *harled* [dragged] through the house (by spirits, we are given to understand), and soon afterwards died. Another daughter," he says, was "possessed by an evil spirit."

My friend, Mr. Sharpe, gives another edition of the tale. According to his information, it was the bridegroom who wounded the bride. The marriage, according to this account, had been against her mother's inclination, who had given her consent in these ominous words: "You may marry him, but soon shall you repent it."

I find still another account darkly insinuated in some highly scurrilous and abusive verses. They are docketed as being written "Upon the late Viscount Stair and his family, by Sir William Hamilton of Whitelaw. The marginals by William Dunlop, writer in Edinburgh, a son of the Laird of Househill, and nephew to the said Sir William Hamilton." There was a bitter and personal quarrel and rivalry betwixt the author of this libel, a name which it richly deserves, and Lord President Stair; and the lampoon, which is written with much more malice than art, bears the following motto:

"Stair's neck, mind, wife, sons, grandson, and the rest,
Are wry, false, witch, pests, parricide, possessed."

This malignant satirist, who calls up all the misfortunes of the family, does not forget the fatal bridal of Baldoon. He seems, though his verses are as obscure as unpoetical, to intimate, that the violence done to the bridegroom was by the intervention of the foul fiend to whom the young lady had resigned herself, in case she should break her contract with her first lover. His hypothesis is inconsistent with the account given in the note upon Law's Memorials, but easily reconcilable to the family tradition.

"In al Stair's offspring we no difference know,
They doe the females as the males bestow;
So he of's daughter's marriage gave the ward,
Like a true vassal, to Glenluce's Laird;

He knew what she did to her suitor plight,
If she her faith to Rutherfurd should slight,
Which, like his own, for greed he broke outright.
Nick did Baldoon's posterior right deride,
And, as first substitute, did seize the bride;
Whate'er he to his mistress did or said,
He threw the bridegroom from the nuptial bed,
Into the chimney did so his rival maul,
His bruised bones ne'er were cured but by the fall."

One of the marginal notes ascribed to William Dunlop applies to the above lines. "She had betrothed herself to Lord Rutherfoord under horrid imprecations, and afterwards married Baldoon, his nevoy, and her mother was the cause of her breach of faith."

The same tragedy is alluded to in the following couplet and note:

"What train of curses that base brood pursues,
When the young nephew wed's old uncle's spouse."

The note on the word *uncle* explains it as meaning "Rutherfoord, who should have married the Lady Baldoon, was Baldoon's uncle." The poetry of this satire on Lord Stair and his family was, as already noticed, written by Sir William Hamilton of Whitelaw, a rival of Lord Stair for the situation of President of the Court of Session; a person much inferior to that great lawyer in talents, and equally ill-treated by the calumny or just satire of his contemporaries, as an unjust and partial judge. Some of the notes are by that curious and laborious antiquary, Robert Milne, who, as a virulent Jacobite, willingly lent a hand to blacken the family of Stair.

Another poet of the period, with a very different purpose, has left an elegy, in which he darkly hints at and bemoans the fate of the ill-starred young person, whose very uncommon calamity Whitelaw, Dunlop, and Milne thought a fitting subject for buffoonery and ribaldry. This bard of milder mood was Andrew Symson, before the Revolution minister of Kirkinner, in Galloway, and after his expulsion as an Episcopalian, following the humble occupation of a printer in Edinburgh. He furnished the family of Baldoon, with which he appears to have been intimate, with an elegy on the tragic event in their family. In this piece he treats the mournful occasion of the bride's death with mysterious solemnity.

The verses bear this title—"On the unexpected death of the virtuous Lady Mrs. Janet Dalrymple, Lady Baldoon, younger," and afford us the precise dates of the catastrophe, which could not otherwise have been easily ascertained. "Nupta August 12. Domum Ducta August 24. Obiit September 12. Sepult. September 30, 1669." The form of the elegy is a dialogue betwixt a passenger and a domestic servant. The first, recollecting that he had passed that way lately, and seen all around enlivened by the appearances of mirth and festivity, is desirous to know what had changed so gay a scene into mourning. We preserve the reply of the servant as a specimen of Mr. Symson's verses, which are not of the first quality:

"———— Sir, 'tis truth you've told,
We did enjoy great mirth; but now, ah me!
Our joyful song's turned to an elegie.
A virtuous lady, not long since a bride,
Was to a hopeful plant by marriage tied,
And brought home hither. We did all rejoice,
Even for her sake. But presently our voice
Was turn'd to mourning for that little time
That she'd enjoy: She waned in her prime,
For Atropos, with her impartial knife,
Soon cut her thread, and therewithal her life;
And for the time we may it well remember,
It being in unfortunate September;
Where we must leave her till the resurrection,
'Tis then the Saints enjoy their full perfection."

SAMUEL LOVER

(1797?–1868)

Samuel Lover was born in Dublin of an English Protestant family. He studied painting at an early age, and though he continued to practise that art, he soon discovered his talent for writing. Many of his most delightful sketches of Irish life appeared in various Dublin periodicals in the early thirties. In 1832 he published his *Legends and Stories of Ireland*, in which *The White Trout* is found. The best known of his novels is *Handy Andy*.

The White Trout is reprinted from Yeats' *Irish Fairy and Folk Tales*; New York, no date.

THE WHITE TROUT

THERE was wanst upon a time, long ago, a beautiful lady that lived in a castle upon the lake beyant, and they say she was promised to a king's son, and they wor to be married, when all of a sudden he was murthered, the crathur (Lord help us), and threwn into the lake above, and so, of course, he couldn't keep his promise to the fairy lady—and more's the pity.

Well, the story goes that she went out iv her mind, bekase av loosin' the king's son—for she was tendher-hearted, God help her, like the rest iv us!—and pined away after him, until at last, no one about seen her, good or bad; and the story wint that the fairies took her away.

Well, sir, in coorse o' time, the White Throut, God bless it, was seen in the sthrame beyant, and sure the people didn't know what to think av the crathur, seein' as how a *white* throut was never heard av afor, nor since; and years upon years the throut was there, just where you seen it this blessed minit, longer nor I can tell—aye throth, and beyant the memory o' th' ouldest in the village.

At last the people began to think it must be a fairy; for what else could it be?—and no hurt nor harm was iver put an the white throut, until some wicked sinners of sojers kem to these parts, and laughed at all the people, and gibed and jeered them for thinkin' o' the likes; and one o' them in partic'lar (bad luck to him; God forgi' me for saying it!) swore he'd catch the throut and ate it for his dinner—the blackguard!

Well, what would you think o' the villainy of the sojer? Sure enough he cotch the throut, and away wid him home, and puts an the fryin'-pan, and into it he pitches the purty little thing. The throut squeeled all as one as a christian crathur, and, my dear, you'd think the sojer id split his sides laughin'—for he was a harden'd villain; and when he thought one side was done, he turns it over to fry the other; and, what would you think, but the divil a taste of a burn was an it at all at all; and sure the sojer thought it was a *quare* throut that could not be briled. "But," says he, "I'll give it another turn by and by," little thinkin' what was in store for him, the haythen.

Well, when he thought that side was done he turns it agin, and lo and behold you, the divil a taste more done that side was nor the other. "Bad luck to me," says the sojer, "but that bates the world," says he; "but I'll thry you agin, my darlint," says he, "as cunnin' as you think yourself"; and so with that he turns it over and over, but not a sign of the fire was on the purty throut. "Well," says the desperate villain—(for sure, sir, only he was a desperate villain *entirely*, he might know he was doing a wrong thing, seein' that all his endeavors was no good)—"Well," says he, "my jolly little throut, maybe you're fried enough, though you don't seem over well dress'd; but you may be better than you look, like a singed cat, and a tit-bit afther all," says he; and with that he ups with his knife and fork to taste a piece o' the throut; but, my jew'l, the minit he puts his knife into the fish, there was a murtherin' screech, that you'd think the life id lave you if you hurd it, and away jumps the throut out av the fryin'-pan into the middle o' the flure; and an the spot where it fell, up riz a lovely lady—the beautifullest crathur that eyes ever seen, dressed in white, and a band o' goold in her hair, and a sthrame o' blood runnin' down her arm.

"Look where you cut me, you villain," says she, and she held out her arm to him—and, my dear, he thought the sight id lave his eyes.

"Couldn't you lave me cool and comfortable in the river where you snared me, and not disturb me in my duty?" says she.

Well, he thrimbled like a dog in a wet sack, and at last he stammered out somethin', and begged for his life, and ax'd her ladyship's pardin, and said he didn't know she was on duty, or he was too good a sojer not to know betther nor to meddle wid her.

"I *was* on duty, then," says the lady; "I was watchin' for my true love that is comin' by wather to me," says she, "an' if he comes while I'm away, an' that I miss iv him, I'll turn you into a pinkeen, and I'll hunt you up and down for evermore, while grass grows or wather runs."

Well, the sojer thought the life id lave him, at the thoughts iv his bein' turned into a pinkeen, and begged for mercy; and with that says the lady:

"Renounce your evil coorses," says she, "you villain, or you'll repint it too late; be a good man for the futhur, and go to your duty reg'lar, and now," says she, "take me back and put me into the river again, where you found me."

"Oh, my lady," says the sojer, "how could I have the heart to drownd a beautiful lady like you?"

But before he could say another word, the lady was vanished, and there he saw the little throut an the ground. Well, he put it in a clean plate, and away he runs for the bare life, for fear her lover would come while she was away; and he run, and he run, even till he came to the cave agin, and threw the throut into the river. The minit he did, the wather was as red as blood for a little while, by rayson av the cut, I suppose, until the sthrame washed the stain away; and to this day there's a little red mark an the throut's side, where it was cut.

Well, sir, from that day out the sojer was an altered man, and reformed his ways, and went to his duty reg'lar, and fasted three times a week—though it was never fish he tuk an fastin' days, for afther the fright he got, fish id never rest an his stomach—savin' your presence.

But anyhow, he was an altered man, as I said before, and in coorse o' time he left the army, and turned hermit at last; and they say he *used to pray evermore for the soul of the White Throut.*

CHARLES DICKENS

(1812–1870)

The son of a government clerk, Charles Dickens was born at Portsea in 1812. His family moved to London shortly after his birth. The early London life of the Dickens family was utilized in several of the son's novels, especially in *David Copperfield.* His first great success was with the *Pickwick Papers,* which appeared serially in 1836. Then followed the novels which have become celebrated and are read the world over. Dickens was an indefatigable writer, editor and, later in life, a public reader. He wrote a number of short stories, of which *The Old Man's Tale of the Queer Client* is probably the most skilfully constructed and best written. It is related by one of the characters in the *Pickwick Papers.*

THE OLD MAN'S TALE OF THE QUEER CLIENT

(From the *Pickwick Papers*)

"It matters little," said the old man, "where, or how, I picked up this brief history. If I were to relate it in the order in which it reached me, I should commence in the middle, and when I had arrived at the conclusion, go back for a beginning. It is enough for me to say that some of its circumstances passed before my own eyes. For the remainder I know them to have happened, and there are some persons yet living who will remember them but too well.

"In the Borough High Street, near St. George's Church, and on the same side of the way, stands, as most people know, the smallest of our debtors' prisons, the Marshalsea. Although in later times it has been a very different place from the sink of filth and dirt it once was, even its improved condition holds out but little temptation to the extravagant, or consolation to the provident. The condemned felon has as good a yard for air and exercise in Newgate, as the insolvent debtor in the Marshalsea Prison.

"It may be my fancy, or it may be that I cannot separate the place from the old recollections associated with it, but this part of London I cannot bear. The street is broad, the shops are spacious, the noise of passing vehicles, the footsteps of a perpetual stream of people—all the busy sounds of traffic, resound in it from morn to midnight, but the streets around are mean and close; poverty and debauchery lie festering in the crowded alleys; want and misfortune are pent up in the narrow prison; an air of gloom and dreariness seems, in my eyes at least, to hang about the scene, and to impart to it a squalid and sickly hue.

"Many eyes, that have long since been closed in the grave, have looked round upon that scene lightly enough, when entering the gate of the old Marshalsea Prison for the first time: for despair seldom comes with the first severe shock of misfortune. A man has confidence in untried friends, he remembers the many offers of service so freely made by his boon companions when he wanted them not; he has hope—the hope of happy inexperience—and however he may bend beneath the first shock, it springs up in his bosom, and flourishes there for a brief space, until it droops beneath the blight of disappointment and neglect. How soon have those same eyes, deeply sunken in the head, glared from faces wasted with famine, and sallow from confinement, in days when it was no figure of speech to say that debtors rotted in prison, with no hope of release, and no prospect of liberty! The atrocity in its full extent no longer exists, but there is enough of it left to give rise to occurrences that make the heart bleed.

"Twenty years ago, that pavement was worn with the footsteps of a mother and child, who, day by day, so surely as the morning came, presented themselves at the prison gate; often, after a night of restless misery and anxious thoughts, were they there, a full hour too soon, and then the young mother turning meekly away, would lead the child to the old bridge, and raising him in her arms to show him the glistening water, tinted with the light of the morning's sun, and stirring with all the bustling preparations for business and pleasure that the river presented at that early hour, endeavor to interest his thoughts in the objects before him. But she would quickly set him down, and, hiding her face in her shawl, give vent to the tears that blinded her; for no expression of interest or amusement lighted up his thin and sickly face. His recollections were few enough, but they were all of one kind: all connected with the poverty and misery of his parents. Hour after hour had he sat on his mother's knee, and with childish sympathy watched the tears that stole down her face, and then crept quietly away into some dark corner, and sobbed himself to sleep. The hard realities of the world, with many of its worst privations—hunger and thirst, and cold and want—had all come home to him, from the first dawnings of reason; and though the form of childhood was there, its light heart, its merry laugh, and sparkling eyes, were wanting.

"The father and mother looked on upon this, and upon each other, with thoughts of agony they dared not breathe in words. The healthy, strong-made man, who could have borne almost any fatigue of active exertion, was wasting beneath the close confinement and unhealthy atmosphere of a crowded prison. The slight and delicate woman was sinking beneath the combined effects of bodily and mental illness. The child's young heart was breaking.

"Winter came, and with it weeks of cold and heavy rain. The poor girl had removed to a wretched apartment close to the spot of her husband's imprisonment; and though the change had been rendered necessary by their increasing poverty, she was happier now, for she was nearer him. For two months, she and her little companion watched the opening of the gate as usual. One day she failed to come, for the first time. Another morning arrived, and she came alone. The child was dead.

"They little know, who coldly talk of the poor man's bereavements, as a happy release from pain to the departed, and a merciful relief from expense to the survivor—they little know, I say, what the agony of those bereavements is. A silent look of affection and regard when all other eyes are turned coldly away—the consciousness that we possess the sympathy and affection of one being when all others have deserted us—is a hold, a stay, a comfort, in the deepest affliction, which no wealth could purchase, or power bestow. The child had sat at his parents' feet for hours together, with his little hands patiently folded in each other, and his thin wan face raised towards them. They had seen him pine away, from day to day; and though his brief existence had been a joyless one, and he was now removed to that peace and rest which, child as he was, he had never known in this world, they were his parents, and his loss sunk deep into their souls.

"It was plain to those who looked upon the mother's altered face, that death must soon close the scene of her adversity and trial. Her husband's fellow-prisoners shrank from obtruding on his grief and misery, and left to himself alone the small room he had previously occupied in common with two companions. She shared it with him: and lingering on without pain, but without hope, her life ebbed slowly away.

"She had fainted one evening in her husband's arms, and he had borne her to the open window, to revive her with the air, when the light of the moon falling full upon her face showed him a change upon her features, which made him stagger beneath her weight, like a helpless infant.

" 'Set me down, George,' she said faintly. He did so, and seating himself beside her, covered his face with his hands, and burst into tears.

" 'It is very hard to leave you, George,' she said, 'but it is God's will, and you must bear it for my sake. Oh! how I thank Him for having taken our boy! He is happy, and in Heaven now. What would he have done here without his mother!'

" 'You shall not die, Mary, you shall not die!' said the husband, starting up. He paced hurriedly to and fro, striking his head with his clenched fists; then reseating himself beside her, and supporting her in his arms, added more calmly, 'Rouse yourself, my dear girl. Pray, pray do. You will revive yet.'

"'Never again, George; never again,' said the dying woman. 'Let them lay me by my poor boy now, but promise me that if ever you leave this dreadful place, and should grow rich, you will have us removed to some quiet country churchyard, a long, long way off—very far from here, where we can rest in peace. Dear George, promise me you will.'

"'I do, I do,' said the man throwing himself passionately on his knees before her. 'Speak to me, Mary, another word; one look—but one!'

"He ceased to speak: for the arm that clasped his neck grew stiff and heavy. A deep sigh escaped from the wasted form before him; the lips moved, and a smile played upon the face; but the lips were pallid, and the smile faded into a rigid and ghastly stare. He was alone in the world.

"That night, in the silence and desolation of his miserable room, the wretched man knelt down by the dead body of his wife, and called on God to witness a terrible oath, that from that hour he devoted himself to revenge her death and that of his child; that thenceforth to the last moment of his life, his whole energies should be directed to this one object; that his revenge should be protracted and terrible; that his hatred should be undying and inextinguishable; and should hunt its object through the world.

"The deepest despair, and passion scarcely human, had made such fierce ravages on his face and form, in that one night, that his companions in misfortune shrunk affrighted from him as he passed by. His eyes were bloodshot and heavy, his face a deadly white, and his body bent as if with age. He had bitten his under lip nearly through in the violence of his mental suffering, and the blood which had flowed from the wound had trickled down his chin, and stained his shirt and neckerchief. No tear or sound of complaint escaped him: but the unsettled look, and disordered haste with which he paced up and down the yard, denoted the fever which was burning within.

"It was necessary that his wife's body should be removed from the prison, without delay. He received the communication with perfect calmness, and acquiesced in its propriety. Nearly all the inmates of the prison had assembled to witness its removal; they fell back on either side when the widower appeared; he walked hurriedly forward, and stationed himself, alone, in a little railed area close to the lodge gate, from whence the crowd, with an instinctive feeling of delicacy, had retired. The rude coffin was borne slowly forward on men's shoulders. A dead silence pervaded the throng, broken only by the audible lamentations of the women, and the shuffling steps of the bearers on the stone pavement. They reached the spot where the bereaved husband stood: and stopped. He laid his hand upon the coffin, and mechanically adjusting the pall with which it was covered, motioned them onward. The turnkeys in the prison lobby took off their hats as it passed through, and in another moment the heavy gate closed behind it. He looked vacantly upon the crowd, and fell heavily to the ground.

"Although for many weeks after this he was watched, night and day, in the wildest ravings of fever, neither the consciousness of his loss, nor the recollection of the vow he had made, ever left him for a moment. Scenes changed before his eyes, place succeeded place, and event followed event, in all the hurry of delirium; but they were all connected in some way with the great object of his mind. He was sailing over a boundless expanse of sea, with a blood-red sky above, and the angry waters, lashed into fury beneath, boiling and eddying up on every side. There was another vessel before them, toiling and laboring in the howling storm: her canvas fluttering in ribbons from the mast, and her deck thronged with figures who were lashed to the sides, over which huge waves every instant burst, sweeping away some devoted creatures into the foaming sea. Onward they bore, amidst the roaring mass of water, with a speed and force which nothing could resist; and striking the stern of the foremost vessel, crushed her beneath their keel. From the huge whirlpool which the sinking wreck occasioned, arose a shriek so loud and shrill—the death-cry of a hundred drowning creatures, blended into one fierce yell—that it rung far above the war-cry of the elements, and echoed and reechoed till it seemed to pierce air, sky, and ocean. But what was that—that old gray head that rose above the water's surface, and with looks of agony, and screams for aid, buffeted with the waves! One look, and he had sprung from the vessel's side, and with vigorous strokes was swimming towards it. He reached it; he was close upon it. They were *his* features. The old man saw him coming, and vainly strove to elude his grasp. But he clasped him tight, and dragged him beneath the water. Down, down with him, fifty fathoms down; his struggles grew fainter and fainter, until they wholly ceased. He was dead; he had killed him, and had kept his oath.

"He was traversing the scorching sands of a mighty desert, barefooted and alone. The sand choked and blinded him; its fine thin grains entered the very pores of his skin, and irritated him almost to madness. Gigantic masses of the same material, carried forward by the wind, and shone through by the burning sun, stalked in the distance like pillars of living fire. The bones of men, who had perished in the dreary waste, lay scattered at his feet; a fearful light fell on everything around; so far as the eye could reach, nothing but objects of dread and horror presented themselves. Vainly striving to utter a cry of terror, with his tongue cleaving to his mouth, he rushed madly forward. Armed with supernatural strength, he waded through the sand, until exhausted with fatigue and thirst, he fell senseless on the earth. What fragrant coolness revived him; what gushing sound was that? Water! It was indeed a well; and the clear fresh stream was running at his feet. He drank deeply of it, and throwing his aching limbs upon the bank, sank into a delicious trance. The sound of approaching footsteps aroused him. An old gray-headed man tottered forward to slake his burning thirst. It was *he* again! He wound his arms round the old man's body, and held him back. He struggled, and shrieked for water, for but one drop of water to save his life! But he held the old man firmly, and watched his agonies with greedy eyes; and when his lifeless head fell forward on his bosom, he rolled the corpse from him with his feet.

"When the fever left him, and consciousness returned, he awoke to find himself rich and free: to hear that the parent who would have let him die in jail—*would!* who *had* let those who were far dearer to him than his own existence die of want and sickness of heart that medicine cannot cure—had been found dead on his bed of down. He had had all the heart to leave his son a beggar, but proud even of his health and strength, had put off the act till it was too late, and now might gnash his teeth in the other world, at the thought of the wealth his remissness had left him. He awoke to this, and he awoke to more. To recollect the purpose for which he lived, and to remember that his enemy was his wife's own father—the man who had cast him into prison, and who, when his daughter and her child sued at his feet for mercy, had spurned them from his door. Oh, how he cursed the weakness that prevented him from being up, and active, in his scheme of vengeance!

"He caused himself to be carried from the scene of his loss and misery, and conveyed to a quiet residence on the sea coast, not in the hope of recovering his peace of mind or happiness, for both were fled forever; but to restore his prostrate energies, and meditate on his darling object. And here, some evil spirit cast in his way the opportunity for his first, most horrible revenge.

"It was summer-time; and wrapped in his gloomy thoughts, he would issue from his solitary lodgings early in the evening, and wandering along a narrow path beneath the cliffs, to a wild and lonely spot that had struck his fancy in his ramblings, seat himself on some fallen fragment of the rock, and burying his face in his hands, remain there for hours—sometimes until night had completely closed in, and the long shadows of the frowning cliffs above his head cast a thick black darkness on every object near him.

"He was seated here, one calm evening, in his old position, now and then raising his head to watch the flight of a sea-gull, or carry his eye along the glorious crimson path, which, commencing in the middle of the ocean, seemed to lead to its very verge where the sun was setting, when the profound stillness of the spot was broken by a loud cry for help; he listened, doubtful of his having heard aright, when the cry was repeated with even greater vehemence than before, and starting to his feet, he hastened in the direction whence it proceeded.

"The tale told itself at once; some scattered garments lay on the beach; a human head was just visible above the waves at a little distance from the shore; and an old man, wringing his hands in agony, was running to and fro, shrieking for assistance. The invalid, whose strength was now sufficiently restored, threw off his coat, and rushed towards the sea, with the intention of plunging in, and dragging the drowning man ashore.

" 'Hasten here, sir, in God's name; help, help, sir, for the love of Heaven. He is my son, sir, my only son!' said the old man, frantically, as he advanced to meet him. 'My only son, sir, and he is dying before his father's eyes!'

"At the first word the old man uttered, the stranger checked himself in his career, and, folding his arms, stood perfectly motionless.

" 'Great God!' exclaimed the old man, recoiling. 'Heyling!'

"The stranger smiled, and was silent.

" 'Heyling!' said the old man, wildly: 'My boy, Heyling, my dear boy, look, look!' Gasping for breath, the miserable father pointed to the spot where the young man was struggling for life.

" 'Hark!' said the old man. 'He cries once more. He is alive yet. Heyling, save him, save him!'

"The stranger smiled again, and remained immovable as a statue.

" 'I have wronged you,' shrieked the old man, falling on his knees, and clasping his hands together. 'Be revenged; take my all, my life; cast me into the water at your feet, and, if human nature can repress a struggle, I will die, without stirring hand or foot. Do it, Heyling, do it, but save my boy; he is so young, Heyling, so young to die!'

" 'Listen,' said the stranger, grasping the old man fiercely by the wrist: 'I will have life for life, and here is ONE. *My* child died, before his father's eyes, a far more agonizing and painful death than that young slanderer of his sister's worth is meeting while I speak. You laughed—laughed in your daughter's face, where death had already set his hand—at our sufferings, then. What do you think of them now? See there, see there!'

"As the stranger spoke, he pointed to the sea. A faint cry died away upon its surface; the last powerful struggle of the dying man agitated the rippling waves for a few seconds: and the spot where he had gone down into his early grave was indistinguishable from the surrounding water.

"Three years had elapsed, when a gentleman alighted from a private carriage at the door of a London attorney, then well known as a man of no great nicety in his professional dealings; and requested a private interview on business of importance. Although evidently not past the prime of life, his face was pale, haggard, and dejected; and it did not require the acute perception of the man of business, to discern at a glance that disease or suffering had done more to work a change in his appearance than the mere hand of time could have accomplished in twice the period of his whole life.

" 'I wish you to undertake some legal business for me,' said the stranger.

"The attorney bowed obsequiously, and glanced at a larger packet which the gentleman carried in his hand. His visitor observed the look, and proceeded:

" 'It is no common business,' said he, 'nor have these papers reached my hands without long trouble and great expense.'

"The attorney cast a still more anxious look at the packet: and his visitor, untying the string that bound it, disclosed a quantity of promissory notes, with copies of deeds, and other documents.

" 'Upon these papers,' said the client, 'the man whose name they bear, has raised, as you will see, large sums of money, for some years past. There was a tacit understanding between him and the men into whose hands they originally went—and from whom I have by degrees purchased the whole, for treble and quadruple their nominal value—that these loans should be from time to time renewed, until a given period had elapsed. Such an understanding is nowhere expressed. He has sustained many losses of late; and these obligations accumulating upon him at once would crush him to the earth.'

" 'The whole amount is many thousands of pounds,' said the attorney, looking over the papers.

" 'It is,' said the client.

" 'What are we to do?' inquired the man of business.

" 'Do!' replied the client, with sudden vehemence. 'Put every engine of the law in force, every trick that ingenuity can devise and rascality execute; fair means and foul; the open oppression of the law, aided by all the craft of its most ingenious practitioners. I would have him die a harassing and lingering death. Ruin him, seize and sell his lands and goods, drive him from house and home, and drag him forth a beggar in his old age, to die in a common jail.'

" 'But the costs, my dear sir, the costs of all this,' reasoned the attorney, when he had recovered from his momentary surprise. 'If the defendant be a man of straw, who is to pay the costs, sir?'

" 'Name any sum,' said the stranger, his hand trembling so violently with excitement that he could scarcely hold the pen he seized as he spoke; 'any sum, and it is yours. Don't be afraid to name it, man. I shall not think it dear, if you gain my object.'

"The attorney named a large sum, at hazard, as the advance he should require to secure himself against the possibility of loss; but more with the view of ascertaining how far his client was really disposed to go, than with any idea that he would comply with the demand. The stranger wrote a check upon his banker, for the whole amount, and left him.

"The draft was duly honored, and the attorney, finding that his strange client might be safely relied upon, commenced his work in earnest. For more than two years afterwards, Mr. Heyling would sit whole days together, in the office, poring over the papers as they accumulated, and reading again and again, his eyes gleaming with joy, the letters of remonstrance, the prayers for a little delay, the representations of the certain ruin in which the opposite party must be involved, which poured in, as suit after suit, and process after process, was commenced. To all applications for a brief indulgence, there was but one reply—the money must be paid. Land, house, furniture, each in its turn, was taken under some one of the numerous executions which were issued; and the old man himself would have been immured in prison had he not escaped the vigilance of the officers, and fled.

"The implacable animosity of Heyling, so far from being satiated by the success of his persecution, increased a hundred-fold with the ruin he inflicted. On being informed of the old man's flight, his fury was unbounded. He gnashed his teeth with rage; tore the hair from his head, and assailed with horrid imprecations the men who had been entrusted with the writ. He was only restored to comparative calmness by repeated assurances of the certainty of discovering the fugitive. Agents were sent in quest of him, in all directions; every stratagem that could be invented was resorted to, for the purpose of discovering his place of retreat; but it was all in vain. Half a year had passed over, and he was still undiscovered.

"At length, late one night, Heyling, of whom nothing had been seen for many weeks before, appeared at his attorney's private residence, and sent up word that a gentleman wished to see him instantly. Before the attorney, who had recognized his voice from above stairs, could order the servant to admit him, he had rushed up the staircase, and entered the drawing-room, pale and breathless. Having closed the door, to prevent being overheard, he sank into a chair, and said, in a low voice:

" 'Hush! I have found him at last.'

" 'No!' said the attorney. 'Well done, my dear sir; well done.'

" 'He lies concealed in a wretched lodging in Camden Town,' said Heyling. 'Perhaps it is as well we *did* lose sight of him, for he has been living alone there, in the most abject misery, all the time, and he is poor—very poor.'

" 'Very good,' said the attorney. 'You will have the capture made to-morrow, of course?'

" 'Yes,' replied Heyling. 'Stay! no! The next day. You are surprised at my wishing to postpone it,' he added, with a ghastly smile; 'but I had forgotten. The next day is an anniversary in his life: let it be done then.'

" 'Very good,' said the attorney. 'Will you write down instructions for the officer?'

" 'No; let him meet me here, at eight in the evening, and I will accompany him myself.'

"They met on the appointed night, and, hiring a hackney coach, directed the driver to stop at that corner of the old Pancras Road, at which stands the parish workhouse. By the time they alighted there, it was quite dark; and, proceeding by the dead wall in front of the Veterinary Hospital, they entered a small by-street, which is, or was at that time, called Little College Street, and which, whatever it may be now, was in those days a desolate place enough, surrounded by little else than fields and ditches.

"Having drawn the traveling cap he had on half over his face, and muffled himself in his cloak, Heyling stopped before the meanest-looking house in the street, and knocked gently at the door. It was at once opened by a woman, who dropped a curtsey of recognition, and Heyling, whispering the officer to remain below, crept gently upstairs, and, opening the door of the front room, entered at once.

"The object of his search and his unrelenting animosity, now a decrepit old man, was seated at a bare deal table, on which stood a miserable candle. He started on the entrance of the stranger, and rose feebly to his feet.

" 'What now, what now?' said the old man. 'What fresh misery is this? What do you want here?'

" 'A word with *you*,' replied Heyling. As he spoke, he seated himself at the other end of the table, and, throwing off his cloak and cap, disclosed his features.

"The old man seemed instantly deprived of the power of speech. He fell backward in his chair, and, clasping his hands together, gazed on the apparition with a mingled look of abhorrence and fear.

" 'This day six years,' said Heyling, 'I claimed the life you owed me for my child's. Beside the lifeless form of your daughter, old man, I swore to live a life of revenge. I have never swerved from my purpose for a moment's space; but if I had, one thought of her uncomplaining, suffering look, as she drooped away, or of the starving face of our innocent child, would have nerved me to my task. My first act of requital you well remember: this is my last.'

"The old man shivered, and his hands dropped powerless by his side.

" 'I leave England to-morrow,' said Heyling, after a moment's pause. 'To-night I consign you to the living death to which you devoted her—a hopeless prison—'

"He raised his eyes to the old man's countenance, and paused. He lifted the light to his face, set it gently down, and left the apartment.

"'You had better see to the old man,' he said to the woman, as he opened the door and motioned the officer to follow him into the street. 'I think he is ill.' The woman closed the door, ran hastily upstairs, and found him lifeless.

"Beneath a plain gravestone, in one of the most peaceful and secluded churchyards in Kent, where wild flowers mingle with the grass, and the soft landscape around forms the fairest spot in the garden of England, lie the bones of the young mother and her gentle child. But the ashes of the father do not mingle with theirs; nor, from that night forward, did the attorney ever gain the remotest clue to the subsequent history of his queer client."

WILKIE COLLINS

(1824–1889)

WILLIAM WILKIE COLLINS was born at London in 1824. Like his friend Dickens, he was a voluminous writer of novels and tales, an editor and a dramatist. He was rather more interested in the short story form than Dickens, and a more accomplished master of it. *A Terribly Strange Bed* is one of the best known examples of the tale that is related for the sake of the thrill.

The story is reprinted from the volume *After Dark*, first published in London, 1856.

A TERRIBLY STRANGE BED

SHORTLY after my education at college was finished, I happened to be staying at Paris with an English friend. We were both young men then, and lived, I am afraid, rather a wild life, in the delightful city of our sojourn. One night we were idling about the neighborhood of the Palais Royal, doubtful to what amusement we should next betake ourselves. My friend proposed a visit to Frascati's; but his suggestion was not to my taste. I knew Frascati's, as the French saying is, by heart; had lost and won plenty of five-franc pieces there, merely for amusement's sake, until it was amusement no longer, and was thoroughly tired, in fact, of all the ghastly respectabilities of such a social anomaly as a respectable gambling-house.

"For Heaven's sake," said I to my friend, "let us go somewhere where we can see a little genuine, blackguard, poverty-stricken gaming, with no false gingerbread glitter thrown over it at all. Let us get away from fashionable Frascati's, to a house where they don't mind letting in a man with a ragged coat, or a man with no coat, ragged or otherwise."

"Very well," said my friend, "we needn't go out of the Palais Royal to find the sort of company you want. Here's the place just before us; as blackguard a place, by all report, as you could possibly wish to see."

In another minute we arrived at the door, and entered the house.

When we got upstairs, and had left our hats and sticks with the door-keeper, we were admitted into the chief gambling-room. We did not find many people assembled there. But, few as the men were who looked up at us on our entrance, they were all types—lamentably true types—of their respective classes.

We had come to see blackguards; but these men were something worse. There is a comic side, more or less appreciable, in all blackguardism: here there was nothing but tragedy—mute, weird tragedy. The quiet in the room was horrible. The thin, haggard, long-haired young man, whose sunken eyes fiercely watched the turning up of the cards, never spoke; the flabby, fat-faced, pimply player, who pricked his piece of pasteboard perseveringly, to register how often black won, and how often red, never spoke; the dirty, wrinkled old man, with the vulture eyes and the darned great-coat, who had lost his last sou, and still looked on desperately after he could play no longer, never spoke. Even the voice of the croupier sounded as if it were strangely dulled and thickened in the atmosphere of the room. I had entered the place to laugh, but the spectacle before me was something to weep over. I soon found it necessary to take refuge in excitement from the depression of spirits which was fast stealing on me. Unfortunately I sought the nearest excitement, by going to the table and beginning to play. Still more unfortunately, as the event will show, I won—won prodigiously; won incredibly; won at such a rate that the regular players at the table crowded round me; and staring at my stakes with hungry, superstitious eyes, whispered to one another that the English stranger was going to break the bank.

The game was Rouge et Noir. I had played at it in every city in Europe, without, however, the care or the wish to study the Theory of Chances—that philosopher's stone of all gamblers! And a gambler, in the strict sense of the word, I had never been. I was heart-whole from the corroding passion for play. My gaming was a mere idle amusement. I never resorted to it by necessity, because I never knew what it was to want money. I never practised it so incessantly as to lose more than I could afford, or to gain more than I could coolly pocket without being thrown off my balance by my good luck. In short, I had hitherto frequented gambling-tables—just as I frequented ball-rooms and opera-houses—because they amused me, and because I had nothing better to do with my leisure hours.

But on this occasion it was very different—now, for the first time in my life, I felt what the passion for play really was. My successes first bewildered, and then, in the most literal meaning of the word, intoxicated me. Incredible as it may appear, it is nevertheless true, that I only lost when I attempted to estimate chances, and played according to previous calculation. If I left everything to luck, and staked without any care or consideration, I was sure to win—to win in the face of every recognized probability in favor of the bank. At first some of the men present ventured their money safely enough on my color; but I speedily increased my stakes to sums which they dared not risk. One after another they left off playing, and breathlessly looked on at my game.

Still, time after time, I staked higher and higher, and still won. The excitement in the room rose to fever pitch. The silence was interrupted by a deep-muttered chorus of oaths and exclamations in different languages, every time the gold was shoveled across to my side of the table—even the imperturbable croupier dashed his rake on the floor in a (French) fury of astonishment at my success. But one man present preserved his self-possession, and that man was my friend. He came to my side, and whispering in English, begged me to leave the place, satisfied with what I had already gained. I must do him the justice to say that he repeated his warnings and entreaties several times, and only left me and went away, after I had rejected his advice (I was to all intents and purposes gambling drunk) in terms which rendered it impossible for him to address me again that night.

Shortly after he had gone, a hoarse voice behind me cried, "Permit me, my dear sir—permit me to restore to their proper place, two napoleons which you have dropped. Wonderful luck, sir! I pledge you my word of honor, as an old soldier, in the course of my long experience in this sort of thing, I never saw such luck as yours—never! Go on, sir—*Sacre mille bombes!* Go on boldly, and break the bank!"

I turned round and saw, nodding and smiling at me with inveterate civility, a tall man, dressed in a frogged and braided surtout.

If I had been in my senses, I should have considered him, personally, as being rather a suspicious specimen of an old soldier. He had goggling, bloodshot eyes, mangy mustaches, and a broken nose. His voice betrayed a barrack-room intonation of the worst order, and he had the dirtiest pair of hands I ever saw—even in France. These little personal peculiarities exercised, however, no repelling influence on me. In the mad excitement, the reckless triumph of that moment, I was ready to "fraternize" with anybody who encouraged me in my game. I accepted the old soldier's offered pinch of snuff; clapped him on the back, and swore he was the honestest fellow in the world—the most glorious relic of the Grand Army that I had ever met with. "Go on!" cried my military friend, snapping his fingers in ecstasy—"Go on, and win! Break the bank—*Mille tonnerres!* my gallant English comrade, break the bank!"

And I *did* go on—went on at such a rate, that in another quarter of an hour the croupier called out, "Gentlemen, the bank has discontinued for to-night." All the notes, and all the gold in that "bank," now lay in a heap under my hands; the whole floating capital of the gambling-house was waiting to pour into my pockets!

"Tie up the money in your pocket-handkerchief, my worthy sir," said the old soldier, as I wildly plunged my hands into my heap of gold. "Tie it up, as we used to tie up a bit of dinner in the Grand Army; your winnings are too heavy for any breeches-pockets that ever were sewed. There! that's it—shovel them in, notes and all! *Credie!* what luck! Stop! another napoleon on the floor. *Ah! sacre petit polisson de Napoleon!* have I found thee at last? Now then, sir—two tight double knots each way with your honorable permission, and the money's safe. Feel it! feel it, fortunate sir! hard and round as a cannon-ball— *À bas* if they had only fired such cannon-balls at us at Austerlitz—*nom d'une pipe!* if they only had! And now, as an ancient grenadier, as an ex-brave of the French army, what remains for me to do? I ask what? Simply this, to entreat my valued English friend to drink a bottle of champagne with me, and toast the goddess Fortune in foaming goblets before we part!"

"Excellent ex-brave! Convivial ancient grenadier! Champagne by all means! An English cheer for an old soldier! Hurrah! hurrah! Another English cheer for the goddess Fortune! Hurrah! hurrah! hurrah!"

"Bravo! the Englishman; the amiable, gracious Englishman, in whose veins circulates the vivacious blood of France! Another glass? *À bas!*—the bottle is empty! Never mind! *Vive le vin!* I, the old soldier, order another bottle, and half a pound of *bonbons* with it!"

"No, no, ex-brave; never—ancient grenadier! *Your* bottle last time; *my* bottle this! Behold it! Toast away! The French Army! the great Napoleon! the present company! the croupier! the honest croupier's wife and daughters—if he has any! the ladies generally! everybody in the world!"

By the time the second bottle of champagne was emptied, I felt as if I had been drinking liquid fire—my brain seemed all aflame. No excess in wine had ever had this effect on me before in my life. Was it the result of a stimulant acting upon my system when I was in a highly excited state? Was my stomach in a particularly disordered condition? Or was the champagne amazingly strong?

"Ex-brave of the French Army!" cried I, in a mad state of exhilaration, "*I* am on fire! how are *you*? You have set me on fire! Do you hear, my hero of Austerlitz? Let us have a third bottle of champagne to put the flame out!"

The old soldier wagged his head, rolled his goggle-eyes, until I expected to see them slip out of their sockets; placed his dirty forefinger by the side of his broken nose; solemnly ejaculated "Coffee!" and immediately ran off into an inner room.

The word pronounced by the eccentric veteran seemed to have a magical effect on the rest of the company present. With one accord they all rose to depart. Probably they had expected to profit by my intoxication; but finding that my new friend was benevolently bent on preventing me from getting dead drunk, had now abandoned all hope of thriving pleasantly on my winnings. Whatever their motive might be, at any rate they went away in a body. When the old soldier returned and sat down again opposite to me at the table, we had the room to ourselves. I could see the croupier, in a sort of vestibule which opened out of it, eating his supper in solitude. The silence was now deeper than ever.

A sudden change, too, had come over the "ex-brave." He assumed a portentously solemn look; and when he spoke to me again, his speech was ornamented by no oaths, enforced by no finger-snapping, enlivened by no apostrophes or exclamations.

"Listen, my dear sir," said he, in mysteriously confidential tones—"listen to an old soldier's advice. I have been to the mistress of the house (a very charming woman, with a genius for cookery!) to impress on her the necessity of making us some particularly strong and good coffee. You must drink this coffee in order to get rid of your little amiable exaltation of spirits before you think of going home—you *must*, my good and gracious friend! With all that money to take home to-night, it is a sacred duty to yourself to have your wits about you. You are known to be a winner to an enormous extent by several gentlemen present to-night, who, in a certain point of view, are very worthy and excellent fellows; but they are mortal men, my dear sir, and they have their amiable weaknesses! Need I say more? Ah, no, no! you understand me! Now, this is what you must do—send for a cabriolet when you feel quite well again—draw up all the windows when you get into it—and tell the driver to take you home only through the large and well-lighted thoroughfares. Do this; and you and your money will be safe. Do this; and to-morrow you will thank an old soldier for giving you a word of honest advice."

Just as the ex-brave ended his oration in very lachrymose tones, the coffee came in, ready poured out in two cups. My attentive friend handed me one of the cups with a bow. I was parched with thirst, and drank it off at a draft. Almost instantly afterward I was seized with a fit of giddiness, and felt more completely intoxicated than ever. The room whirled round and round furiously; the old soldier seemed to be regularly bobbing up and down before me like the piston of a steam-engine. I was half deafened by a violent singing in my ears; a feeling of utter bewilderment, helplessness, idiocy, overcame me. I rose from my chair, holding on by the table to keep my balance; and stammered out that I felt dreadfully unwell—so unwell that I did not know how I was to get home.

"My dear friend," answered the old soldier—and even his voice seemed to be bobbing up and down as he spoke—"my dear friend, it would be madness to go home in *your* state; you would be sure to lose your money; you might be robbed and murdered with the greatest ease. *I* am going to sleep here: *do* you sleep here, too—they make up capital beds in this house—take one; sleep off the effects of the wine, and go home safely with your winnings to-morrow—to-morrow, in broad day-light."

I had but two ideas left: one, that I must never let go hold of my handkerchief full of money; the other, that I must lie down somewhere immediately, and fall off into a comfortable sleep. So I agreed to the proposal about the bed, and took the offered arm of the old soldier, carrying my money with my disengaged hand. Preceded by the croupier, we passed along some passages and up a flight of stairs into the bed-room which I was to occupy. The ex-brave shook me warmly by the hand, proposed that we should breakfast together, and then, followed by the croupier, left me for the night.

I ran to the wash-hand stand; drank some of the water in my jug; poured the rest out, and plunged my face into it; then sat down in a chair and tried to compose myself. I soon felt better. The change for my lungs, from the fetid atmosphere of the gambling-house to the cool air of the apartment I now occupied, the almost equally refreshing change for my eyes, from the glaring gaslights of the "salon" to the dim, quiet flicker of one bedroom-candle, aided wonderfully the restorative effects of cold water. The giddiness left me, and I began to feel a little like a reasonable being again. My first thought was of the risk of sleeping all night in a gambling-house; my second, of the still greater risk of trying to get out after the house was closed, and of going home alone at night through the streets of Paris with a large sum of money about me. I had slept in worse places than this on my travels; so I determined to lock, bolt, and barricade my door, and take my chance till the next morning.

Accordingly, I secured myself against all intrusion; looked under the bed, and into the cupboard; tried the fastening of the window; and then, satisfied that I had taken every proper precaution, pulled off my upper clothing, put my light, which was a dim one, on the hearth among a feathery litter of wood-ashes, and got into bed, with the handkerchief full of money under my pillow.

I soon felt not only that I could not go to sleep, but that I could not even close my eyes. I was wide awake, and in a high fever. Every nerve in my body trembled—every one of my senses seemed to be preternaturally sharpened. I tossed and rolled, and tried every kind of position and perseveringly sought out the cold corners of the bed, and all to no purpose. Now I thrust my arms over the clothes; now I poked them under the clothes; now I violently shot my legs straight out down to the bottom of the bed; now I convulsively coiled them up as near my chin as they would go; now I shook out my crumpled pillow, changed it to the cool side, patted it flat, and lay down quietly on my back; now I fiercely doubled it in two, set it up on end, thrust it against the board of the bed, and tried a sitting posture. Every effort was in vain; I groaned with vexation as I felt that I was in for a sleepless night.

What could I do? I had no book to read. And yet, unless I found out some method of diverting my mind, I felt certain that I was in the condition to imagine all sorts of horrors; to rack my brain with forebodings of every possible and impossible danger; in short, to pass the night in suffering all conceivable varieties of nervous terror.

I raised myself on my elbow, and looked about the room—which was brightened by a lovely moonlight pouring straight through the window—to see if it contained any pictures or ornaments that I could at all clearly distinguish. While my eyes wandered from wall to wall, a remembrance of Le Maistre's delightful little book, "Voyage autour de ma Chambre," occurred to me. I resolved to imitate the French author, and find occupation and amusement enough to relieve the tedium of my wakefulness, by making a mental inventory of every article of furniture I could see, and by following up to their sources the multitude of associations which even a chair, a table, or a wash-hand stand may be made to call forth.

In the nervous, unsettled state of my mind at that moment, I found it much easier to make my inventory than to make my reflections, and thereupon soon gave up all hope of thinking in Le Maistre's fanciful track—or, indeed, of thinking at all. I looked about the room at the different articles of furniture, and did nothing more.

There was, first, the bed I was lying in; a four-post bed, of all things in the world to meet with in Paris—yes, a thorough clumsy British four-poster, with a regular top lined with chintz—the regular fringed valance all round—the regular stifling, unwholesome curtains, which I remembered having mechanically drawn back against the posts without particularly noticing the bed when I first got into the room. Then there was the marble-topped wash-hand stand, from which the water I had spilled, in my hurry to pour it out, was still dripping, slowly and more slowly, on to the brick floor. Then two small chairs, with my coat, waistcoat, and trousers flung on them. Then a large elbow-chair covered with dirty white dimity, with my cravat and shirt collar thrown over the back. Then a chest of drawers with two of the brass handles off, and a tawdry, broken china inkstand placed on it by way of ornament for the top. Then the dressing-table, adorned by a very small looking-glass, and a very large pincushion. Then the window—an unusually large window. Then a dark old picture, which the feeble candle dimly showed me. It was the picture of a fellow in a high Spanish hat, crowned with a plume of towering feathers. A swarthy, sinister ruffian, looking upward, shading his eyes with his hand, and looking intently upward—it might be at some tall gallows on which he was going to be hanged. At any rate, he had the appearance of thoroughly deserving it.

This picture put a kind of constraint upon me to look upward too—at the top of the bed. It was a gloomy and not an interesting object, and I looked back at the picture. I counted the feathers in the man's hat—they stood out in relief—three white, two green. I observed the crown of his hat, which was of a conical shape, according to the fashion supposed to have been favored by Guido Fawkes. I wondered what he was looking up at. It couldn't be at the stars; such a desperado was neither astrologer nor astronomer. It must be at the high gallows, and he was going to be hanged presently. Would the executioner come into possession of his conical crowned hat and plume of feathers? I counted the feathers again—three white, two green.

While I still lingered over this very improving and intellectual employment, my thoughts insensibly began to wander. The moonlight shining into the room reminded me of a certain moonlight night in England—the night after a picnic party in a Welsh valley. Every incident of the drive homeward, through lovely scenery, which the moonlight made lovelier than ever, came back to my remembrance, though I had never given the picnic a thought for years; though, if I had *tried* to recollect it, I could certainly have recalled little or nothing of that scene long past. Of all the wonderful faculties that help to tell us we are immortal, which speaks the sublime truth more eloquently than memory? Here was I, in a strange house of the most suspicious character, in a situation of uncertainty, and even of peril, which might seem to make the cool exercise of my recollection almost out of the question; nevertheless, remembering, quite involuntarily, places, people, conversations, minute circumstances of every kind, which I had thought forgotten forever; which I could not possibly have recalled at will, even under the most favorable auspices. And what cause had produced in a moment the whole of this strange, complicated, mysterious effect? Nothing but some rays of moonlight shining in at my bedroom window.

I was still thinking of the picnic—of our merriment on the drive home—of the sentimental young lady who *would* quote *Childe Harold* because it was moonlight. I was absorbed by these past scenes and past amusements, when, in an instant, the thread on which my memories hung snapped asunder; my attention immediately came back to present things more vividly than ever, and I found myself, I neither knew why nor wherefore, looking hard at the picture again.

Looking for what?

Good God! the man had pulled his hat down on his brows! No! the hat itself was gone! Where was the conical crown? Where the feathers—three white, two green? Not there! In place of the hat and feathers, what dusky object was it that now hid his forehead, his eyes, his shading hand?

Was the bed moving?

I turned on my back and looked up. Was I mad? drunk? dreaming? giddy again? or was the top of the bed really moving down—sinking slowly, regularly, silently, horribly, right down throughout the whole of its length and breadth—right down upon me, as I lay underneath?

My blood seemed to stand still. A deadly, paralyzing coldness stole all over me as I turned my head round on the pillow and determined to test whether the bed-top was really moving or not, by keeping my eye on the man in the picture.

The next look in that direction was enough. The dull, black, frowsy outline of the valance above me was within an inch of being parallel with his waist. I still looked breathlessly. And steadily and slowly—very slowly—I saw the figure, and the line of frame below the figure, vanish, as the valance moved down before it.

I am, constitutionally, anything but timid. I have been on more than one occasion in peril of my life, and have not lost my self-possession for an instant; but when the conviction first settled on my mind that the bed-top was really moving, was steadily and continuously sinking down upon me, I looked up shuddering, helpless, panic-stricken, beneath the hideous machinery for murder, which was advancing closer and closer to suffocate me where I lay.

I looked up, motionless, speechless, breathless. The candle, fully spent, went out; but the moonlight still brightened the room. Down and down, without pausing and without sounding, came the bed-top, and still my panic terror seemed to bind me faster and faster to the mattress on which I lay—down and down it sank, till the dusty odor from the lining of the canopy came stealing into my nostrils.

At that final moment the instinct of self-preservation startled me out of my trance, and I moved at last. There was just room for me to roll myself sidewise off the bed. As I dropped noiselessly to the floor, the edge of the murderous canopy touched me on the shoulder.

Without stopping to draw my breath, without wiping the cold sweat from my face, I rose instantly on my knees to watch the bed-top. I was literally spellbound by it. If I had heard footsteps behind me, I could not have turned round; if a means of escape had been miraculously provided for me, I could not have moved to take advantage of it. The whole life in me was, at that moment, concentrated in my eyes.

It descended—the whole canopy, with the fringe round it, came down —down—close down; so close that there was not room now to squeeze my finger between the bed-top and the bed. I felt at the sides, and discovered that what had appeared to me from beneath to be the ordinary light canopy of a four-post bed was in reality a thick, broad mattress, the substance of which was concealed by the valance and its fringe. I looked up and saw the four posts rising hideously bare. In the middle of the bed-top was a huge wooden screw that had evidently worked it down through a hole in the ceiling, just as ordinary presses are worked down on the substance selected for compression. The frightful apparatus moved without making the faintest noise. There had been no creaking as it came down; there was now not the faintest sound from the room above. Amidst a dead and awful silence I beheld before me—in the Nineteenth Century, and in the civilized capital of France—such a machine for secret murder by suffocation as might have existed in the worst days of the Inquisition, in the lonely inns among the Hartz Mountains, in the mysterious tribunals of Westphalia! Still, as I looked on it, I could not move, I could hardly breathe, but I began to recover the power of thinking, and in a moment I discovered the murderous conspiracy framed against me in all its horror.

My cup of coffee had been drugged, and drugged too strongly. I had been saved from being smothered by having taken an overdose of some narcotic. How I had chafed and fretted at the fever fit which had preserved my life by keeping me awake! How recklessly I had confided myself to the two wretches who had led me into this room, determined, for the sake of my winnings, to kill me in my sleep by the surest and most horrible contrivance for secretly accomplishing my destruction! How many men, winners like me, had slept, as I had proposed to sleep, in that bed, and had never been seen or heard of more! I shuddered at the bare idea of it.

But ere long all thought was again suspended by the sight of the murderous canopy moving once more. After it had remained on the bed—as nearly as I could guess—about ten minutes, it began to move up again. The villains who worked it from above evidently believed that their purpose was now accomplished. Slowly and silently, as it had descended, that horrible bed-top rose toward its former place. When it reached the upper extremities of the four posts, it reached the ceiling too. Neither hole nor screw could be seen; the bed became in appearance an ordinary bed again—the canopy an ordinary canopy—even to the most suspicious eyes.

Now, for the first time, I was able to move—to rise from my knees—to dress myself in my upper clothing—and to consider of how I should escape. If I betrayed by the smallest noise that the attempt to suffocate me had failed, I was certain to be murdered. Had I made any noise already? I listened intently, looking toward the door.

No! No footsteps in the passage outside—no sound of a tread, light or heavy, in the room above—absolute silence everywhere. Besides locking and bolting my door, I had moved an old wooden chest against it, which I had found under the bed. To remove this chest (my blood ran cold as I thought of what its contents *might* be!) without making some disturbance was impossible; and, moreover, to think of escaping through the house, now barred up for the night, was sheer insanity. Only one chance was left me—the window. I stole to it on tiptoe.

My bedroom was on the first floor, above an entresol, and looked into the back street. I raised my hand to open the window, knowing that on that action hung, by the merest hair-breadth, my chance of safety. They keep vigilant watch in a House of Murder. If any part of the frame cracked, if the hinge creaked, I was a lost man! It must have occupied me at least five minutes, reckoning by time—five *hours* reckoning by suspense—to open that window. I succeeded in doing it silently—in doing it with all the dexterity of a house-breaker—and then looked down into the street. To leap the distance beneath me would be almost certain destruction! Next, I looked round at the sides of the house. Down the left side ran a thick water-pipe—it passed close by the outer edge of the window. The moment I saw the pipe, I knew I was saved. My breath came and went freely for the first time since I had seen the canopy of the bed moving down upon me!

To some men the means of escape which I had discovered might have seemed difficult and dangerous enough—to *me* the prospect of slipping down the pipe into the street did not suggest even a thought of peril. I had always been accustomed, by the practise of gymnastics, to keep up my school-boy powers as a daring and expert climber; and knew that my head, hands, and feet would serve me faithfully in any hazards of ascent or descent. I had already got one leg over the window-sill, when I remembered the handkerchief filled with money under my pillow. I could well have afforded to leave it behind me, but I was revengefully determined that the miscreants of the gambling-house should miss their plunder as well as their victim. So I went back to the bed and tied the heavy handkerchief at my back by my cravat.

Just as I had made it tight and fixed it in a comfortable place, I thought I heard a sound of breathing outside the door. The chill feeling of horror ran through me again as I listened. No! Dead silence still in the passage—I had only heard the night air blowing softly into the room. The next moment I was on the window-sill—and the next I had a firm grip on the water-pipe with my hands and knees.

I slid down into the street easily and quietly, as I thought I should, and immediately set off at the top of my speed to a branch "Prefecture" of Police, which I knew was situated in the immediate neighborhood. A "Sub-prefect," and several picked men among his subordinates, happened to be up, maturing, I believe, some scheme for discovering the perpetrator of a mysterious murder which all Paris was talking of just then. When I began my story, in a breathless hurry and in very bad French, I could see that the Sub-prefect suspected me of being a drunken Englishman who had robbed somebody; but he soon altered his opinion as I went on, and before I had anything like concluded, he shoved all the papers before him into a drawer, put on his hat, supplied me with another (for I was bareheaded), ordered a file of soldiers, desired his expert followers to get ready all sorts of tools for breaking open doors and ripping up brick flooring, and took my arm, in the most friendly and familiar manner possible, to lead me with him out of the house. I will venture to say that when the Sub-prefect was a little boy, and was taken for the first time to the play, he was not half as much pleased as he was now at the job in prospect for him at the gambling-house!

Away we went through the streets, the Sub-prefect cross-examining and congratulating me in the same breath as we marched at the head of our formidable *posse comitatus*. Sentinels were placed at the back and front of the house the moment we got to it, a tremendous battery of knocks was directed against the door; a light appeared at a window; I was told to conceal myself behind the police—then came more knocks, and a cry of "Open in the name of the law!" At that terrible summons bolts and locks gave way before an invisible hand, and the moment after the Sub-prefect was in the passage, confronting a waiter half dressed and ghastly pale. This was the short dialogue which immediately took place:

"We want to see the Englishman who is sleeping in this house?"

"He went away hours ago."

"He did no such thing. His friend went away; *he* remained. Show us to his bedroom!"

"I swear to you, Monsieur le Sous-prefet, he is not here! He—"

"I swear to you, Monsieur le Garçon, he is. He slept here—he didn't find your bed comfortable—he came to us to complain of it—here he is among my men—and here am I ready to look for a flea or two in his bedstead. Renaudin!" (calling to one of the subordinates, and pointing to the waiter), "collar that man, and tie his hands behind him. Now then, gentlemen, let us walk upstairs!"

Every man and woman in the house was secured—the "Old Soldier" the first. Then I identified the bed in which I had slept, and then we went into the room above.

No object that was at all extraordinary appeared in any part of it. The Sub-prefect looked round the place, commanded everybody to be silent, stamped twice on the floor, called for a candle, looked attentively at the spot he had stamped on, and ordered the flooring there to be carefully taken up. This was done in no time. Lights were produced, and we saw a deep raftered cavity between the floor of this room and the ceiling of the room beneath. Through this cavity there ran perpendicularly a sort of case of iron thickly greased; and inside the case appeared the screw, which communicated with the bed-top below. Extra lengths of screw, freshly oiled; levers covered with felt; all the complete upper works of a heavy press—constructed with infernal ingenuity so as to join the fixtures below, and when taken to pieces again to go into the smallest possible compass—were next discovered and pulled out on the floor. After some little difficulty the Sub-prefect succeeded in putting the machinery together, and, leaving his men to work it, descended with me to the bedroom. The smothering canopy was then lowered, but not so noiselessly as I had seen it lowered. When I mentioned this to the Sub-prefect, his answer, simple as it was, had a terrible significance, "My men," said he, "are working down the bed-top for the first time—the men whose money you won were in better practise."

We left the house in the sole possession of two police agents—every one of the inmates being removed to prison on the spot. The Sub-prefect, after taking down my "procès verbal" in his office, returned with me to my hotel to get my passport. "Do you think," I asked, as I gave it to him, "that any men have really been smothered in that bed, as they tried to smother *me?*"

"I have seen dozens of drowned men laid out at the Morgue," answered the Sub-prefect, "in whose pocketbooks were found letters stating that they had committed suicide in the Seine, because they had lost everything at the gaming-table. Do I know how many of those men entered the same gambling-house that *you* entered? won as *you* won? took that bed as *you* took it? slept in it? were smothered in it? and were privately thrown into the river, with a letter of explanation written by the murderers and placed in their pocketbooks? No man can say how many or how few have suffered the fate from which you have escaped. The people of the gambling-house kept their bedstead machinery a secret from us—even from the police! The dead kept the rest of the secret for them. Good-night, or rather good-morning, Monsieur Faulkner! Be at my office again at nine o'clock—in the meantime, au revoir!"

The rest of my story is soon told. I was examined and reexamined; the gambling-house was strictly searched all through from top to bottom; the prisoners were separately interrogated; and two of the less guilty among them made a confession. I discovered that the Old Soldier was the master of the gambling-house—*justice* discovered that he had been drummed out of the army as a vagabond years ago; that he had been guilty of all sorts of villainies since; that he was in possession of stolen property, which the owners identified; and that he, the croupier, another accomplice, and the woman who had made my cup of coffee, were all in the secret of the bedstead. There appeared some reason to doubt whether the inferior persons attached to the house knew anything of the suffocating machinery; and they received the benefit of that doubt, by being treated simply as thieves and vagabonds. As for the Old Soldier and his two head myrmidons, they went to the galleys; the woman who had drugged my coffee was imprisoned for I forget how many years; the regular attendants at the gambling-house were considered "suspicious," and placed under "surveillance"; and I became, for one whole week (which is a long time), the head "lion" in Parisian society. My adventure was dramatized by three illustrious play-makers, but never saw theatrical daylight; for the censorship forbade the introduction on the stage of a correct copy of the gambling-house bedstead.

One good result was produced by my adventure, which any censorship must have approved: it cured me of ever again trying "Rouge et Noir" as an amusement. The sight of a green cloth, with packs of cards and heaps of money on it, will henceforth be forever associated in my mind with the sight of a bed canopy descending to suffocate me in the silence and darkness of the night.

THOMAS HARDY

(1840—)

THOMAS HARDY was born in Dorsetshire in 1840. At an early age he went to Dorchester to study architecture, and later to London. His first novel (published 1871) was read and appreciated by George Meredith, who saw it in MS. After its publication Hardy returned to Dorchester, where he has lived for the past half-century. Among his many volumes of fiction there are four collections of short stories. Hardy's chief qualities—his grasp of character and his ability to create atmosphere—are observable in his short tales quite as clearly as in his greater and more extensive novels.

The present story is reprinted, by permission of the publisher, from *A Group of Noble Dames*, Macmillan and Co.

SQUIRE PETRICK'S LADY

(From *A Group of Noble Dames*)

FOLK who are at all acquainted with the traditions of Stapleford Park will not need to be told that in the middle of the last century it was owned by that trump of mortgagees, Timothy Petrick, whose skill in gaining possession of fair estates by granting sums of money on their title-deeds has seldom if ever been equaled in our part of England. Timothy was a lawyer by profession, and agent to several noblemen, by which means his special line of business became opened to him by a sort of revelation. It is said that a relative of his, a very deep thinker, who afterwards had the misfortune to be transported for life for mistaken notions on the signing of a will, taught him considerable legal lore, which he creditably resolved never to throw away for the benefit of other people, but to reserve it entirely for his own.

However, I have nothing in particular to say about his early and active days, but rather of the time when, an old man, he had become the owner of vast estates by the means I have signified—among them the great manor of Stapleford, on which he lived, in the splendid old mansion now pulled down; likewise estates at Marlott, estates near Sherton Abbas, nearly all the borough of Millpool, and many properties near Ivell. Indeed, I can't call to mind half his landed possessions, and I don't know that it matters much at this time of day, seeing that he's been dead and gone many years. It is said that when he bought an estate he would not decide to pay the price till he had walked over every single acre with his own two feet, and prodded the soil at every point with his own spud, to test its quality, which, if we regard the extent of his properties, must have been a stiff business for him.

At the time I am speaking of he was a man over eighty, and his son was dead; but he had two grandsons, the eldest of whom, his namesake, was married, and was shortly expecting issue. Just then the grandfather was taken ill, for death, as it seemed, considering his age. By his will the old man had created an entail (as I believe the lawyers call it), devising the whole of the estates to his elder grandson and his issue male, failing which, to his younger grandson and his issue male, failing which, to remoter relatives, who need not be mentioned now.

While old Timothy Petrick was lying ill, his elder grandson's wife, Annetta, gave birth to her expected child, who, as fortune would have it, was a son. Timothy, her husband, though sprung of a scheming family, was no great schemer himself; he was the single one of the Petricks then living whose heart had ever been greatly moved by sentiments which did not run in the groove of ambition; and on this account he had not married well, as the saying is, his wife having been the daughter of a family of no better beginnings than his own; that is to say, her father was a country townsman of the professional class. But she was a very pretty woman, by all accounts, and her husband had seen, courted, and married her in a high tide of infatuation, after a very short acquaintance, and with very little knowledge of her heart's history. He had never found reason to regret his choice as yet, and his anxiety for her recovery was great.

She was supposed to be out of danger, and herself and the child progressing well, when there was a change for the worse, and she sank so rapidly that she was soon given over. When she felt that she was about to leave him, Annetta sent for her husband, and, on his speedy entry and assurance that they were alone, she made him solemnly vow to give the child every care in any circumstances that might arise, if it should please Heaven to take her. This, of course, he readily promised. Then, after some hesitation, she told him that she could not die with a falsehood upon her soul, and dire deceit in her life; she must make a terrible confession to him before her lips were sealed forever. She thereupon related an incident concerning the baby's parentage which was not as he supposed.

Timothy Petrick, though a quick-feeling man, was not of a sort to show nerves outwardly; and he bore himself as heroically as he possibly could do in this trying moment of his life. That same night his wife died; and while she lay dead, and before her funeral, he hastened to the bedside of his sick grandfather, and revealed to him all that had happened—the baby's birth, his wife's confession, and her death, beseeching the aged man, as he loved him, to bestir himself now, at the eleventh hour, and alter his will so as to dish the intruder. Old Timothy, seeing matters in the same light as his grandson, required no urging against allowing anything to stand in the way of legitimate inheritance; he executed another will, limiting the entail to Timothy, his grandson, for life, and his male heirs thereafter to be born; after them to his other grandson, Edward, and Edward's heirs. Thus the newly born infant, who had been the center of so many hopes, was cut off and scorned as none of the elect.

The old mortgagee lived but a short time after this, the excitement of the discovery having told upon him considerably, and he was gathered to his fathers like the most charitable man in his neighborhood. Both wife and grandparent being buried, Timothy settled down to his usual life as well as he was able, mentally satisfied that he had, by prompt action, defeated the consequences of such dire domestic treachery as had been shown towards him, and resolving to marry a second time as soon as he could satisfy himself in the choice of a wife.

But men do not always know themselves. The imbittered state of

Timothy Petrick's mind bred in him by degrees such a hatred and mistrust of womankind that, though several specimens of high attractiveness came under his eyes, he could not bring himself to the point of proposing marriage. He dreaded to take up the position of husband a second time, discerning a trap in every petticoat, and a Slough of Despond in possible heirs. "What has happened once, when all seemed so fair, may happen again," he said to himself. "I'll risk my name no more." So he abstained from marriage, and overcame his wish for a lineal descendant to follow him in the ownership of Stapleford.

Timothy had scarcely noticed the unfortunate child that his wife had borne, after arranging for a meager fulfilment of his promise to her to take care of the boy, by having him brought up in his house. Occasionally, remembering his promise, he went and glanced at the child, saw that he was doing well, gave a few special directions, and again went his solitary way. Thus he and the child lived on in the Stapleford mansion-house till two or three years had passed by. One day he was walking in the garden, and by some accident left his snuff-box on a bench. When he came back to find it he saw the little boy standing there; he had escaped his nurse, and was making a plaything of the box, in spite of the convulsive sneezings which the game brought in its train. Then the man with the incrusted heart became interested in the little fellow's persistence in his play under such discomforts; he looked in the child's face, saw there his wife's countenance, though he did not see his own, and fell into thought on the piteousness of childhood—particularly of despised and rejected childhood, like this before him.

From that hour, try as he would to counteract the feeling, the human necessity to love something or other got the better of what he had called his wisdom, and shaped itself in a tender anxiety for the youngster Rupert. This name had been given him by his dying mother when, at her request, the child was baptized in her chamber, lest he should not survive for public baptism; and her husband had never thought of it as a name of any significance till, about this time, he learned by accident that it was the name of the young Marquis of Christminster, son of the Duke of Southwesterland, for whom Annetta had cherished warm feelings before her marriage. Recollecting some wandering phrases in his wife's last words, which he had not understood at the time, he perceived at last that this was the person to whom she had alluded when affording him a clew to little Rupert's history.

He would sit in silence for hours with the child, being no great speaker at the best of times; but the boy, on his part, was too ready with his tongue for any break in discourse to arise because Timothy Petrick had nothing to say. After idling away his mornings in this manner, Petrick would go to his own room and swear in long, loud whispers, and walk up and down, calling himself the most ridiculous dolt that ever lived, and declaring that he would never go near the little fellow again; to which resolve he would adhere for the space, perhaps, of a day. Such cases are happily not new to human nature, but there never was a case in which a man more completely befooled his former self than in this.

As the child grew up, Timothy's attachment to him grew deeper, till Rupert became almost the sole object for which he lived. There had been enough of the family ambition latent in him for Timothy Petrick to feel a little envy when, some time before this date, his brother Edward had been accepted by the Honorable Harriet Mountclere, daughter of the second viscount of that name and title; but having discovered, as I have before stated, the paternity of his boy Rupert to lurk in even a higher stratum of society, those envious feelings speedily dispersed. Indeed, the more he reflected thereon, after his brother's aristocratic marriage, the more content did he become. His late wife took softer outline in his memory, as he thought of the lofty taste she had displayed, though only a plain burgher's daughter, and the justification for his weakness in loving the child—the justification that he had longed for—was afforded now in the knowledge that the boy was by nature, if not by name, a representative of one of the noblest houses in England.

"She was a woman of grand instincts, after all," he said to himself, proudly. "To fix her choice upon the immediate successor in that ducal line—it was finely conceived! Had he been of low blood like myself or my relations she would scarce have deserved the harsh measure that I have dealt out to her and her offspring. How much less, then, when such groveling tastes were farthest from her soul! The man Annetta loved was noble, and my boy is noble in spite of me."

The after-clap was inevitable, and it soon came. "So far," he reasoned, "from cutting off his child from inheritance of my estates, as I have done, I should have rejoiced in the possession of him! He is of pure stock on one side at least, while in the ordinary run of affairs he would have been a commoner to the bone."

Being a man, whatever his faults, of good old beliefs in the divinity of kings and those about 'em, the more he overhauled the case in this light the more strongly did his poor wife's conduct in improving the blood and breed of the Petrick family win his heart. He considered what ugly, idle, hard-drinking scamps many of his own relations had been; the miserable scriveners, usurers, and pawnbrokers that he had numbered among his forefathers, and the probability that some of their bad qualities would have come out in a merely corporeal child, to give him sorrow in his old age, turn his black hairs gray, his gray hairs white, cut down every stick of timber, and Heaven knows what all, had he not, like a this right-minded man fell down on his knees every night and morning skilful gardener, minded his grafting and changed the sort; till at length and thanked God that he was not as other meanly descended fathers in such matters.

It was in the peculiar disposition of the Petrick family that the satisfaction which ultimately settled in Timothy's breast found nourishment. The Petricks had adored the nobility, and plucked them at the same time. That excellent man Izaak Walton's feelings about fish were much akin to those of old Timothy Petrick, and of his descendants in a lesser degree, concerning the landed aristocracy. To torture and to love simultaneously is a proceeding strange to reason, but possible to practise, as these instances show.

Hence, when Timothy's brother Edward said slightingly one day that Timothy's son was well enough, but that he had nothing but shops ana offices in his backward perspective, while his own children, should he have any, would be far different, in possessing such a mother as the Honorable Harriet, Timothy felt a bound of triumph within him at the power he possessed of contradicting that statement if he chose.

So much was he interested in his boy in this new aspect that he now began to read up chronicles of the illustrious house ennobled as the Dukes of Southwesterland, from their very beginning in the glories of the Restoration of the blessed Charles till the year of his own time. He mentally noted their gifts from royalty, grants of lands, purchases, intermarriages, plantings, and buildings; more particularly their political and military achievements, which had been great, and their performances in arts and letters, which had been by no means contemptible. He studied prints of the portraits of that family, and then, like a chemist watching a crystallization, began to examine young Rupert's face for the unfolding of those historic curves and shades that the painters Vandyke and Lely had perpetuated on canvas.

When the boy reached the most fascinating age of childhood, and his shouts of laughter rang through Stapleford House from end to end, the remorse that oppressed Timothy Petrick knew no bounds. Of all people in the world this Rupert was the one on whom he could have wished the estates to devolve; yet Rupert, by Timothy's own desperate strategy at the time of his birth, had been ousted from all inheritance of them; and, since he did not mean to remarry, the manors would pass to his brother and his brother's children, who would be nothing to him, whose boasted pedigree on one side would be nothing to his Rupert's.

Had he only left the first will of his grandfather alone!

His mind ran on the wills continually, both of which were in existence, and the first, the canceled one, in his own possession. Night after night, when the servants were all abed, and the click of safety-locks sounded as loud as a crash, he looked at that first will, and wished it had been the second and not the first.

The crisis came at last. One night, after having enjoyed the boy's company for hours, he could no longer bear that his beloved Rupert should be dispossessed, and he committed the felonious deed of altering the date of the earlier will to a fortnight later, which made its execution appear subsequent to the date of the second will already proved. He then boldly propounded the first will as the second.

His brother Edward submitted to what appeared to be not only incontestible fact, but a far more likely disposition of old Timothy's property; for, like many others, he had been much surprised at the limitations defined in the other will, having no clew to their cause. He joined his brother Timothy in setting aside the hitherto accepted document, and matters went on in their usual course, there being no dispositions in the substituted will differing from those in the other, except such as related to a future which had not yet arrived.

The years moved on. Rupert had not yet revealed the anxiously expected historic lineaments which should foreshadow the political abilities of the ducal family aforesaid, when it happened on a certain day that Timothy Petrick made the acquaintance of a well-known physician of Budmouth, who had been the medical adviser and friend of the late Mrs. Petrick's family for many years, though after Annetta's marriage, and consequent removal to Stapleford, he had seen no more of her, the neighboring practitioner who attended the Petricks having then become her doctor as a matter of course. Timothy was impressed by the insight and knowledge disclosed in the conversation of the Budmouth physician, and the acquaintance ripening to intimacy, the physician alluded to a form of hallucination to which Annetta's mother and grandmother had been subject—that of believing in certain dreams as realities. He delicately inquired if Timothy had ever noticed anything of the sort in his wife during her lifetime; he, the physician, had fancied that he discerned germs of the same peculiarity in Annetta when he attended her in her girlhood. One explanation begat another, till the dumbfounded Timothy Petrick was persuaded in his own mind that Annetta's confession to him had been based on a delusion.

"You look down in the mouth!" said the doctor, pausing.

"A bit unmanned. 'Tis unexpected-like," sighed Timothy.

But he could hardly believe it possible; and, thinking it best to be frank with the doctor, told him the whole story which, till now, he had never related to living man, save his dying grandfather. To his surprise, the physician informed him that such a form of delusion was precisely what he would have expected from Annetta's antecedents at such a physical crisis in her life.

Petrick prosecuted his inquiries elsewhere; and the upshot of his labors was, briefly, that a comparison of dates and places showed irrefutably that his poor wife's assertion could not possibly have foundation in fact. The young Marquis of her tender passion—a highly moral and bright-minded nobleman—had gone abroad the year before Annetta's marriage, and had not returned until after her death. The young girl's love for him had been a delicate ideal dream—no more.

Timothy went home, and the boy ran out to meet him; whereupon a strangely dismal feeling of discontent took possession of his soul. After all, then, there was nothing but plebeian blood in the veins of the heir to his name and estates; he was not to be succeeded by a noble-natured line. To be sure, Rupert was his son; but that glory and halo he believed him to have inherited from the ages, outshining that of his brother's children, had departed from Rupert's brow forever; he could no longer read history in the boy's face and centuries of domination in his eyes.

His manner towards his son grew colder and colder from that day forward; and it was with bitterness of heart that he discerned the characteristic features of the Petricks unfolding themselves by degrees. Instead of the elegant knife-edged nose, so typical of the Dukes of Southwesterland, there began to appear on his face the broad nostril and hollow bridge of his grandfather Timothy. No illustrious line of politicians was promised a continuator in that graying blue eye, for it was acquiring the expression of the orb of a particularly objectionable cousin of his own; and, instead of the mouth-curves which had thrilled Parliamentary audiences in speeches now bound in calf in every well-ordered library, there was the bull-lip of that very uncle of his who had had the misfortune with the signature of a gentleman's will, and had been transported for life in consequence.

To think how he himself, too, had sinned in this same matter of a will for this mere fleshly reproduction of a wretched old uncle whose very name he wished to forget! The boy's Christian name, even, was an imposture and an irony, for it implied hereditary force and brilliancy to which he plainly would never attain. The consolation of real sonship was always left him certainly; but he could not help groaning to himself, "Why cannot a son be one's own and somebody else's likewise?"

The Marquis was shortly afterwards in the neighborhood of Stapleford, and Timothy Petrick met him, and eyed his noble countenance admiringly. The next day, when Petrick was in his study, somebody knocked at the door.

"Who's there?"

"Rupert."

"I'll Rupert thee, you young impostor! Say, only a poor commonplace Petrick!" his father grunted. "Why didn't you have a voice like the Marquis I saw yesterday!" he continued, as the lad came in. "Why haven't you his looks, and a way of commanding as if you'd done it for centuries—hey?"

"Why? How can you expect it, father, when I'm not related to him?"
"Ugh! Then you ought to be!" growled his father.

ROBERT LOUIS STEVENSON

(1850–1894)

Stevenson was born at Edinburgh in 1850. He studied first for the law, and then turned to writing. His earliest books were essays and travel sketches. In the early eighties he tried his hand at short stories, and throughout his career he turned often to the short story medium for the expression of a mood or the recounting of a picturesque episode. He travelled a great deal, both in Europe and in the United States, and, ever in search of a climate that would suit his frail health, he went in 1889 to Samoa, where he lived with his family until his death in 1894. Stevenson is a romantic of the line of Scott and Dumas, but differing from his masters in that he was primarily a literary writer, whose first care was the perfection of a beautiful style.

Thrawn Janet first appeared in a magazine in 1882, and was included in the volume *The Merry Men*, published in 1886 by Chatto and Windus, by whose permission, and that of Mr. Lloyd Osbourne, it is here reprinted.

THRAWN JANET

THE Reverend Murdoch Soulis was long minister of the moorland parish of Balweary, in the vale of Dule. A severe, bleak-faced old man, dreadful to his hearers, he dwelt in the last years of his life, without relative or servant or any human company, in the small and lonely manse under the Hanging Shaw. In spite of the iron composure of his features, his eye was wild, scared, and uncertain; and when he dwelt, in private admonitions, on the future of the impenitent, it seemed as if his eye pierced through the storms of time to the terrors of eternity. Many young persons, coming to prepare themselves against the season of the Holy Communion, were dreadfully affected by his talk. He had a sermon on 1st Peter, v. and 8th, "The devil as a roaring lion," on the Sunday after every seventeenth of August, and he was accustomed to surpass himself upon that text both by the appalling nature of the matter and the terror of his bearing in the pulpit. The children were frightened into fits, and the old looked more than usually oracular, and were, all that day, full of those hints that Hamlet deprecated. The manse itself, where it stood by the water of Dule among some thick trees, with the

Shaw overhanging it on the one side, and on the other many cold, moorish hilltops rising toward the sky, had begun, at a very early period of Mr. Soulis's ministry, to be avoided in the dusk hours by all who valued themselves upon their prudence; and guidmen sitting at the clachan alehouse shook their heads together at the thought of passing late by that uncanny neighborhood. There was one spot, to be more particular, which was regarded with especial awe. The manse stood between the high road and the water of Dule, with a gable to each; its back was toward the kirktown of Balweary, nearly half a mile away; in front of it, a bare garden, hedged with thorn, occupied the land between the river and the road. The house was two stories high, with two large rooms on each. It opened not directly on the garden, but on a causewayed path, or passage, giving on the road on the one hand, and closed on the other by the tall willows and elders that bordered on the stream. And it was this strip of causeway that enjoyed among the young parishioners of Balweary so infamous a reputation. The minister walked there often after dark, sometimes groaning aloud in the instancy of his unspoken prayers; and when he was from home, and the manse door was locked, the more daring schoolboys ventured, with beating hearts, to "follow my leader" across that legendary spot.

This atmosphere of terror, surrounding, as it did, a man of God of spotless character and orthodoxy, was a common cause of wonder and subject of inquiry among the few strangers who were led by chance or business into that unknown, outlying country. But many even of the people of the parish were ignorant of the strange events which had marked the first year of Mr. Soulis's ministrations; and among those who were better informed, some were naturally reticent, and others shy of that particular topic. Now and again, only, one of the older folk would warm into courage over his third tumbler, and recount the cause of the minister's strange looks and solitary life.

Fifty years syne, when Mr. Soulis cam' first into Ba'weary, he was still a young man—a callant, the folk said—fu' o' book learnin' and grand at the exposition, but, as was natural in sae young a man, wi' nae leevin' experience in religion. The younger sort were greatly taken wi' his gifts and his gab; but auld, concerned, serious men and women were moved even to prayer for the young man, whom they took to be a self-deceiver, and the parish that was like to be sae ill-supplied. It was before the days o' the moderates—weary fa' them; but ill things are like guid —they baith come bit by bit, a pickle at a time; and there were folk even then that said the Lord had left the college professors to their ain devices, an' the lads that went to study wi' them wad hae done mair and better sittin' in a peat-bog, like their forebears of the persecution, wi' a Bible under their oxter and a speerit o' prayer in their heart. There was nae doubt, onyway, but that Mr. Soulis had been ower lang at the college. He was careful and troubled for mony things besides the ae thing needful. He had a feck o' books wi' him—mair than had ever been seen before in a' that presbytery; and a sair wark the carrier had wi' them, for they were a' like to have smoored in the Deil's Hag between this and Kilmackerlie. They were books o' divinity, to be sure, or so they ca'd them; but the serious were o' opinion there was little service for sae mony, when the hail o' God's Word would gang in the neuk of a plaid. Then he wad sit half the day and half the nicht forbye, which was scant decent—writin', nae less; and first, they were feared he wad read his sermons; and syne it proved he was writin' a book himsel', which was surely no fittin' for ane of his years an' sma' experience.

Onyway it behooved him to get an auld, decent wife to keep the manse for him an' see to his bit denners; and he was recommended to an auld limmer—Janet M'Clour, they ca'd her—and sae far left to himsel' as to be ower persuaded. There was mony advised him to the contrar, for Janet was mair than suspeckit by the best folk in Ba'weary. Lang or that, she had had a wean to a dragoon; she hadnae come forrit for maybe thretty year; and bairns had seen her mumblin' to hersel' up on Key's Loan in the gloamin', whilk was an unco time an' place for a God-fearin' woman. Howsoever, it was the laird himsel' that had first tauld the minister o' Janet; and in thae days he wad have gane a far gate to pleesure the laird. When folk tauld him that Janet was sib to the deil, it was a' superstition by his way of it; an' when they cast up the Bible to him an' the witch of Endor, he wad threep it doun their thrapples that thir days were a' gane by, and the deil was mercifully restrained.

Weel, when it got about the clachan that Janet M'Clour was to be servant at the manse, the folk were fair mad wi' her an' him thegether; and some o' the guidwives had nae better to dae than get round her door cheeks and chairge her wi' a' that was ken't again her, frae the sodger's bairn to John Tamson's twa kye. She was nae great speaker; folk usually let her gang her ain gate, an' she let them gang theirs, wi' neither Fair-guid-een nor Fair-guid-day; but when she buckled to she had a tongue to deave the miller. Up she got, an' there wasnae an auld story in Ba'weary but she gart somebody lowp for it that day; they couldnae say ae thing but she could say twa to it; till, at the hinder end, the guidwives up and claught haud of her, and clawed the coats aff her back, and pu'd her doun the clachan to the water o' Dule, to see if she were a witch or no, soum or droun. The carline skirled till ye could hear her at the Hangin' Shaw, and she focht like ten; there was mony a guidwife bure the mark of her neist day, an' mony a lang day after; and just in the hettest o' the collieshangie, wha suld come up (for his sins) but the new minister.

"Women," said he (and he had a grand voice), "I charge you in the Lord's name to let her go."

Janet ran to him—she was fair wud wi' terror—an' clang to him an' prayed him, for Christ's sake, save her frae the cummers; an' they, for their pairt, tauld him a' that was ken't, and maybe mair.

"Woman," says he to Janet, "is this true?"

"As the Lord sees me," says she, "as the Lord made me, no a word o't. Forbye the bairn," says she, "I've been a decent woman a' my days."

"Will you," says Mr. Soulis, "in the name of God, and before me, His unworthy minister, renounce the devil and his works?"

Weel, it wad appear that when he askit that, she gave a girn that fairly frichtit them that saw her, an' they could hear her teeth play dirl thegether in her chafts; but there was naething for it but the ae way or the ither; an' Janet lifted up her hand and renounced the deil before them a'.

"And now," said Mr. Soulis to the guidwives, "home with ye, one and all, and pray to God for His forgiveness."

And he gied Janet his arm, though she had little on her but a sark, and took her up the clachan to her ain door like a leddy of the land; an' her skreighin' and laughin' as was a scandal to be heard.

There were mony grave folk lang ower their prayers that nicht; but when the morn cam' there was sic a fear fell upon a' Ba'weary that the bairns hid theirsels, and even the men-folk stood and keekit frae their doors. For there was Janet comin' doun the clachan—her or her likeness, nane could tell—wi' her neck thrawn, and her heid on ae side, like a body that has been hangit, and a girn on her face like an unstreakit corp. By an' by they got used wi' it, and even speered at her to ken what was wrang; but frae that day forth she couldnae speak like a Christian woman, but slavered and played click wi' her teeth like a pair o' shears; and frae that day forth the name o' God cam' never on her lips. Whiles she wad try to say it, but it michtnae be. Them that kenned best said least; but they never gied that Thing the name o' Janet M'Clour; for the auld Janet, by their way o't, was in muckle hell that day. But the minister was neither to haud nor to bind; he preached about naething but the folks' cruelty that had gi'en her a stroke of the palsy; he skelpt the bairns that meddled her; and he had her up to the manse that same nicht and dwalled there a' his lane wi' her under the Hangin' Shaw.

Weel, time gaed by: and the idler sort commenced to think mair lichtly o' that black business. The minister was weel thocht o'; he was aye late at the writing, folk wad see his can'le doun by the Dule water after twal' at e'en; and he seemed pleased wi' himsel' and upsitten as at first, though a' body could see that he was dwining. As for Janet she cam' an' she gaed; if she didnae speak muckle afore, it was reason she should speak less then; she meddled naebody; but she was an eldritch thing to see, an' nane wad hae mistrysted wi' her for Ba'weary glebe. About the end o' July there cam' a spell o' weather, the like o't never was in that countryside; it was lown an' het an' heartless; the herds couldnae win up the Black Hill, the bairns were ower weariet to play; an' yet it was gousty too, wi' claps o' het wund that rumm'led in the glens, and bits o' shouers that slockened naething. We aye thocht it but to thun'er on the morn; but the morn cam', and the morn's morning, and it was aye the same uncanny weather, sair on folks and bestial. Of a' that were the waur, nane suffered like Mr. Soulis; he could neither sleep nor eat, he tauld his elders; an' when he wasnae writin' at his weary book, he wad be stravaguin' ower a' the countryside like a man possessed, when a' body else was blythe to keep caller ben the house.

Abune Hangin' Shaw, in the bield o' the Black Hill, there's a bit inclosed grund wi' an iron yett; and it seems in the auld days, that was the kirkyaird o' Ba'weary, and consecrated by the Papists before the blessed licht shone upon the kingdom. It was a great howff o' Mr. Soulis's, onyway; there he would sit an' consider his sermons; and indeed it's a bieldy bit. Weel, as he cam' ower the wast end o' the Black Hill, ae day, he saw first twa, an' syne fower, an' syne seeven corbie craws fleein' round an' round abune the auld kirkyaird. They flew laigh and heavy, an' squawked to ither as they gaed; and it was clear to Mr. Soulis that something had put them frae their ordinar. He wasnae easy fleyed, an' gaed straucht up to the wa's; an' what suld he find there but a man, or the appearance of a man, sittin' in the inside upon a grave. He was of a great stature, an' black as hell, and his een were singular to see. Mr. Soulis had heard tell o' black men, mony's the time; but there was something unco about this black man that daunted him. Het as he was, he took a kind o' cauld grue in the marrow o' his banes; but up he spak for a' that; an' says he: "My friend, are you a stranger in this place?" The black man answered never a word; he got upon his feet, an' begude to hirstle to the wa' on the far side; but he aye lookit at the minister; an' the minister stood an' lookit back, till a' in a meenute the black man was over the wa' an' rinnin' for the bield o' the trees. Mr. Soulis, he hardly kenned why, ran after him; but he was sair forjaskit wi' his walk an' the het, unhalesome weather, and rin as he likit, he got nae mair than a glisk o' the black man amang the birks, till he won doun to the foot o' the hillside, an' there he saw him ance mair, gaun, hap, step, an' lowp, ower Dule water to the manse.

Mr. Soulis wasnae weel pleased that this fearsome gangrel suld mak' sae free wi' Ba'weary manse; an' he ran the harder, an', wet shoon, ower the burn, an' up the walk; but the deil a black man was there to see. He stepped out upon the road, but there was naebody there; he gaed a' ower the gairden, but na, nae black man. At the hinder end, and a bit feared as was but natural, he lifted the hasp and into the manse; and there was Janet M'Clour before his een, wi' her thrawn craig, and nane sae pleased to see him. And he aye minded sinsyne, when first he set his een upon her, he had the same cauld and deidly grue.

"Janet," says he, "have you seen a black man?"

"A black man?" quo' she. "Save us a'! Ye're no wise, minister. There's nae black man in a' Ba'weary."

But she didnae speak plain, ye maun understand; but yam-yammered; like a powney wi' the bit in its moo.

"Weel," says he, "Janet, if there was nae black man, I have spoken with the Accuser of the Brethren."

And he sat down like ane wi' a fever, an' his teeth chittered in his heid.

"Hoots," says she, "think shame to yoursel', minister"; an' gied him a drap brandy that she keept aye by her.

Syne Mr. Soulis gaed into his study amang a' his books. It's a lang, laigh, mirk chalmer, perishin' cauld in winter, an' no very dry even in the tap o' the simmer, for the manse stands near the burn. Sae doun he sat, and thocht of a' that had come an' gane since he was in Ba'weary, an' his hame, an' the days when he was a bairn an' ran daffin' on the braes; and that black man aye ran in his heid like the owercome of a sang. Aye the mair he thocht, the mair he thocht o' the black man. He tried the prayer, an' the words wouldnae come to him; an' he tried, they say, to write at his book, but he couldnae mak' nae mair o' that. There was whiles he thocht the black man was at his oxter, an' the swat stood upon him cauld as well-water; and there was other whiles, when he cam' to himself' like a christened bairn and minded naething.

The upshot was that he gaed to the window an' stood glowrin' at Dule water. The trees are unco thick, an' the water lies deep an' black under the manse; an' there was Janet washin' the cla'es wi' her coats kilted. She had her back to the minister, an' he, for his pairt, hardly kenned what he was lookin' at. Syne she turned round an' shawed her face; Mr. Soulis had the same cauld grue as twice that day afore, an' it was borne in upon him what folk said, that Janet was deid lang syne, an' this was a bogle in her clay cauld flesh. He drew back a pickle and he scanned her narrowly. She was tramp-trampin' in the cla'es, croonin' to hersel'; and eh! Gude guide us, but it was a fearsome face. Whiles she sang louder, but there was nae man born o' woman that could tell the words o' her sang; an' whiles she lookit side-lang doun, but there was naething there for her to look at. There gaed a scunner through the flesh upon his banes; and that was Heeven's advertisement. But Mr. Soulis just blamed himsel', he said, to think sae ill of a puir, auld afflicted wife that hadnae a freend forby himsel'; and he put up a bit prayer for him and her, an' drank a little caller water—for his heart rose again the meat—an' gaed up to his naked bed in the gloaming.

That was a nicht that has never been forgotten in Ba'weary, the nicht o' the seeventeenth of August, seeventeen hun'er an' twal'. It had been het afore, as I hae said, but that nicht it was hetter than ever. The sun gaed doun amang unco-lookin' clouds; it fell as mirk as the pit; no a star, no a breath o' wund; ye couldnae see your han' before your face, and even the auld folk cuist the covers frae their beds and lay pechin' for their breath. Wi' a' that he had upon his mind, it was gey and unlikely Mr. Soulis wad get muckle sleep. He lay an' he tummled; the gude, caller bed that he got into brunt his very banes; whiles he slept, and whiles he waukened; whiles he heard the time o' nicht, and whiles a tyke yowlin' up the muir, as if somebody was deid; whiles he thocht he heard bogles claverin' in his lug, an' whiles he saw spunkies in the room. He behooved, he judged, to be sick; an' sick he was—little he jaloosed the sickness.

At the hinder end, he got a clearness in his mind, sat up in his sark on the bedside, and fell thinkin' ance mair o' the black man an' Janet. He couldnae weel tell how—maybe it was the cauld to his feet—but it cam' in upon him wi' a spate that there was some connection between thir twa, an' that either or baith o' them were bogles. And just at that moment, in Janet's room, which was neist to his, there cam' a stramp o' feet as if men were wars'lin', an' then a loud bang; an' then a wund gaed reishling round the fower quarters of the house; an' then a' was aince mair as seelent as the grave.

Mr. Soulis was feared for neither man nor deevil. He got his tinder box, an' lighted a can'le, an' made three steps o't ower to Janet's door. It was on the hasp, an' he pushed it open, an' keeked bauldly in. It was a big room, as big as the minister's ain, an' plenished wi' grand, auld, solid gear, for he had naething else. There was a fower-posted bed wi' auld tapestry; and a braw cabinet of aik, that was fu' o' the minister's divinity books, an' put there to be out o' the gate; an' a wheen duds o' Janet's lying here and there about the floor. But nae Janet could Mr. Soulis see; nor ony sign of a contention. In he gaed (an' there's few that wad ha'e followed him) an' lookit a' round, an' listened. But there was naethin' to be heard, neither inside the manse nor in a' Ba'weary parish, an' naethin' to be seen but the muckle shadows turnin' round the can'le. An' then a' at aince, the minister's heart played dunt an' stood stock-still; an' a cauld wund blew amang the hairs o' his heid. Whaten a weary sicht was that for the puir man's een! For there was Janet hangin' frae a nail beside the auld aik cabinet: her heid aye lay on her shouther, her een were steeked, the tongue projekit frae her mouth, and her heels were twa feet clar abune the floor.

"God forgive us all!" thocht Mr. Soulis; "poor Janet's dead."

He cam' a step nearer to the corp; an' then his heart fair whammled in his inside. For by what cantrip it wad ill-beseem a man to judge, she was hingin' fae a single nail an' by a single wursted thread for darnin' hose.

It's an awfu' thing to be your lane at nicht wi' siccan prodigies o' darkness; but Mr. Soulis was strong in the Lord. He turned an' gaed his ways oot o' that room, and lockit the door ahint him; and step by step, doon the stairs, as heavy as leed; and set doon the can'le on the table at the stairfoot. He couldnae pray, he couldnae think, he was dreepin' wi' caul' swat, an' naething could he hear but the dunt-dunt-duntin' o' his ain heart. He micht maybe have stood there an hour, or maybe twa, he minded sae little; when a' o' a sudden he heard a laigh, uncanny steer upstairs; a foot gaed to an' fro in the cha'mer whaur the corp was hingin'; syne the door was opened, though he minded weel that he had lockit it; an' syne there was a step upon the landin', an' it seemed to him as if the corp was lookin' ower the rail and doun upon him whaur he stood.

He took up the can'le again (for he couldnae want the licht) and, as saftly as ever he could, gaed straucht out o' the manse an' to the far end o' the causeway. It was aye pitmirk; the flame o' the can'le, when he set it on the grund, brunt steedy and clear as in a room; naething moved, but the Dule water seepin' and sabbin' doon the glen, an' yon unhaly footstep that cam' ploddin' doun the stairs inside the manse. He kenned the foot ower weel, for it was Janet's; and at ilka step that cam' a wee thing nearer, the cauld got deeper in his vitals. He commended his soul to Him that made an' keepit him; "and O Lord," said he, "give me strength this night to war against the powers of evil."

By this time the foot was comin' through the passage for the door; he could hear a hand skirt alang the wa', as if the fearsome thing was feelin' for its way. The saughs tossed an' maned thegether, a lang sigh cam' ower the hills, the flame o' the can'le was blawn aboot; an' there stood the corp of Thrawn Janet, wi' her grogram goun an' her black mutch, wi' the heid aye upon the shouther, an' the girn still upon the face o't—leevin', ye wad hae said—deid, as Mr. Soulis weel kenned—upon the threshold o' the manse.

It's a strange thing that the saul of man should be that thirled into his perishable body; but the minister saw that, an' his heart didnae break.

She didnae stand there lang; she began to move again an' cam' slowly toward Mr. Soulis whaur he stood under the saughs. A' the life o' his body, a' the strength o' his speerit, were glowerin' frae his een. It seemed she was gaun to speak, but wanted words, an' made a sign wi' the left hand. There cam' a clap o' wund, like a cat's fuff; oot gaed the can'le, the saughs skrieghed like folk; an' Mr. Soulis kenned that, live or die, this was the end o't.

"Witch, beldam, devil!" he cried, "I charge you, by the power of

God, begone—if you be dead, to the grave—if you be damned, to hell."

An' at that moment the Lord's ain hand out o' the Heevens struck the Horror whaur it stood; the auld, deid, desecrated corp o' the witch-wife, sae lang keepit frae the grave and hirsled round by deils, lowed up like a brunstane spunk and fell in ashes to the grund; the thunder followed, peal on dirling peal, the rairing rain upon the back o' that; and Mr. Soulis lowped through the garden hedge, and ran, wi' skelloch upon skelloch, for the clachan.

That same mornin', John Christie saw the Black Man pass the Muckle Cairn as it was chappin' six; before eicht, he gaed by the change-house at Knockdow; an' no lang after, Sandy M'Lellan saw him gaun linkin' doun the braes frae Kilmackerlie. There's little doubt it was him that dwalled sae lang in Janet's body; but he was awa' at last; and sinsyne the deil has never fashed us in Ba'weary.

But it was a sair dispensation for the minister; lang, lang he lay ravin' in his bed; and frae that hour to this, he was the man ye ken the day.

OSCAR WILDE

(1854–1900)

WILDE was born in Dublin in 1854, the son of distinguished parents. His mother, Lady Wilde, was famous for her volumes of Irish stories. Wilde went first to Trinity College, Dublin, and later to Oxford. His first published work was a volume of poems in 1881. From that time until 1895 he wrote plays, poems, essays, a novel, and several short stories and fairy tales. Wilde's jewelled style was never employed to better purpose than in the group of tales from which *The Selfish Giant* has been selected. In 1895 he was sentenced to two years' hard labor as a result of a notorious trial. After his release he travelled in Italy and France, and died in 1900 at Paris.

The Selfish Giant is reprinted, by permission of Mr. Philip Nutt, from *The Happy Prince and Other Tales*, published by Gerald Duckworth and Co. in 1885.

THE SELFISH GIANT

EVERY afternoon, as they were coming from school, the children used to go and play in the Giant's garden.

It was a large lovely garden, with soft green grass. Here and there over the grass stood beautiful flowers like stars, and there were twelve peach-trees that in the Spring-time broke out into delicate blossoms of pink and pearl, and in the autumn bore rich fruit. The birds sat on the trees and sang so sweetly that the children used to stop their games in order to listen to them. "How happy we are here!" they cried to each other.

One day the Giant came back. He had been to visit his friend the Cornish ogre, and had stayed with him for seven years. After the seven years were over he had said all that he had to say, for his conversation was limited, and he determined to return to his own castle. When he arrived he saw the children playing in the garden.

"What are you doing there?" he cried in a very gruff voice, and the children ran away.

"My own garden is my own garden," said the Giant; "anyone can understand that, and I will allow nobody to play in it but myself." So he built a high wall all round it, and put up a notice-board.

TRESPASSERS WILL BE PROSECUTED

He was a very selfish Giant.

The poor children had now nowhere to play. They tried to play on the road, but the road was very dusty and full of hard stones, and they did not like it. They used to wander round the high wall when their lessons were over, and talk about the beautiful garden inside. "How happy we were there," they said to each other.

Then the Spring came, and all over the country there were little blossoms and little birds. Only in the garden of the Selfish Giant it was still winter. The birds did not care to sing in it, as there were no children, and the trees forgot to blossom. Once a beautiful flower put its head out from the grass, but when it saw the notice-board it was so sorry for the children that it slipped back into the ground again, and went off to sleep. The only people who were pleased were the Snow and the Frost. "Spring has forgotten this garden," they cried, "so we will live here all the year round." The Snow covered up the grass with her great white cloak, and the Frost painted all the trees silver. Then they invited the North Wind to stay with them, and he came. He was wrapped in furs, and he roared all day about the garden, and blew the chimney-pots down. "This is a delightful spot," he said; "we must ask the Hail on a visit." So the Hail came. Every day for three hours he rattled on the roof of the castle till he broke most of the slates, and then he ran round and round the garden as fast as he could go. He was dressed in gray, and his breath was like ice.

"I can not understand why the Spring is so late in coming," said the Selfish Giant, as he sat at the window and looked out at his cold white garden; "I hope there will be a change in the weather."

But the Spring never came, nor the Summer. The Autumn gave golden fruit to every garden, but to the Giant's garden she gave none. "He is too selfish," she said. So it was always Winter there, and the North Wind, and the Hail, and the Frost, and the Snow danced about through the trees.

One morning the Giant was lying awake in bed when he heard some lovely music. It sounded so sweet to his ears that he thought it must be the King's musicians passing by. It was really only a little linnet singing outside his window, but it was so long since he had heard a bird sing in his garden that it seemed to him to be the most beautiful music in the world. Then the Hail stopped dancing over his head, and the North Wind ceased roaring, and a delicious perfume came to him through the open casement. "I believe the Spring has come at last," said the Giant; and he jumped out of bed and looked out.

What did he see?

He saw a most wonderful sight. Through a little hole in the wall the children had crept in, and they were sitting in the branches of the trees. In every tree that he could see there was a little child. And the trees were so glad to have the children back again that they had covered themselves with blossoms, and were waving their arms gently above the children's heads. The birds were flying about and twittering with delight, and the flowers were looking up through the green grass and laughing. It was a lovely scene, only in one corner it was still winter. It was the farthest corner of the garden, and in it was standing a little boy. He was so small that he could not reach up to the branches of the tree, and he was wandering all round it, crying bitterly. The poor tree was still quite covered with frost and snow, and the North Wind was blowing and roaring above it. "Climb up, little boy," said the Tree, and it bent its branches down as low as it could; but the boy was too tiny.

And the Giant's heart melted as he looked out. "How selfish I have been!" he said; "now I know why the Spring would not come here. I will put that poor little boy on the top of the tree, and then I will knock down the wall, and my garden shall be the children's playground for ever and ever." He was really very sorry for what he had done.

So he crept downstairs and opened the front door quite softly, and went out into the garden. But when the children saw him they were so frightened that they all ran away, and the garden became winter again. Only the little boy did not run, for his eyes were so full of tears that he did not see the Giant coming. And the Giant stole up behind him and took him gently in his hand, and put him up into the tree. And the tree broke at once into blossoms, and the birds came and sang on it, and the little boy stretched out his two arms and flung them round the Giant's neck, and kissed him. And the other children, when they saw that the Giant was not wicked any longer, came running back, and with them came the Spring. "It is your garden now, little children," said the Giant, and he took a great axe and knocked down the wall. And when the people were going to market at twelve o'clock they found the Giant playing with the children in the most beautiful garden they had ever seen.

All day long they played, and in the evening they came to the Giant to bid him good-bye.

"But where is your little companion?" he said: "the boy I put into the tree." The Giant loved him the best because he had kissed him.

"We don't know," answered the children; "he has gone away."

"You must tell him to be sure and come here to-morrow," said the Giant. But the children said that they did not know where he lived, and had never seen him before; and the Giant felt very sad.

Every afternoon, when school was over, the children came and played with the Giant. But the little boy whom the Giant loved was never seen again. The Giant was very kind to all the children, yet he longed for his first little friend, and often spoke of him. "How I would like to see him!" he used to say.

Years went over, and the Giant grew very old and feeble. He could not play about any more, so he sat in a huge armchair, and watched the children at their games, and admired his garden. "I have many beautiful flowers," he said; "but the children are the most beautiful flowers of all."

One winter morning he looked out of his window as he was dressing. He did not hate the Winter now, for he knew that it was merely the Spring asleep, and that the flowers were resting.

Suddenly he rubbed his eyes in wonder, and looked and looked. It certainly was a marvelous sight. In the farthest corner of the garden was a tree quite covered with lovely white blossoms. Its branches were all golden, and silver fruit hung down from them, and underneath it stood the little boy he had loved.

Downstairs ran the Giant in great joy, and out into the garden. He hastened across the grass, and came near to the child. And when he came quite close his face grew red with anger, and he said, "Who hath dared to wound thee?" For on the palms of the child's hands were the prints of two nails, and the prints of two nails were on the little feet.

"Who hath dared to wound thee?" cried the Giant; "tell me, that I may take my big sword and slay him."

"Nay!" answered the child; "but these are the wounds of Love."

"Who art thou?" said the Giant, and a strange awe fell on him, and he knelt before the little child.

And the child smiled on the Giant, and said to him, "You let me play once in your garden, to-day you shall come with me to my garden, which is Paradise."

And when the children ran in that afternoon, they found the Giant lying dead under the tree, all covered with white blossoms.

GEORGE MOORE

(1852—)

George Moore was born in County Mayo, in 1852, of a well-to-do family. At an early age he wished to become a painter, and went to Paris for that purpose. Finding that he had no real gift for painting, he turned to literature. His earliest efforts were plays and imitative verses. He spent the period between 1872 and 1882 in Paris, and when he returned to London to earn his livelihood, he was a confirmed Naturalist of the school of Zola. Under Zola's influence he wrote his first successful novel, *A Mummer's Wife*. During the eighties and nineties he wrote several novels of contemporary English and Irish life, including his masterpiece, *Esther Waters*. Most of Moore's short stories are in the volume *The Untilled Field* (1903). These are beautifully written studies of Irish life.

Julia Cahill's Curse is reprinted from *The Untilled Field*, by permission of the author and the publisher, William Heinemann. Copyright, 1903.

JULIA CAHILL'S CURSE

"AND what has become of Margaret?"

"Ah, didn't her mother send her to America as soon as the baby was born? Once a woman is wake here she has to go. Hadn't Julia to go in the end, and she the only one that ever said she didn't mind the priest?"

"Julia who?" said I.

"Julia Cahill."

The name struck my fancy, and I asked the driver to tell me her story.

"Wasn't it Father Madden who had her put out of the parish, but she put her curse on it, and it's on it to this day."

"Do you believe in curses?"

"Bedad I do, sir. It's a terrible thing to put a curse on a man, and the curse that Julia put on Father Madden's parish was a bad one, the divil a worse. The sun was up at the time, and she on the hilltop raising both her hands. And the curse she put on the parish was that every year a roof must fall in and a family go to America. That was the curse, your honor, and every word of it has come true. You'll see for yourself as soon as we cross the mearing."

"And what has become of Julia's baby?"

"I never heard she had one, sir."

He flicked his horse pensively with his whip, and it seemed to me that the disbelief I had expressed in the power of the curse disinclined him for further conversation.

"But," I said, "who is Julia Cahill, and how did she get the power to put a curse upon the village?"

"Didn't she go into the mountains every night to meet the fairies, and who else could've given her the power to put a curse upon the village?"

"But she couldn't walk so far in one evening."

"Them that's in league with the fairies can walk that far and much farther in an evening, your honor. A shepherd saw her; and you'll see the ruins of the cabins for yourself as soon as we cross the mearing, and I'll show you the cabin of the blind woman that Julia lived with before she went away."

"And how long is it since she went?"

"About twenty year, and there hasn't been a girl the like of her in these parts since. I was only a gossoon at the time, but I've heard tell she was as tall as I'm myself, and as straight as a poplar. She walked with a little swing in her walk, so that all the boys used to be looking after her, and she had fine black eyes, sir, and she was nearly always laughing. Father Madden had just come to the parish; and there was courting in these parts then, for aren't we the same as other people—we'd like to go out with a girl well enough if it was the custom of the country. Father Madden put down the ball alley because he said the boys stayed there instead of going into Mass, and he put down the cross-road dances because he said dancing was the cause of many a bastard, and he wanted none in his parish. Now there was no dancer like Julia; the boys used to gather about to see her dance, and whoever walked with her under the hedges in the summer could never think about another woman. The village was cracked about her. There was fighting, so I suppose the priest was right: he had to get rid of her. But I think he mightn't have been as hard on her as he was.

"One evening he went down to the house. Julia's people were well-to-do people, they kept a grocery-store in the village; and when he came into the shop who should be there but the richest farmer in the country, Michael Moran by name, trying to get Julia for his wife. He didn't go straight to Julia, and that's what swept him. There are two counters in that shop, and Julia was at the one on the left hand as you go in. And many's the pound she had made for her parents at that counter.

Michael Moran says to the father, 'Now, what fortune are you going to give with Julia?' And the father says there was many a man who would take her without any; and that's how they spoke, and Julia listening quietly all the while at the opposite counter. For Michael didn't know what a spirited girl she was, but went on arguing till he got the father to say fifty pounds, and thinking he had got him so far he said, 'I'll never drop a flap to her unless you give the two heifers.' Julia never said a word, she just sat listening. It was then that the priest came in. And over he goes to Julia. 'And now,' says he, 'aren't you proud to hear that you'll have such a fine fortune, and it's I that'll be glad to see you married, for I can't have any more of your goings-on in my parish. You're the encouragement of the dancing and courting here, but I'm going to put an end to it.' Julia didn't answer a word, and he went over to them that were arguing about the sixty pounds. 'Now, why not make it fifty-five?' says he. So the father agreed to that, since the priest had said it, and all three of them thought the marriage was settled. 'Now what will you be taking, Father Tom?' says Cahill, 'and you, Michael?' Sorra one of them thought of asking her if she was pleased with Michael; but little did they know what was passing in her mind, and when they came over to the counter to tell her what they had settled, she said, 'Well, I've just been listening to you, and 'tis well for you to be wasting your time talking about me,' and she tossed her head, saying she would just pick the boy out of the parish that pleased her best. And what angered the priest most of all was her way of saying it—that the boy that would marry her would be marrying herself and not the money that would be paid when the book was signed or when the first baby was born. Now it was agin girls marrying according to their fancy that Father Madden had set himself. He had said in his sermon the Sunday before that young people shouldn't be allowed out by themselves at all, but that the parents should make up the marriages for them. And he went fairly wild when Julia told him the example she was going to set. He tried to keep his temper, sir, but it was getting the better of him all the while. And Julia said, 'My boy isn't in the parish now, but maybe he is on his way here, and he may be here to-morrow or the next day.' And when Julia's father heard her speak like that he knew that no one would turn her from what she was saying, and he said, 'Michael Moran, my good man, you may go your way: you will never get her.' Then he went back to hear what Julia was saying to the priest, but it was the priest that was talking. 'Do you think,' says he, 'I am going to let you go on turning the head of every boy in the parish? Do you think,' says he, 'I'm going to see you gallivanting with one and then with the other? Do you think I am going to see fighting and quarreling for your like? Do you think I am going to hear stories like I heard last week about poor Patsy Carey, who has gone out of his mind, they say, on account of your treatment? No,' says he, 'I'll have no more of that. I'll have you out of my parish, or I'll have you married.' Julia didn't answer the priest; she tossed her head, and went on making up parcels of tea and sugar, and getting the steps and taking down candles, though she didn't want them, just to show the priest that she didn't mind what he was saying. And all the while her father trembling, not knowing what would happen, for the priest had a big stick, and there was no saying that he wouldn't strike her. Cahill tried to quiet the priest, he promising him that Julia shouldn't go out any more in the evenings, and bedad, sir, she was out the same evening with a young man and the priest saw them, and the next evening she was out with another and the priest saw them, nor was she minded at the end of the month to marry any of them. Then the priest went down to the shop to speak to her a second time, and he went down again a third time, though what he said the third time no one knows, no one being there at the time. And next Sunday he spoke out, saying that a disobedient daughter would have the worst devil in hell to attend on her. I've heard tell that he called her the evil spirit that set men mad. But most of the people that were there are dead or gone to America, and no one rightly knows what he did say, only that the words came out of his mouth, and the people when they saw Julia crossed themselves, and even the boys that were most mad after Julia were afraid to speak to her. Cahill had to put her out."

"Do you mean to say that the father put his daughter out?"

"Sure, didn't the priest threaten to turn him into a rabbit if he didn't, and no one in the parish would speak to Julia, they were so afraid of Father Madden, and if it hadn't been for the blind woman that I was speaking about a while ago, sir, it is to the Poor House she'd have to go. The blind woman has a little cabin at the edge of the bog—I'll point it out to you, sir; we do be passing it by—and she was with the blind woman for nearly two years disowned by her own father. Her clothes wore out, but she was as beautiful without them as with them. The boys were told not to look back, but sure they couldn't help it.

"Ah, it was a long while before Father Madden could get shut of her. The blind woman said she wouldn't see Julia thrown out on the roadside, and she was as good as her word for well-nigh two years, till Julia went to America, so some do be saying, sir, whilst others do be saying she joined the fairies. But 'tis for sure, sir, that the day she left the parish Pat Quinn heard a knocking at his window and somebody asking if he would lend his cart to go to the railway station. Pat was a heavy sleeper and he didn't get up, and it is thought that it was Julia who wanted Pat's cart to take her to the station; it's a good ten mile; but she got there all the same!"

"You said something about a curse?"

"Yes, sir. You'll see the hill presently. And a man who was taking some sheep to the fair saw her there. The sun was just getting up and he saw her cursing the village, raising both her hands, sir, up to the sun, and since that curse was spoken every year a roof has fallen in, sometimes two or three."

I could see he believed the story, and for the moment I, too, believed in an outcast Venus becoming the evil spirit of a village that would not accept her as divine.

"Look, sir, the woman coming down the road is Bridget Coyne. And that's her house," he said, and we passed a house built of loose stone without mortar, but a little better than the mud cabins I had seen in Father MacTurnan's parish.

"And now, sir, you will see the loneliest parish in Ireland."

And I noticed that though the land was good, there seemed to be few people on it, and, what was more significant, that the untilled fields were the ruins, for they were not the cold ruins of twenty, or thirty, or forty years ago when the people were evicted and their tillage turned into pasture—the ruins I saw were the ruins of cabins that had been lately abandoned, and I said:

"It wasn't the landlord who evicted these people."

"Ah, it's the landlord who would be glad to have them back, but there's no getting them back. Every one here will have to go, and 'tis said that the priest will say Mass in an empty chapel, sorra a one will be there but Bridget, and she'll be the last he'll give communion to. It's said, your honor, that Julia has been seen in America, and I'm going there this autumn. You may be sure I'll keep a lookout for her."

"But all this is twenty years ago. You won't know her. A woman changes a good deal in twenty years."

"There will be no change in her, your honor. Sure, hasn't she been with the fairies?"

ARTHUR MORRISON

(1863—)

ARTHUR MORRISON is one of the few writers of his period—for he belongs to the "School" of the Nineties—whose work is still widely popular. He is known almost exclusively for his small volume of stories called *Tales of Mean Streets*, from which *That Brute Simmons* has been selected. The entire collection, says Mencken, reveals "the amazing life of the London East End, the sewer of England and of Christendom."

Reprinted from *Tales of Mean Streets*, Methuen, 1894, by permission of the author and publishers.

THAT BRUTE SIMMONS

SIMMONS'S infamous behavior toward his wife is still matter for profound wonderment among the neighbors. The other women had all along regarded him as a model husband, and certainly Mrs. Simmons was a most conscientious wife. She toiled and slaved for that man, as any woman in the whole street would have maintained, far more than any husband had a right to expect. And now this was what she got for it. Perhaps he had suddenly gone mad.

Before she married Simmons, Mrs. Simmons had been the widowed Mrs. Ford. Ford had got a berth as donkey-man on a tramp steamer, and that steamer had gone down with all hands off the cape—a judgment, the widow woman feared, for long years of contumacy which had culminated in the wickedness of taking to the sea, and taking to it as a donkey-man, an immeasurable fall for a capable engine-fitter. Twelve years as Mrs. Ford had left her still childless, and childless she remained as Mrs. Simmons.

As for Simmons, he, it was held, was fortunate in that capable wife. He was a moderately good carpenter and joiner, but no man of the world, and he wanted to be one. Nobody could tell what might not have happened to Tommy Simmons if there had been no Mrs. Simmons to take care of him. He was a meek and quiet man, with a boyish face and sparse, limp whiskers. He had no vices (even his pipe departed him after his marriage), and Mrs. Simmons had ingrafted on him divers exotic virtues. He went solemnly to chapel every Sunday, under a tall hat, and put a penny—one returned to him for the purpose out of his week's wages—in the plate. Then, Mrs. Simmons overseeing, he took off his best clothes and brushed them with solicitude and pains. On Saturday afternoons he cleaned the knives, the forks, the boots, the kettles and the windows, patiently and conscientiously. On Tuesday evenings he took the clothes to the mangling. And on Saturday nights he attended Mrs. Simmons in her marketing, to carry the parcels.

Mrs. Simmons's own virtues were native and numerous. She was a wonderful manager. Every penny of Tommy's thirty-six or thirty-eight shillings a week was bestowed to the greatest advantage, and Tommy never ventured to guess how much of it she saved. Her cleanliness in housewifery was distracting to behold. She met Simmons at the front door whenever he came home, and then and there he changed his boots for slippers, balancing himself painfully on alternate feet on the cold flags. This was because she scrubbed the passage and doorstep turn about with the wife of the downstairs family, and because the stair-carpet was her own. She vigilantly supervised her husband all through the process of "cleaning himself" after work, so as to come between her walls and the possibility of random splashes; and if, in spite of her diligence, a spot remained to tell the tale, she was at pains to impress the fact on Simmons's memory, and to set forth at length all the circumstances of his ungrateful selfishness. In the beginning she had always escorted him to the ready-made clothes shop, and had selected and paid for his clothes —for the reason that men are such perfect fools, and shopkeepers do as they like with them. But she presently improved on that. She found a man selling cheap remnants at a street corner, and straightway she conceived the idea of making Simmons's clothes herself. Decision was one of her virtues, and a suit of uproarious check tweeds was begun that afternoon from the pattern furnished by an old one. More: it was finished by Sunday, when Simmons, overcome by astonishment at the feat, was indued in it, and pushed off to chapel ere he could recover his senses. The things were not altogether comfortable, he found; the trousers clung tight against his shins, but hung loose behind his heels; and when he sat, it was on a wilderness of hard folds and seams. Also his waistcoat collar tickled his nape, but his coat collar went straining across from shoulder to shoulder, while the main garment bagged generously below his waist. Use made a habit of his discomfort, but it never reconciled him to the chaff of his shopmates; for as Mrs. Simmons elaborated successive suits, each one modeled on the last, the primal accidents of her design developed into principles, and grew even bolder and more hideously pronounced. It was vain for Simmons to hint—as hint he did —that he shouldn't like her to overwork herself, tailoring being bad for the eyes, and there was a new tailor's in the Mile End Road, very cheap, where . . . "Ho yus," she retorted, "you're very consid'rit I dessay sittin' there actin' a livin' lie before your own wife, Thomas Simmons, as though I couldn't see through you like a book; a lot you care about overworkin' me as long as *your* turn's served throwin' away money like dirt in the street on a lot o' swindling tailors an' me workin' an' slavin' 'ere to save a 'apenny an' this is my return for it; any one 'ud think you could pick up money in the 'orseroad an' I b'lieve I'd be thought better of if I laid in bed all day like some would, that I do." So that Thomas Simmons avoided the subject, nor even murmured when she resolved to cut his hair.

So his placid fortune endured for years. Then there came a golden summer evening when Mrs. Simmons betook herself with a basket to do some small shopping, and Simmons was left at home. He washed and put away the tea-things, and then he fell to meditating on a new pair of trousers, finished that day and hanging behind the parlor door. There they hung, in all their decent innocence of shape in the seat, and they were shorter of leg, longer of waist, and wilder of pattern than he had ever worn before. And as he looked on them the small devil of original sin awoke and clamored in his breast. He was ashamed of it, of course, for well he knew the gratitude he owed his wife for those same trousers, among other blessings. Still, there the small devil was, and the small devil was fertile in base suggestions, and could not be kept from hinting at the new crop of workshop gibes that would spring at Tommy's first public appearance in such things.

"Pitch 'em in the dust-bin!" said the small devil, at last; "it's all they're fit for."

Simmons turned away in sheer horror of his wicked self, and for a moment thought of washing the tea-things over again by way of discipline. Then he made for the back room, but saw from the landing that the front door was standing open, probably by the fault of the child downstairs. Now, a front door standing open was a thing that Mrs. Simmons would *not* abide; it looked low. So Simmons went down, that she might not be wroth with him for the thing when she came back; and, as he shut the door, he looked forth into the street.

A man was loitering on the pavement, and prying curiously about the door. His face was tanned, his hands were deep in the pockets of his unbraced blue trousers, and well back on his head he wore the high-crowned peaked cap topped with a knob of wool, which is affected by Jack ashore about the docks. He lurched a step nearer to the door, and: "Mrs. Ford ain't in, is she?" he said.

Simmons stared at him for a matter of five seconds, and then said: "Eh?"

"Mrs. Ford as was, then—Simmons now, ain't it?"

He said this with a furtive leer that Simmons neither liked nor understood.

"No," said Simmons, "she ain't in now."

"You ain't her 'usband, are ye?"

"Yus."

The man took his pipe from his mouth, and grinned silently and long. "Blimy," he said, at length, "you look the sort o' bloke she'd like." And with that he grinned again. Then, seeing that Simmons made ready to shut the door, he put a foot on the sill and a hand against the panel. "Don't be in a 'urry, matey," he said; "I come 'ere t'ave a little talk with you, man to man, d'ye see?" And he frowned fiercely.

Tommy Simmons felt uncomfortable, but the door would not shut, so he parleyed. "Wotjer want?" he asked. "I dunno you."

"Then if you'll excuse the liberty, I'll interdooce meself, in a manner of speaking." He touched his cap with a bob of mock humility. "I'm Bob Ford," he said, "come back out o' kingdom-come, so to say. Me as went down with the 'Mooltan'—safe dead five years gone. I come to see my wife."

During this speech Thomas Simmons's jaw was dropping lower and lower. At the end of it he poked his fingers up through his hair, looked down at the mat, then up at the fanlight, then out into the street, then hard at his visitor. But he found nothing to say.

"Come to see my wife," the man repeated. "So now we can talk it over—as man to man."

Simmons slowly shut his mouth, and led the way upstairs mechanically, his fingers still in his hair. A sense of the state of affairs sunk gradually into his brain, and the small devil woke again. Suppose this man *was* Ford? Suppose he did claim his wife? Would it be a knockdown blow? Would it hit him out?—or not? He thought of the trousers, the tea-things, the mangling, the knives, the kettles and the windows; and he thought of them in the way of a backslider.

On the landing Ford clutched at his arm, and asked, in a hoarse whisper: "'Ow long 'fore she's back?"

"'Bout a hour, I expect," Simmons replied, having first of all repeated the question in his own mind. And then he opened the parlor door.

"Ah," said Ford, looking about him, "you've bin pretty comf'table. Them chairs an' things"—jerking his pipe toward them—"was hers—mine, that is to say, speaking straight, and man to man." He sat down, puffing meditatively at his pipe, and presently: "Well," he continued, "'ere I am agin, ol' Bob Ford dead an' done for—gawn down in the 'Mooltan.' On'y I *ain't* done for, see?"—and he pointed the stem of his pipe at Simmons's waistcoat—"I ain't done for, 'cause why? Cons'kence o' bein' picked up by a ol' German sailin'-'utch an' took to 'Frisco 'fore the mast. I've 'ad a few years o' knockin' about since then, an' now"—looking hard at Simmons—"I've come back to see my wife."

"She—she don't like smoke in 'ere," said Simmons, as it were, at random.

"No, I bet she don't," Ford answered, taking his pipe from his mouth, and holding it low in his hand. "I know 'Anner. 'Ow d'you find 'er? Do she make ye clean the winders?"

"Well," Simmons admitted, uneasily, "I—I do 'elp 'er sometimes, o' course."

"Ah! An' the knives too, I bet, an' the bloomin' kittles. I know. Wy"—he rose and bent to look behind Simmons's head—"s'elp me, I b'lieve she cuts yer 'air! Well, I'm damned! Jes' wot she would do, too."

He inspected the blushing Simmons from divers points of vantage. Then he lifted a leg of the trousers hanging behind the door. "I'd bet a trifle," he said, "she made these 'ere trucks. Nobody else 'ud do 'em like that. Damme—they're wuss'n wot you're got on."

The small devil began to have the argument all its own way. If this man took his wife back, perhaps he'd have to wear those trousers.

"Ah!" Ford pursued, "she ain't got no milder. An', my davy, wot a jore!"

Simmons began to feel that this was no longer his business. Plainly, 'Anner was this other man's wife, and he was bound in honor to acknowledge the fact. The small devil put it to him as a matter of duty.

"Well," said Ford, suddenly, "time's short, an' this ain't business. I won't be 'ard on you, matey. I ought prop'ly to stand on my rights, but seein' as you're a well-meanin' young man, so to speak, an' all settled an' a-livin 'ere quiet an' matrimonual, I'll"—this with a burst of generosity—"damme, yus, I'll compound the felony, an' take me 'ook. Come, I'll name a figure, as man to man, fust an' last, no less an' no more. Five pound does it."

Simmons hadn't five pounds—he hadn't even five pence—and he said so. "An' I wouldn't think for to come between a man an' 'is wife," he added, "not on no account. It may be rough on me, but it's a dooty. *I'll* 'ook it."

"No," said Ford, hastily, clutching Simmons by the arm, "don't do that. I'll make it a bit cheaper. Say three quid—come, that's reasonable, ain't it? Three quid ain't much compensation for me goin' away forever—where the stormy winds do blow, so to say—an' never as much as seein' me own wife agin for better nor wuss. Between man an' man now—three quid; an' I'll shunt. That's fair, ain't it?"

"Of course it's fair," Simmons replied, effusively. "It's more'n fair; it's noble—downright noble, *I* call it. But I ain't goin' to take a mean advantage o' your good-'artedness, Mr. Ford. She's your wife, an' I oughtn't to 'a' come between you. I apologize. You stop an' 'ave yer proper rights. It's me as ought to shunt, an' I will." And he made a step toward the door.

" 'Old on," quoth Ford, and got between Simmons and the door; "don't do things rash. Look wot a loss it'll be to you with no 'ome to go to, an' nobody to look after ye, an' all that. It'll be dreadful. Say a couple—there, we won't quarrel, jest a single quid, between man an' man, an' I'll stand a pot o' the money. You can easy raise a quid—the clock 'ud pretty nigh do it. A quid does it; an' I'll—"

There was a loud double-knock at the front door. In the East End a double-knock is always for the upstairs lodgers.

"Oo's that?" asked Bob Ford, apprehensively.

"I'll see," said Thomas Simmons in reply, and he made a rush for the staircase.

Bob Ford heard him open the front door. Then he went to the window, and just below him, he saw the crown of a bonnet. It vanished, and borne to him from within the door there fell upon his ear the sound of a well-remembered female voice.

"Where ye goin' now with no 'at?" asked the voice, sharply.

"Awright, 'Anner—there's—there's somebody upstairs to see you," Simmons answered. And, as Bob Ford could see, a man went scuttling down the street in the gathering dusk. And behold, it was Thomas Simmons.

Ford reached the landing in three strides. His wife was still at the front door, staring after Simmons. He flung into the back room, threw open the window, dropped from the wash-house roof into the back-yard, scrambled desperately over the fence, and disappeared into the gloom. He was seen by no living soul. And that is why Simmons's base desertion—under his wife's very eyes, too—is still an astonishment to the neighbors.

Germany

INTRODUCTION

THE contribution of German writers to the technical development and the sum total of the world's stories has been especially rich. Owing doubtless to the political vicissitudes of the German-speaking peoples, and to the widely varying elements that combined through the ages to produce it, the short-story literature of the Germans offers a greater diversity in subject-matter and treatment than that of France or Italy or Spain. There is a substratum of pre-Christian folklore and tradition that has persisted through the centuries, lending to the stories of even the most recent writers a certain air of romance and mystery that is often lacking among the best productions of other lands.

The earliest specimen of German vernacular literature, the *Lay of Hildebrand*, a precious document dating from the early Ninth Century, happens to be a well-told short story. The author was an Austrian, but it must be remembered that German literature as a whole embraces certain adjacent countries which, like parts of Switzerland and Austria, are essentially German, racially and intellectually.

As early as the second decade of the Eleventh Century there existed a fairly well-defined fiction form. *Ruodlieb*, though it is too long for inclusion in this volume, is a genuine long-short story. It was written about the year 1030. Not long afterward came the romances and Lays of chivalry, like the *Gudrun*, and somewhat later *The Lay of the Nibelungs*. During the Twelfth and Thirteenth Centuries the courtly romances flourished; it was the age of the great Minnesingers, Wolfram von Eschenbach, Hartmann von Aue, and Gottfried von Strassburg, all of whom drew largely on France for their plots and characters. It is possible to select from the romances of these poets an infinity of episodes, like *The Coming of Gandin* (which appears in the following pages), which are true short stories.

With the decline of Chivalry and the growth of the merchant classes, the courtly tales languished. They gave way to such realistic work as Wernher the Gardner's *Farmer Helmbrecht* (1250), and *Reynard the Fox* which, though in fable-form, was a realistic work. This was followed by several imitations. Passing rapidly now to the period of the

Reformation, we find a growing literature of and by the people—often formless and rambling like Brant's *Ship of Fools*, which dates from the early Sixteenth Century. Far better artistically is Wickram's *Galmy* (1539), usually regarded as the first German novel.

The same century was especially rich in the collections of episodes like the celebrated *Till Eulenspiegel*, Pauli's *Jest and Earnest*, and the Faust chapbooks. These popular works were accumulations of folklore, history, gossip, and the odds and ends of other literatures. The Italian Renaissance had also affected Germany, and influences from France continued as before. Boccaccio and Rabelais, together with their followers and imitators, were well-known by the end of the Sixteenth Century.

Of a more original character is the work of Moscherosch, Grimmelhausen and his follower, Christian Weise. Grimmelhausen was the creator of the famous character of Simplicissimus. The *Adventures* of that remarkable person are still read with interest.

Under the influence of the pseudo-classical Gottsched, about the middle of the Eighteenth Century, a new era dawned. Its most important contribution was the short verse fable and tale, which was perfected by Gellert, though others, like Lessing, tried their hand at it. By the end of the century, the *Storm and Stress* and later the Romantic movements, helped on by Goethe and Schiller, the Schlegels and several others, prepared the way for the first of the moderns, Hauff and Hoffmann and Zschokke.

The Nineteenth Century produced a large number of romantic writers who, in common with the French, evolved a highly finished type of short story. Supreme among these writers were Keller and Heyse, though the novelists Freytag, Auerbach, Spielhagen, Baumbach, and Reuter (to mention only a few) all wrote short tales. Toward the end of the century the short story became with certain writers, like Ludwig Thoma and others, the vehicle for the interpretation of peasant life, while with writers like Schnitzler and Bahr, Hartleben and Wedekind, it was largely an expression of the Time Spirit of all Europe.

The more recent writers, like Heinrich and Thomas Mann, Zweig, Wassermann, Sternheim and Kellermann are developing new varieties of form, and reveal the influence of the Russians to a marked extent.

THE LAY OF HILDEBRAND

(Anonymous: Early 9th Century, A.D.)

The fragmentary *Lay of Hildebrand* is the very earliest surviving specimen of literature in the German language. Beyond the fact that he was an Austrian, nothing is known of the writer. The fragment consists of sixty-nine lines of verse, and relates the greater part of an incident which belongs to the much longer Dietrich saga. Fortunately, what we possess of *The Lay of Hildebrand* is really, so far as it goes, a short story in itself. It bears a striking resemblance to the old story of Sohrab and Rustem.

The present version is reprinted from W. Taylor's *Historic Survey of German Poetry*, etc., London, 1830. There is no title in the original.

THE LAY OF HILDEBRAND

I HAVE heard say that Hildebrand and Amelung agreed to go on a warlike expedition. These kinsmen made ready their horses, prepared their war-shirts and girded on their chain-hilted swords.

As they rode to the meeting of heroes Hildebrand, Hildebrand's son (he was one of the wise and questioned in few words), said to his companion: "If thou wilt tell me who was thy father and of what people thou art sprung, I will give thee three garments."

"I am a child of the Huns," answered Amelung, "and our old people have told me that my father's name was Hildebrand. In former times he came from the east, flying the enmity of Otto-asa, and put himself with Theodoric and his blades.

"He left behind in the land a bride in childbed and a child without inheritance; and went to the south with Theodoric, where he stood many brunts.

"He was a man without connections, not a match for Otto-asa; but he was a good soldier, while he strove under Theodoric, acquired domains, was his people's father, and dear to brave men. I do not believe that he is living."

"My worthy god Irmin in heaven above," quoth Hildebrand, "do not let me fight with so near a kinsman." Then he untwisted golden bracelets from his arm, and imperial rings which his king had given him, saying: "This I give thee not without good will. I am thy father Hildebrand."

Amelung answered: "With willing soul be gifts taken, tit for tat. Thou art not of his age. Craftily thou seekest to deceive me: but I will convict thee out of thy own mouth. Thou art so advanced in years, and thou must be older than he. And shipwrecked men told me that he died by the Wendel-Sea in the west."

Then Hildebrand answered: "I well see thou hast in thy breast no Lord God, and carest nought for his kingdom. Go now, so God be willing," said Hildebrand; "I would we were parted. Sixty summers have I wandered out of my country, and sometimes I have joined archers but in no borough did ever fasten my legs: and now my nearest kinsman would aim his battle-ax at my neck, or I must bind his legs. Yet you may now easily, if your valor is up, win the spoils of the dead from one you should venerate, if you have any sense of right. He would be a base Ostrogoth," continued Hildebrand, "who should refuse thee battle, seeing thou so greatly desirest it. Good commoners, be judges which it is who flinches in the field, and which it is who ought to have our two coats of mail."

Then they let them fly their ashen spears with such force that they stuck in the shields. Then they struck together their stone axes, and uplifted hostilely their white shields, till their loins and bellies quivered.

But the lady Utta rushed in between them: "I know," said she, "the cross of gold which I gave him for his shield; this is my Hildebrand. You, Amelung, sheath your sword; this is your father."

Then she led both champions into her hall, and gave them meat and wine and many embraces.

SIEGFRIED AND KRIEMHILD

(Anonymous: End of 12th Century)

THE unknown writer of the *Nibelungenlied*, or *Lay of the Nibelungs*, was an Austrian. Nothing is known of him except that he wrote his celebrated ballad-epic toward the end of the Twelfth Century. Rediscovered toward the end of the Eighteenth Century, the *Lay* is, in the words of Prof. Calvin Thomas, "a powerful poem and a human document of many-sided interest." The component episodes are related with great vivacity, and the characters developed by means of a powerful imagination. The *Lay* was founded upon earlier versions of various legends, traditions, and songs that were current in pre-Christian times. Many of the same stories are found in the two Icelandic *Eddas* and in the *Volsunga Saga*.

The present version comprises two chapters, or "Adventures" (the fourth and fifth) of *The Fall of the Nibelungs*, translated by Margaret Armour, Everyman's Library. Reprinted by permission of the publishers, J. M. Dent and Sons. There is no title in the original.

SIEGFRIED AND KRIEMHILD

(From *The Lay of the Nibelungs*)

NOW there were brought into Gunther's land strange tidings by envoys sent from afar by foreign princes that hated him; and when they heard the message they were troubled. The kings were as I will tell you: Ludger of the Saxons, a high and mighty prince; and Ludgast of Denmark, and many bold warriors with them.

These envoys, sent by his foemen, came into Gunther's land, and the strangers were asked their business, and brought before the king.

The king greeted them fair, and said, "I know not who hath sent you hither, and would hear it." So spake the good king, and they greatly feared his wrath.

"If thou wilt have our message, O king, we will tell it plain, and name thee the princes that have sent us. They are Ludgast and Ludger, and will come against thee into thy land. Thou art fallen in their displeasure, and we know that they bear thee bitter hate. They come hither with an armed force to Worms by the Rhine—they and their warriors. Wherefore be warned. Inside of twelve days they will ride. If thou hast trusty friends, let it appear now; let them help thee to keep thy castles and thy country, for, or long, there will be smiting of helmets and shields here. Or wouldst thou treat with them, then declare it straightway, that thy foemen come not nigh thee to thy hurt, and that goodly knights perish not thereby."

"Tarry a while—ye shall have answer betimes—that I may bethink me," said the good king. "If I have true liegemen, I will not hide it from them, but will take counsel with them on this hard matter."

Heavy enow of his cheer was Gunther. He pondered the message secretly in his heart, and summoned Hagen, and others of his men, and sent to the court in haste for Gernot. His best knights drew round him, and he said, "Without cause, and with a mighty array, foemen come hither against us into our land."

Thereto answered Gernot, a hardy and bold warrior, "We shall hinder that with our swords. They only perish that fate dooms. Let them die. They shall not turn me from honor. Our foemen are welcome."

Spake Hagen of Trony then, "Methinketh that were unwise. Ludgast and Ludger are proud men withal, and we can hardly in so few days muster our men." Therefore the bold knight said, "Tell Siegfried."

They bade lodge the envoys in the town. Albeit they were his foemen, Gunther, the great king, commanded the folk to entreat them well—rightly he did so—till that he knew the friends that would stand by him.

The king was heavy of his cheer, and Siegfried, the good knight, saw that he was downcast, but wist not the reason, and asked King Gunther what ailed him. "I marvel much," said Siegfried, "that thou takest no part in our sports as heretofore." And Gunther, the doughty knight, answered him, "Not to every man may I declare the secret heaviness of my heart; only unto true friends shall the heart tell its dole."

Siegfried changed color, and grew red and white, and he said to the king, "I have denied thee naught, and now I would help thee. If thou seekest friends, I will be one of them, and stand to it truly to my life's end."

"Now God requite thee, Sir Siegfried, for I like thy word; and albeit thy might availed me nothing, I would rejoice none the less that thou art well-minded toward me; as much and more will I do to thee if I live. I will tell thee the cause of my trouble. Envoys from my foemen have brought a message that with an army they will come against me; such inroad of warriors hath not been aforetime in this country."

"Be not sorrowful for that," answered Siegfried; "be of good cheer, and do now as I say. I will win for thee honor and profit or ever thy foemen reach this land. Had thy stark adversaries thirty thousand warriors at their back, and I but one thousand, I would withstand them—trust me for that."

King Gunther answered, "Thou shalt be well paid for this."

"Give me a thousand of thy knights, since of mine own I have but twelve here with me, and I will keep thy land for thee. The hand of Siegfried will serve thee truly. Hagen shall help us in this, and also Ortwin, Dankwart, and Sindolt, thy loving knights, and eke Folker, the bold man, who shall bear the standard: better knight thou wilt not find. Bid the envoys return to their country; tell them they shall see us there soon enow. So shall our castles go scatheless."

The king let summon his kinsmen and his liegemen, and Ludger's messengers went to the court. They were glad to be gone. Gunther, the good king, gave them gifts and an escort, whereat they were well content.

Spake Gunther, "Thou shalt say on this wise to my haughty foemen: 'They did wisely to turn from their journey, for if my friends fail me not, and they seek me here in my land, they will find work enow.'"

They brought out rich gifts for the envoys, whereof Gunther had to spare, and these said not "nay." Then they took their leave, and departed rejoicing.

When the messengers were come again to Denmark, and told Ludgast how that the Rhine-men would ride thither, he was wroth at their boldness. They made report to him of the many brave men Gunther had, and how that they had seen a knight there amidst of them that hight Siegfried, a hero from the Netherland, the which was heavy news for Ludgast.

When they of Denmark heard it, they hasted the more to summon their friends, till that Ludgast had ready for the onset twenty thousand warriors withal.

On like manner Ludger of Saxony summoned his men to the number of forty thousand, ready to march into Burgundy.

The same also did King Gunther to his liegemen, and to his brothers with their vassals, and to Hagen and his knights. These were sorry enow at the news; by reason thereof many a knight looked on death.

They hasted and made ready for the journey. Brave Folker bare the standard. They purposed to cross the Rhine from Worms. Hagen of Trony led the force. Sindolt and bold Hunolt were there, that they might deserve King Gunther's gold; also Hagen's brother Dankwart, and Ortwin, fit men and worthy for the undertaking.

"Sit thou at home, O King," spake Siegfried. "Since thy knights are willing to follow me, stay here by the women and be of good cheer; for, by my troth, I will guard for thee both goods and honor. I will see to it, that they that seek thee here at Worms by the Rhine bide where they are; we will pierce deep into their country, till their vaunting is turned to sorrow."

They passed from the Rhine through Hesse against Saxony, where the battle was fought afterward. With plunder and with fire they laid waste the land, the which both the princes found to their cost.

When they were come to the marches, the warriors hasted forward, and Siegfried began to ask them, "Which of us shall guard the rest from surprise?" More to their hurt the Saxons never took the field.

They answered, "Let bold Dankwart guard the younger knights. He is a good warrior. So shall we come in less scathe by Ludger's men. He and Ortwin shall guard the rear."

"I myself will ride forward," said Siegfried, "and spy out the foe, that I may know rightly who the warriors be."

Fair Sieglind's son did on his armor in haste. He gave his knights in charge to Hagen and bold Gernot when he set out. He rode into Saxony all alone, and won honor by his quest. He perceived a great host encamped on a field, that loomed mightily against him, beyond the strength of one man: forty thousand or more. And the high heart of Siegfried rejoiced.

One of the enemy's knights kept watch warily, and perceived Siegfried, and Siegfried him, and they glared fiercely on each other. I will tell you who he was that kept watch. On his arm he bare a glittering shield of gold. It was King Ludgast that kept ward over his host.

The noble stranger pricked toward him fiercely. Ludgast dressed him also. They put spurs to their horses and smote with all their strength on the shields with their spears, that it was like to go hard with the king.

On their horses, pricked forward by the spur, the princes bare down on each other like the wind. Then they wheeled round deftly—these two fierce men—and fell to hacking with their swords. Sir Siegfried smote, that the field rang therewith; the hero with his mighty blade struck sparks from Ludgast's helmet. Fiercely fought the prince of the Netherland, and Ludgast, likewise, dealt many a grim blow. Each drave with all his might at the other's shield. The combat was spied by thirty of Ludgast's men, but Siegfried, by means of three deep wounds and grisly that he dealt Ludgast through his white harness, overcame the king or these knights came up. His sword drew blood with each stroke, that King Ludgast came in evil plight, and begged for his life, offering his land as the price thereof, and said that his name was Ludgast.

His knights hasted to his rescue, for they had seen the encounter at the ward-post. Siegfried would have led him thence, but thirty of Ludgast's men rode at him. With mighty blows the stark warrior kept his rich captive; and soon his hands did even deadlier deeds. He smote the thirty men dead in his defense, save one that fled and told what had happed, the truth whereof was proven by his bloody helmet.

They of Denmark were aghast when they heard their king was taken captive; they told it to his brother, who fell in a great fury by reason of the disaster.

So the mighty Ludgast was taken by Siegfried's prowess, and given in charge to Hagen. When that good knight heard that it was Ludgast he was not sorry.

They bade raise the standard of Burgundy. "Forward!" cried Siegfried. "More shall be done or the day end, if I lose not my life. The Saxon women shall rue it. Hearken now, ye men of the Rhine. I can lead you to Ludger's army. There ye will see helmets hewn by the good hands of heroes. They shall be in evil case or we turn again."

Then Gernot and his men sprang to horse. The banner was unfurled by Folker, the minstrel knight. He rode before the host, and they all made them ready for battle. They numbered not more than a thousand men, and thereto the twelve strangers. The dust rose from their path, and they rode through the land, their shields flashing.

The Saxons, also, were come up, bearing well-sharpened swords. So hath the story been told me. The swords in the heroes' hands dealt grim blows in defense of their castles and their land.

The marshal led the army, and Siegfried was come forward with the twelve men that he had with him from the Netherland. Many a hand was bloody that day in the battle. Sindolt and Hunolt and eke Gernot smote many heroes dead in the fight, that were bold enow till they felt their prowess. For their sake sorrowed women not a few. Folker and Hagen and Ortwin, the fierce warriors, quenched the flash of many helmets with blood. Dankwart, also, did wonders. The Danes proved their mettle, and loud were heard the hurtling of shields and the clash of sharp swords swung mightily. The Saxons, bold in strife, made havoc enow. Wide were the wounds hewn by the men of Burgundy when they rushed to the encounter. Blood ran down the saddles. So was honor wooed of these knights bold and swift. Loud rang the keen swords in the hands of the heroes of the Netherland, when they rode with their lord into the fray. They rode with Siegfried like good knights. None from the Rhine kept pace with him. By reason of Siegfried's hand streams of blood ran from bright helmets, till that he lit on Ludgast amidst of his men. Thrice he pierced through the army of the Saxons, and thrice returned. Hagen, by this time, was come up with him, that helped him in his quest. They slew many a brave knight.

When bold Ludger found Siegfried with Balmung, the good sword, swung aloft, wherewith he made a mighty slaughter, he was wroth, and of his mood full grim. With a fierce rush and clash of swords the warriors came together. So exceeding furious was their onset that the host gave way. Terrible was their hate. The Saxon king knew well that his brother was taken captive, and he was wroth thereat; but he knew it not for Siegfried's work till now. They had blamed Gernot. Now he found out the truth. Ludger smote so hard that Siegfried's horse reeled under him. But when he was come to, Siegfried was more terrible than afore. Hagen and Gernot, Dankwart and Folker, stood by him. The dead lay in heaps. Sindolt and Hunolt and Ortwin the knight slew many in the strife. The princes held together in the fray. Bright spears in the hands of heroes flashed above the helmets, that clave the shining bucklers in twain. Many a massy shield was red with blood. In the fierce encounter many men fell from their horses. Bold Siegfried and King Ludger strove together, and lances whizzed, and sharp spears. Ludger's shield-plate flew off through the strength of Siegfried's hand. Then the hero of the Netherland thought to have gotten the victory over the Saxons that were hard pressed. Ha! what polished bucklers doughty Dankwart brake!

Of a sudden Ludger espied a crown that was painted on Siegfried's shield, and he knew the mighty man, and cried aloud to his friends, "Forbear, my men all. I have seen the son of Siegmund, even bold Siegfried. The Devil hath sent him hither into Saxony." He bade lower the standard, and sued for peace. They granted this, yet he was compelled by Siegfried to go captive into Gunther's land.

With one accord they ceased from the strife. They threw down their shivered helmets and shields. Blood-red were they all by the hands of the Burgundians. They took captive whom they listed, for they had the power.

Gernot and Hagen gave order to convey the wounded on litters. They led five hundred noble knights as prisoners to the Rhine.

The vanquished warriors rode back to Denmark. Nor had the Saxons fought so as to win them honor, and they were downcast. The dead were mourned by their friends.

They sent the weapons to the Rhine on sumpters. So wondrously had Siegfried done, that all Gunther's men praised him.

Sir Gernot sent word to Worms, and throughout the whole land, to their friends, how it had sped with them; for as bold knights and honorable they had fought. The pages hasted and told it, and the glad news rejoiced the loving ones that had sorrowed. The noble women ceased not from questioning how it had fared with the great king's men.

Kriemhild bade a messenger to her in secret; publicly she durst not, for to one of them she bare dear heart's love.

When the messenger was come to her chamber, Kriemhild, the beautiful maiden, spake him fair. "Now tell me glad tidings; thou shalt have gold therefor; and, sayest thou sooth, I will ever be beholden to thee. How sped my brother Gernot in the battle, and the rest of my friends? Are there many dead? Who did most valiantly? Now tell me."

Whereto the messenger answered truthfully, "We had no coward among us. Yet since thou wilt hear it, noble princess, none rode in the thick of the fight like the knight of the Netherland. Marvelous was the work of Siegfried's hand. All that the knights did in battle—Dankwart and Hagen and the rest—though with honor fought they all, was but as a wind matched with the prowess of Siegfried, the son of Siegmund. Many heroes have they slain, yet of the deeds of Siegfried, done in battle, none shall tell to the end. By reason of him many maidens mourn for their kin. Low lieth the dear one of many a bride. Loud smote he on the helmets, that they ran blood. In all things he is a knight bold and good.

"Ortwin of Metz, also, won worship. Whoso came within range of his sword lieth wounded or dead. Thy brother, too, made fierce havoc in the battle. To his prowess must all testify. The proud Burgundians have so fought that none may question their honor. For many a saddle was emptied by them when the field rang loud with gleaming swords. On such wise fought the knights of the Rhine that their foemen had done better to flee. The brave men of Trony rode fiercely in the strife. Hagen with his hand slew many, whereof Burgundy shall hear. So valiantly fought Sindolt and Hunolt, Gernot's men, and eke Rumolt, that Ludger may well rue that he ever met thy kinsmen by the Rhine. But the mightiest deeds, first and last, were done by Siegfried. He bringeth rich captives into Gunther's land, that his strength hath conquered, by reason whereof King Ludgast and his brother, Ludger of Saxony, suffer dole. For list to the marvel, noble queen: both these princes hath Siegfried's hand taken. Never have so many captives been led into this land as come hither now through his prowess."

The maiden was glad at the tale.

"Of unwounded men they bring five hundred or more, and eighty red biers (I say sooth) of the wounded, fallen, the most part, by Siegfried's might. They that arrogantly withstood the knights of the Rhine are now Gunther's captives. Our men lead them hither rejoicing."

When she had heard the news aright, her fair cheek reddened, and her lovely face was the color of the rose, because it had gone well with young and noble Siegfried, and he was come with glory out of peril. She joyed for her kinsmen also, as in duty bound. And she said, "Thou hast spoken well; for guerdon thereof thou shalt have costly raiment, and ten golden marks, that I will bid them bear to thee." It is good to tell glad tidings to rich women.

He got his envoy's fee of gold and vesture, and the fair maids hasted to the window and looked down the road, where the high-hearted warriors rode home. They drew nigh, whole and wounded, and heard the greeting of friends, unashamed. Light of heart Gunther rode to meet them, for now his grim care was turned to joy. He received his own men well and also the strangers. Not to have thanked them that were come to his court, for that they had done valiantly in battle, would have been unseemly in so great a king. And he asked tidings of his friends, and who were slain. None were lost to him save sixty only, and these were mourned as many a hero hath been mourned since.

They that were unhurt brought many battered shields and shivered helmets back to Gunther's land. The warriors sprang down from their horses before the palace, and there was a joyful noise of welcome.

Order was given to lodge the knights in the town, and the king commanded that his guests should be courteously entreated, and that the wounded should be seen to and given good chambers. So he approved himself generous to his foes. He said to Ludger, "Thou art welcome! Much scathe have I suffered through thee; yet, if I prosper henceforth, I will consider myself well paid. God reward my warriors, for well have they served me!"

"Thou hast cause to thank them," answered Ludger, "for nobler captives were never won for a king; and gold without stint shall be thine, if thou do well by me and my friends."

Said Gunther, "Ye shall both go free. Yet I must have a pledge that my foemen quit not my land till peace be sealed betwixt us." And they promised it, and gave their hand thereon. They led them to their quarters to rest, and saw the wounded men laid softly in their beds. They set before them that were whole meat and good wine, and never were men merrier. They bare the battered shields away into safe keeping; and the bloody saddles, of which there were enow, they hid, that the women might not grieve thereat. Many a weary knight was there.

The king entreated his guests right royally, and the land was full of friends and of strangers. He bade see to the sore wounded ones whose pride was brought low. To them that were skilled in leech craft they offered a rich fee of unweighed silver and yellow gold, that they might heal the heroes of their wounds gotten in battle; the king sent also precious gifts to his guests. They that thought to ride home were bidden stay as friends. And the king took counsel how he might reward his liegemen that had done valiantly for his sake.

Sir Gernot said, "Let them go hence for the present, and summon them after six weeks to a hightide. Many will then be whole that now lie sick of their wounds."

Siegfried of the Netherland would have taken leave also, but, when King Gunther knew his intent, he besought him lovingly to tarry, the which Siegfried had not done but for Gunther's sister's sake. He was too rich to take money, albeit he well deserved it; the king loved him, and also the king's kinsmen that had seen the deeds wrought by his hand in battle. So, for love of the maiden, he agreed to tarry, that haply he might win to see her, the which, or long, came to pass; for he knew her to his heart's desire, and rode home joyfully afterward to his father's land.

The young knights obeyed the king's command willingly, and practised daily at the tourney. Seats were raised on the stand before Worms for the guests that were coming into Burgundy.

When it was time for them to arrive, fair Kriemhild heard the news, that they were about to hold a hightide with their friends. Then the beautiful women busied them with their kirtles and their headgear that they were to wear.

Uta, the great queen, heard of the proud knights that were coming, and gorgeous robes were taken from their wrapping-cloths. For love of her children she bade them bring forth the garments. Many women and maidens were adorned therewith, and, of the young knights of Burgundy, not a few. To many of the strangers, also, she gave goodly apparel.

A vast multitude of them that would attend the hightide drew daily to the Rhine; and unto those that came for love of the king horses were given and goodly raiment, and to each his place, even unto two and thirty princes of the highest and the best. So they tell us.

And the women vied with one another in their attire. Giselher, the youth, and Gernot, and their two squires, rested not from welcoming both friends and strangers. They gave courtly greeting unto the warriors.

The guests brought with them to the Rhine, to the tourney, saddles worked in ruddy gold, and finely wrought shields, and knightly apparel. And the sick rejoiced, and they that lay on their beds sore wounded forgot that death is an hard thing. When the rumor of the festival was noised abroad, no man took heed more of them that groaned, for each thought only how he might sojourn there as a guest. Joy without measure had all they that were found there, and gladness and rejoicing were in Gunther's land.

On Whitsun morning, there drew toward the hightide a goodly company of brave men, fairly clad: five thousand or more, and they made merry far and wide, and strove with one another in friendly combat.

Now Gunther knew well how, truly and from his heart, the hero of the Netherland loved his sister whom he had not yet seen, and whose beauty the people praised before that of all other maidens.

And he said, "Now counsel me, my kinsmen and my lieges, how we may order this hightide, that none may blame us in aught; for only unto such deeds as are good pertaineth lasting fame."

Then answered Ortwin, the knight, to the king, "If thou wilt win for thyself glory from the hightide, let now the maidens that dwell with honor in our midst appear before us. For what shall pleasure or glad a man more than to behold beautiful damsels and fair women? Bid thy sister come forth and show herself to thy guests."

And this word pleased the knights.

"That will I gladly do," said the king; and they that heard him rejoiced. He sent a messenger to Queen Uta, and besought her that she would come to the court with her daughter and her women-folk.

And these took from the presses rich apparel, and what lay therein in wrapping-cloths; they took also brooches, and their silken girdles worked with gold, and attired themselves in haste. Many a noble maiden adorned herself with care, and the youths longed exceedingly to find favor in their eyes, and had not taken a rich king's land in lieu thereof. And they that knew not one another before looked each upon each right gladly.

The rich king commanded an hundred men of his household, his kinsmen and hers, to escort his sister, their swords in their hands. Uta, with an hundred and more of her women, gorgeously attired, came forth from the female apartments, and many noble damsels followed after her daughter. The knights pressed in upon them, thinking thereby to behold the beautiful maiden.

And lo! the fair one appeared, like the dawn from out the dark clouds. And he that had borne her so long in his heart was no more aweary, for the beloved one, his sweet lady, stood before him in her beauty. Bright jewels sparkled on her garments, and bright was the rose-red of her hue, and all they that saw her proclaimed her peerless among maidens.

As the moon excelleth in light the stars shining clear from the clouds, so stood she, fair before the other women, and the hearts of the warriors were uplifted. The chamberlains made way for her through them that pressed in to behold her. And Siegfried joyed, and sorrowed likewise, for he said in his heart, "How should I woo such as thee? Surely it was a vain dream; yet I were liefer dead than a stranger to thee."

Thinking thus he waxed oft white and red; yea, graceful and proud stood the son of Sieglind, goodliest of heroes to behold, as he were drawn on parchment by the skill of a cunning master. And the knights fell back as the escort commanded, and made way for the high-hearted women, and gazed on them with glad eyes. Many a dame of high degree was there.

Said bold Sir Gernot, the Burgundian, then, "Gunther, dear brother, unto the gentle knight, that hath done thee service, show honor now before thy lieges. Of this counsel I shall never shame me. Bid Siegfried go before my sister, that the maiden greet him. Let her, that never greeted knight, go toward him. For this shall advantage us, and we shall win the good warrior for ours."

Then Gunther's kinsmen went to the knight of the Netherland, and said to him, "The king bids thee to the court that his sister may greet thee, for he would do thee honor."

It rejoiced Siegfried that he was to look upon Uta's fair child, and he forgot his sorrow.

She greeted him mild and maidenly, and her color was kindled when she saw before her the high-minded man, and she said, "Welcome, Sir Siegfried, noble knight and good." His courage rose at her words, and graceful, as beseemed a knight, he bowed himself before her and thanked her. And love that is mighty constrained them, and they yearned with their eyes in secret. I know not whether, from his great love, the youth pressed her white hand, but two love-desirous hearts, I trow, had else done amiss.

Nevermore, in summer or in May, bore Siegfried in his heart such high joy as when he went by the side of her whom he coveted for his dear one. And many a knight thought, "Had it been my hap to walk with her, as I have seen him do, or to lie by her side, certes, I had suffered it gladly! Yet never, truly, hath warrior served better to win a queen." From what land soever the guests came, they were ware only of these two. And she was bidden kiss the hero. He had never had like joy before in this world.

Said the King of Denmark then, "By reason of this high greeting many good men lie low, slain by the hand of Siegfried, the which hath been proven to my cost. God grant he return not to Denmark!"

Then they ordered to make way for fair Kriemhild. Valiant knights in stately array escorted her to the minster, where she was parted from

Siegfried. She went thither followed by her maidens; and so rich was her apparel that the other women, for all their striving, were as naught beside her, for to glad the eyes of heroes she was born.

Scarce could Siegfried tarry till they had sung mass, he yearned so to thank her for his gladness, and that she whom he bore in his heart had inclined her desire toward him, even as his was to her, which was meet. Now when Kriemhild was come forth to the front of the minster, they bade the warrior go to her again, and the damsel began to thank him, that before all others he had done valiantly. And she said, "Now, God requite thee, Sir Siegfried, for they tell me thou hast won praise and honor from all knights."

He looked on the maid right sweetly, and he said, "I will not cease to serve them. Never, while I live, will I lay head on pillow, till I have brought their desire to pass. For love of thee, dear lady, I will do this."

And every day of twelve, in the sight of all the people, the youth walked by the side of the maiden as she went to the court. So they showed their love to the knight.

And there was merriment and gladness and delight in the hall of Gunther, without and within, among the valiant men. Ortwin and Hagen did many wonderful deeds, and if any devised a sport, warriors, joyous in strife, welcomed it straightway. So were the knights proven before the guests, and they of Gunther's land won glory. The wounded also came forth to take part with their comrades, to skirmish with the buckler, and to shoot the shaft, and waxed strong thereby, and increased their might.

Gunther gave order that, for the term of the hightide, they should set before them meats of the daintiest, that he might fail in naught as a king, nor the people blame him.

And he came to his guests, and said, "Receive my gifts ere ye go hence, and refuse not the treasure that I would share with you."

The Danes made answer, "Ere we turn again to our land, make thou a lasting peace with us. We have need of such, that have many dear friends, slain by thy warriors."

Ludgast and eke the Saxon were healed of their wounds gotten in battle, but many tarried behind, dead.

Then Gunther sought Siegfried and said, "Now counsel me in this. On the morrow our guests ride forth, and they desire of me and mine a lasting covenant. What they offer I will tell thee: as much gold as five hundred horses may carry, they will give me to go free."

And Siegfried answered, "That were ill done. Send them forth without ransom, that they ride no more hither as foemen. And they shall give thee the hand thereon for surety."

"What thou counselest I will do. They shall depart as thou sayest."

And they told it to his enemies; also that none desired their gold. They said it to the war-tired men, by reason of whom the dear ones of their own land sorrowed.

And the king took shields full of treasure, and divided it among them without weighing it, five hundred marks and more. Gernot, the brave knight, counseled him thereto. And they took their leave, for they were aweary for home. And they passed before Kriemhild and Queen Uta; never were knights dismissed more courteously.

The chambers were void when they left, nevertheless the king abode there still with his lieges and his vassals and knights. And these ceased not to go before Kriemhild.

Then Siegfried, the hero, had also taken leave, for he thought not to attain his desire. But the king heard of it, and Giselher the youth turned him back. "Whither ridest thou, Sir Siegfried? Prithee yield to me in this. Go not from among our knights, and Gunther, and his men. Here are fair maidens enow that thou mayest behold at will."

Said bold Sir Siegfried, "Let stand the horses, bear hence the shields. I would have ridden forth and turned again to my land, but Giselher hath changed my intent."

So he abode among them through love, nor in any land had it been sweeter for him. And Kriemhild, the fair maiden, he saw daily, by reason of whose beauty he tarried.

They passed the time in sports and feats of chivalry. But his heart was weary with love; yea, for love he sorrowed then, and, after, died miserably.

GOTTFRIED VON STRASSBURG

(Died about 1210)

GOTTFRIED was one of the most famous of that group of Minnesingers which included Hartmann von Aue and Wolfram von Eschenbach. These were the most popular writers of the so-called romances of knighthood. Gottfried's *Tristan* was a working-over of a French version of the tale (now existing only in fragmentary form) by Thomas the Trouvère. The German work is a many-coloured story of love and adventure, direct, simple, and devoid of the finer subtleties of psychology. *The Coming of Gandin* is one of the complete episodes which abound throughout the romance.

The present version, translated by Jessie L. Weston, is reprinted by her permission from *Tristan and Iseult*, published by David Nutt in 1899. There is no title in the original.

THE COMING OF GANDIN

(From *Tristan and Iseult*)

FOR in these days a ship came to Mark's haven in Cornwall, and there landed from it a knight, a noble baron of Ireland, named Gandin; he was rich, handsome, and courteous, so manly and strong of limb that all Ireland spake of his valor.

Fairly clad, without shield or spear, he came riding to the king's court. On his back he bare a lute adorned with gold and precious stones, a-strung as a lute should be.

He dismounted, entered the palace, and greeted Mark and Iseult in fitting wise. Many a time and in many ways had he served the queen in her own land, through his knighthood, and the great love he bare her, and for her sake had he journeyed hither from Ireland.

Then Iseult knew him, and greeted him courteously. "God save thee, Sir Gandin."

"Gramercy, fair Iseult, fair and fairer than gold in the eyes of Gandin!"

Iseult spake softly to the king, saying who the knight was and whence he came; and Mark hearkened, wondering much why he bare a lute, and in sooth so did all the folk, for such was not the wont of wandering knights. Nevertheless would Mark do him all the honor he might, both for his own sake and for that of Iseult, since he was the queen's countryman; so he bade the stranger sit beside him, and spake to him of his folk and land, and of knightly deeds.

When the feast was ready, and water was brought round to the guests to wash their hands, then did the courtiers pray the stranger to play the lute before them. The king and queen said nought, they would leave it to his own will; and when he took no heed of their prayers, the courtiers mocked him, calling him "The Knight of the Lute," "The Prince with the Penance"; and Gandin said nought, but sat beside King Mark, and ate and drank, and heeded them not.

When the feast was over, and the tables borne away, then King Mark prayed him, an he could, to pleasure them awhile with his skill on the lute; but Gandin answered: "Sire, I may not, save that I know what my reward may be."

"Sir Knight, what meanest thou? Dost thou desire aught of my possessions? If so, 'tis granted; let us but hearken thy skill, and I will give thee whatever thou desirest."

"So be it," spake the knight of Ireland.

Then he sang a lay which pleased them all well, so that the king desired him to sing another. The traitor laughed in his heart. "Tell me," he said, "what thou wilt, that I may play even as shall please thee."

Now when he had sung another lay, Gandin arose and stood before the king, holding the lute in his hand. "Sir King," he said, "bethink thee of what thou didst promise me."

And Mark answered: "Of good will will I do it. Tell me what wilt thou?"

"Give me Iseult," quoth the knight.

"Friend," said Mark, "whatever else thou desirest thou shalt have, but this may not be."

"Verily, Sir King," said Gandin, "I will neither much nor little, but Iseult alone."

The King spake: "Of a truth, that shall not be!"

"Sire, wilt thou then break thy promise? If thou be thus forsworn, henceforth shall men hold thee unworthy to be king of any land. Bid them read the right of kings, and if this be not so, then will I renounce my claim. Or, dost thou, or any other say that thou didst not swear to give me what I asked, then will I assert my right against thee, or against whomsoever the court may choose. My body shall be overcome with fight ere I renounce my claim. Choose thou a knight to ride in the ring against me, and I will prove by combat that fair Iseult is mine."

The king looked all about and on either side if he might find one who would dare to uphold his cause; but there was no man who would set his life on such a wager, nor would Mark himself fight for his queen, for Gandin was so strong and valiant that none durst take up his challenge.

Now Tristan had ridden forth to the woods to hunt, and as he came homeward to the court he heard on the way the news of what had chanced. 'Twas all true: Gandin had led the queen, weeping and lamenting bitterly from the palace to the seashore. On the shore was pitched a tent, rich and costly, wherein he led the queen that they might wait till tide and river rose and floated the bark, which now lay high on the sand.

When Tristan heard the tale from beginning to end, he mounted his horse and took his harp in his hand, and rode swiftly, even to the haven. There he turned aside secretly, to a grove, made his horse fast to the bough of a tree, and with his harp in his hand took his way to the tent. The knight of Ireland sat there, armed, beside the weeping queen, whom he strove hard to comfort, but little might it avail, till he saw Tristan and his harp.

He greeted Gandin, saying: "God save thee, fair minstrel!"

"Gramercy, gentle knight."

"Sir," he said, "I have hastened hither. Men have told me thou art come from Ireland: I too am from thence. I pray thee, of thine honor, take me back to mine own land."

The Irish knight made answer: "That will I do; but sit thee down, play to me, and if thou canst comfort my lady, whom thou seest weeping sorely, I will give thee the fairest garment that is in this tent."

"'Tis a fair offer, Sir Knight," said Tristan. "I have good hope that I may do so; an her grief be not so great that it will stay not for any man's playing, she must needs be consoled."

Therewith he harped so sweetly that the notes crept into Iseult's heart and bare her thoughts so far hence that she ceased weeping, and thought but of her love.

Now, when the lay was ended, the water had come up to the bark, and it floated, so that they on board cried to the haven: "Sir, sir, come aboard; if my lord Tristan comes whilst thou art yet ashore, we shall have but an ill time! Folk and land alike are in his power—also he himself, so they say, is of such wondrous daring, so valiant and strong, he will likely do thee a mischief."

This was unpleasing to Gandin, and he said angrily: "Now may heaven hate me if I stir hence a moment earlier for that! Comrade, play me the Lay of Dido; thou dost harp so sweetly that I must needs love thee for it. Now, play and banish my lady's sorrow. Out of love for thee will I bear thee hence with her and me, and will give thee all I have promised thee, yea, and more!"

"So be it," quoth Tristan.

The minstrel touched his harp again; and he played so sweetly that Gandin listened eagerly, and Iseult was all intent on the music. And when it had ended the knight took the queen by the hand, and would lead her aboard, but by now was the tide so high and running so strong that no man might reach the bark save on horseback. "What shall we do now?" asked Gandin. "How may my lady come aboard?"

"See, Sir Knight," quoth the minstrel, "since I am sure thou wilt take me hence with thee, I think but little of what I have here in Cornwall. I have a horse near by; I ween he shall be tall enough to carry my lady, thy friend, over to the bark without the sea wetting her."

Gandin said: "Good minstrel, haste, bring thy horse hither, and take also the robe I promised thee."

Tristan fetched his horse swiftly, and when he came back he swung his harp behind him and cried: "Now, knight of Ireland, give me my lady, I will carry her before me through the water."

"Nay, minstrel, thou shalt not touch her; I will carry her myself."

"Nay, sir," said fair Iseult, "'tis needless to say he shall not touch me. Know the truth, I go not aboard save the minstrel bear me."

Then Gandin led her to Tristan. "Comrade," he said, "have a care of her—carry her so gently that I shall be ever grateful to thee."

Now as soon as Tristan held Iseult he spurred his steed forward, and when Gandin saw it he spake in wrath: "Ha, fool, what dost thou?"

"Nay, nay, fool Gandin," quoth Tristan, "'tis thou who art the fool; what thou didst steal from King Mark by the lute, that I do bear away with my harp. Thou didst betray, now art thou betrayed. Tristan has followed thee till he has befooled thee! Friend, thou hast indeed given me a rich garment, even the richest that thy tent did hold."

With that Tristan rode his way, leaving Gandin beyond measure sorrowful; his loss and his shame cut him to the heart; mourning, he returned over-seas.

Tristan and Iseult rode homeward, rejoicing in their love; and when they came to the palace, Tristan led the queen to King Mark, and spake bitterly: "Sire, God knoweth, if thou dost hold thy queen so dear as thou sayest, 'tis a great folly to give her up lightly for mere lute or harp play! The world may well mock! Whoever saw a queen the chattel of a lay? Henceforth bethink thee, and guard my lady better."

BRUIN THE BEAR AND REYNARD THE FOX

(Anonymous: about 1230)

NOTHING is known of the writer of the first version of the celebrated *Reynard the Fox*. The problem of the origin of the book is complicated, but it is generally agreed that a series of incidents attributed to an Alsatian writer of the late Twelfth Century was the basis of the book as it stands in the version here used. This was printed in 1498, though it was probably written about 1230. *Reynard* was soon afterwards translated into nearly every language of Europe. The book, in one form or another, has been a popular favourite among all classes of readers, and has for centuries been rewritten to suit the tastes of each generation.

The present version, translated by Thomas Roscoe, is reprinted from Roscoe's *German Novelists*, London, no date. It is Chapter IV of *The Pleasant History of Reynard the Fox*. The full title of the chapter is *How Bruin the Bear Sped with Reynard the Fox*, followed by a brief description.

BRUIN THE BEAR AND REYNARD THE FOX

(From *Reynard the Fox*)

THE next morning away went Sir Bruin the bear in quest of the fox, armed against all kinds of plots and deceit whatsoever; and as he went along through a dark forest in which Reynard had a by-path which he used when he was out hunting or being hunted, he saw a high mountain, over which he must pass to reach Malepardus. For though Reynard had many houses, Malepardus is his chief and most ancient castle, and there he resorted both for defense and pleasure. When Bruin at length came to the place, he found the gates close shut; at which, after he had knocked, sitting upon his tail, he called aloud, "Sir Reynard, are you at home? I am Bruin, your kinsman, sent by the king to summon you to court, to answer the many foul accusations laid at your door. His majesty hath taken a great vow that if you fail to appear to the summons, your life shall answer for your contempt, and your whole goods and honors become confiscated to the crown. Therefore, fair kinsman, be advised by your friend, and come with me to court, in order to shun the fate that will otherwise overtake you": so said the bear. Reynard, who was lying near the gate, as was his custom, basking in the sun, hearing these words, departed into one of his holes, Malepardus being full of many intricate and curious apartments, through which he could pass in case of danger or for objects of prey, where he determined to commune with himself awhile how best he might counterplot, and bring the bear into disgrace, while he added to his own credit, for he detested the bear; and at last coming forth, said, "Is it you, dear uncle Bruin? you are exceeding welcome, and excuse my delay in saying so; but the truth is, that when you began to speak I was saying my vespers, and devotion must not be neglected for any worldly concerns. Yet I believe he hath done you no good service, nor do I thank him who hath sent you hither, a long and weary journey, in which your sweat and toil far exceed the worth of the labor performed. It is certain, that had you not come, I had tomorrow attended the court of mine own accord. As it is, however, my regret is much diminished, because your counsel just at this time may turn to my double benefit. Alas! uncle, could his majesty find no meaner a messenger than your noble self to employ in these trivial affairs? Truly it appears strange to me, especially since, next his royal self, you are of greatest renown, both in point of blood and riches. For my part, I would that we were both at court, as I fear our journey will be exceedingly troublesome. To say truth, since my entire abstinence from flesh, I have lived upon strange new meats, which have very much disagreed with me, and swelled my body as if it was about to burst." "Alas! dear cousin," said the bear, "what kind of meat can it be that makes you so ill?" "Uncle," he replied, "what will it avail you to know? The food was simple and mean: we poor gentry are no lords, you know, but are glad to eat from necessity what others taste for mere wantonness. Yet not to delay you, that which I ate was honeycombs, large, full, and very pleasant. But, impelled by hunger, I ate so very immoderately that I was afterwards infinitely distempered." "Ay!" quoth Bruin; "honeycombs, do you say? Hold you them in such slight respect, nephew? Why, sir, it is food for the greatest emperors in the world. Help me, fair nephew, to some of these honeycombs, and command me while I live; for only a small share I will be your servant everlastingly." "You are jesting with me, surely, uncle," replied the fox. "Jest with you!" cried Bruin; "beshrew my heart, then; for I am in such serious good earnest, that for a single lick of the same you shall count me among the most faithful of your kindred." "Nay, if you be," returned Reynard, "I will bring you where ten of you would not be able to eat the whole at a meal. This I do out of friendship, for I wish to have yours in return, which above all things I desire." "Not ten of us," cried the bear, "not ten of us! it is impossible; for had I all the honey between Hybla and Portugal, I could eat the whole of it very shortly myself." "Then know, uncle, that near at hand there dwells a husbandman named Lanfert, who is master of so much that you could not consume it in seven years, and this, for your love and friendship's sake, I will put into your possession." Bruin, now mad for the honey, swore that for one good meal he would stop the mouths of all Reynard's enemies. Smiling at his easy credulity, the latter said, "If you would wish for seven ton, uncle, you shall have it"; and these words pleased the bear so much, and made it so pleasant, that he could not actually stand for laughing. "Well," thought the fox, "this is good fortune; though I will assuredly lead him where he shall laugh more in reason." He then said, "Uncle, we must lose no time, and I will spare no pains, such as I would not undertake for any of my kin." The bear gave him thanks, and away they went together, the fox promising as much honey as he could carry, but meaning as many stripes as he could undergo. At length they came to Lanfert's house, the sight of which made the bear caper for joy. This Lanfert was a stout brawny carpenter, who the other day had brought into his yard a large oak, which he had begun to cleave, and struck into it two wedges, so that the cleft lay a great way open, at which the fox rejoiced, as it was just what he wished. Then, with a smiling countenance, turning to the bear, "Behold now," he said, "dear uncle, and be careful of yourself; for within this tree is contained so much honey, that if you can get to it you will find it immeasurable; yet be cautious, good uncle, and eat moderately. The combs are sweet and good, but a surfeit is always dangerous, and may prove troublesome on your journey, which I would not for the world, as no harm can happen to you but must redound to my dishonor." "Concern not yourself for me, faith, nephew Reynard; I am not such a fool but I can temper my appetite if I can only get at the honey." "True, I was perhaps too bold to say what I did, my best uncle; so I pray you enter in at the end, and you shall there find what you want." With all haste the bear entered the tree with his fore feet forward, and thrust his head into the hole quite over the ears. When the fox saw this, he instantly ran and pulled the wedges out of the tree, so that the bear remained locked fast.

Neither flattery nor anger now availed the bear, for his nephew had got him in so fast a prison, that it was impossible to free himself by any maneuver. What profited him his great strength and valor now? They only served to irritate and annoy him; and deprived of all relief, he began to howl and bray, to scratch and tumble, and make such a noise, that Lanfert came running hastily out of the house to see what was the matter. He held a sharp hook in his hand, and while the bear lay tearing and roaring in the tree, the fox cried out in scorn, "He is coming, uncle! I fear you will not like the honey; is it good? Do not eat too much; pleasant things are apt to surfeit, and you will delay your journey back to court. If your belly be too full, Lanfert will give you drink to digest it." Having said which, he set off towards his castle again. Lanfert, finding that the bear was taken fast, ran to his neighbors and desired them to come. The tidings spreading through the town, there was neither man, woman, nor child but ran to see; some with one weapon and some with another, goads, rakes, and broom-staves, and whatever they could lay hands on. The priest bore the handle of a large cross, the clerk had holy water, and the priest's wife, Dame Jullock, brought her distaff, as she happened to be spinning: nay, the old beldams came that had never a tooth in their heads. Hearing the approach of this army, Bruin fell into great fear, there being none but himself to withstand them; and as they came thundering down upon him, he struggled so fiercely that he contrived to get his head out of jeopardy by leaving behind the best part of the skin, along with his ears, insomuch that never age beheld a more foul ugly beast; for the blood covered his face and hands, leaving his claws and skin behind him, so that he could hardly move or see. It was an ill market he came to, for in spite of this torment Lanfert and his crew came upon him, and so belabored him with staves, and hooks, and rakes, that it might well be a warning to every one taken in misery, showing how the weakest must evermore go to the wall. This Bruin cruelly experienced, every one venting their fury upon his hide, even Houghlin with his crooked leg, and Ludolf with the long broad nose; the one armed with a leaden mall, and the other with an iron scourge. None lashed so hard as Sir Bertolf with the long fingers, and none annoyed him more than Lanfert and Ortam, one being armed with a sharp Welsh hook, and the second with a crooked staff heavily leaded at the end, with which he used to play at stab-ball. There was Burkin and Armes Ablequack, Bane the priest with his cross-handle, and Jullock his wife. All these so belabored the poor bear that his life was in extreme jeopardy; he sat and sighed sadly during the massacre, but the thundering weight of Lanfert's fierce blows was the most cruel to bear; for Dame Podge, at Casport, was his mother, and his father was Marob, the staple-maker, a passing stout man when he was alone. From him Bruin received such a shower of stones, at the same time that Lanfert's brother wielded him a savage blow upon the pate, that he could no longer see nor hear, but made a desperate plunge into the adjoining river, through a cluster of old wives standing by, many of whom he threw into the water, which was broad and deep, among whom was the parson's wife. Seeing her floating there like a sea-mew, the holy man left off striking the bear, crying out, "Help, oh, help! Dame Jullock is in the water! I absolve the man, woman, or child that saves her, from all their sins and transgressions, past and to come, and I remit all penance." Hearing this, all left the pursuit of the bear to succor Dame Jullock, upon which Bruin cut the stream with fresh strength, and swam away. The priest only pursued him, crying in great rage, "Turn, villain, turn, that I may be revenged upon thee!" But the bear, having the advantage of the stream, heeded not his calling, for he was proud of the triumph of having escaped from them. He bitterly cursed the honey tree, and more bitterly the fox, who had not only betrayed him, but made him lose his hood from his face and his leather gloves from his fingers. In this condition he swam about three miles down the stream, when he grew so very weary that he was obliged to seek a landing. The blood trickled down his face; he sighed, and drew his breath so short that it seemed as if his last hour was come.

Meanwhile the fox, on his way home, had stolen a fat pullet, and running through a by-path to elude pursuit, he now came towards the river with infinite joy. For he never doubted but the bear was slain, and he therefore said, "My fortune is made, for my greatest enemy at the court is dead, and no one can suspect me." But as he spoke, looking towards the river-side, he espied the bear lying down to ease his grievous wounds. At this sight Reynard's heart misgave him, and he railed bitterly against Lanfert the carpenter, cursing him for a silly fool, that did not know how to kill a bear in a trap. "What madman," he cried, "would have lost such good venison? so fat and wholesome, and which lay taken to his hand. A wise man would have been proud of the fortune which thou, like a fool, hast neglected." Thus fretting and chiding, he came to the river, where he found the bear covered with wounds, which Reynard alone had caused. Yet he said in scorn as he passed, "Monsieur, Dieu vous garde!" "O thou foul red villain!" said the bear to himself. "What impudence can equal thine?" But the fox continued his speech: "What, uncle, have you forgotten everything at Lanfert's, or have you paid for the honeycombs you stole? I would rather pay for them myself than that you should incur any disgrace. If the honey was good, you may have plenty more at the same price. Good uncle, tell me before I go, into what order you mean to enter, that you wear this new-fashioned hood? Will you be a monk, an abbot, or a friar? He that shaved your crown seems also to have cropped your ears; your forelock is lost, and your leather gloves are gone. Fie, sloven! go not bareheaded!

They say you can sing *peccavi* rarely." These taunts made Bruin mad with rage; but because he could not take revenge, he was obliged to let him talk on. At last, to avoid him, he plunged again into the river and landed on the other side, where he began to meditate how best he might reach the court; for he had lost both his ears and his talons, and could scarcely walk. Yet of necessity he must move forward, which he could only do by setting his buttocks upon the ground, and tumbling his body over and over. In this manner he first rolled about half a mile, then rested, and rolled another half-mile, until by dint of perseverance he tumbled his way to court. Witnessing his strange method of approach, a number of courtiers gazed upon him as a sort of prodigy, little deeming that it was the famous Sir Bruin the bear.

The king himself was the first who recognized him, and he said, "It is Sir Bruin my servant: what villains have wounded him thus? Where can he have been, that he could contrive it—to bring his death as it were back with him? let us hear what tidings he has got." "O my dread sovereign lord the king," cried out the bear, "I have to complain grievously. Behold how I am massacred; a massacre I humbly beseech you to revenge on that false malignant Reynard, who hath wrought me this foul disgrace and slaughter, merely because I have done your royal pleasure in conveying him a summons to court." His majesty then said, "How durst he do this thing? Now, by my crown I swear, I will take such revenge as shall make the traitor tremble, and remember the foul deed." So forthwith the king summoned his whole council, and consulted how and in what way to proceed most efficaciously against the wily fox. At length, after much discussion, it was unanimously concluded that he should be again summoned to appear and answer his transgressions in person. The party now appointed to execute the summons was Tibert the cat, being equally recommended for his gravity and his wisdom; an appointment likewise well pleasing to the king.

EULENSPIEGEL AND THE MERCHANT

(Anonymous: about 1500)

THE earliest known version of *Eulenspiegel* dates from 1515, though an edition is said to have been printed in 1483. Nothing at all is known about the author. The merry pranks of Eulenspiegel, like the adventures of Reynard and his companions, formed the basis of several collections of adventures in the late Sixteenth and early Seventeenth Centuries. They were utilized in the Nineteenth Century by the Belgian Charles de Coster. The original book, in the words of Roscoe, is "a national storehouse of amusement from which each successive generation has largely drawn." Like most of the books of its kind, it was derived from fables and popular traditions.

The present version, translated by Thomas Roscoe, is reprinted from Roscoe's *German Novelists*, London, no date. It is one of the separate adventures and has only a descriptive note by way of title.

EULENSPIEGEL AND THE MERCHANT

(From *Eulenspiegel, the Merry Jester*)

IN the town of Herdellem there resided a rich merchant, who, happening one day to be walking in one of his own fields, a short way out of the city, saw Howleglass lying on the green. He inquired who he was. To this Howleglass replied, "I am a cook without a master, and I have been a cook's servant, otherwise a scullion; but that is now not a place for me." The merchant said, "If you like to become my servant, I will give you good board and wages, besides your clothes; you shall have a trial, for my wife is continually bickering one after another with all her cooks." Howleglass promised to do his best to please him; and his new master asked his name, to which our hero replied that it was Bartholomew. "The name," said the merchant, "is too long; you shall be called *Dol*." "Sir," said Howleglass, "just as you like best, it pleases me well." "Then come," added his master, "you are the sort of man I want; let us go directly into my garden to gather herbs for the young boiled chickens, as to-morrow I have a party coming, and we must make merry with the best cheer." So they went to the house, and when the merchant's wife saw them come in, she said, "Heyday, master mine, what kind of a servant have you brought us here? Are you afraid lest the bread should be left to grow moldy? What is he for?" "Oh, you shall see that, my dear, to-morrow. Here, Dol, take this pannier, and follow me to the shambles."

Away they went, and the merchant bought some pieces of roasting meat, saying on his return, "Now, Dol, remember when you put this sirloin down to-morrow, that you leave it to do coolly at a distance, so as not to catch or singe; the boiling piece you may put on a good deal earlier."

"Very good, master," said Howleglass, "it shall be done." So the next morning he rose betimes and brought the meat he was to boil near the fire. But that which he intended to roast he stuck upon the spit, and placed it at a cool distance as he had been told (namely, in the cellar between two barrels of beer) from the fire. Now, before the merchant's guests had assembled, he went to see that all was going on well in the kitchen (for his wife was a fine lady), and he inquired whether the dinner was almost ready, to which Howleglass made answer, "Yes, everything but the roast beef." "Everything but!" exclaimed the merchant; "and where is that?" "It is on the spit," answered Howleglass; "it is doing cool at a distance, as you desired, in the coolest place in the house, which is the beer cellar. You did not say when you would like to have it roasted." While his master was discussing this point with Howleglass, the guests began to arrive, to whom he candidly related the incident, at which some looked grave and others laughed, while his lady was least of all satisfied with the joke. Indeed, she proposed an ejectment of the new cook from the premises forthwith.

"My love," said the merchant, "give yourself no kind of uneasiness about that! To-morrow I am going to Gollai, and he must see me there; but on my return he shall be discharged." Then they all proceeded to dinner, and made as good cheer as they could upon what they had got. In the evening when all was over, his master called Howleglass, and said, "Dol, see that my coach is in readiness early to-morrow morning, for I and the priest are going as far as Gollai, so look that it be well cleaned and greased." Accordingly when the whole family were abed, Howleglass proceeded to grease the chariot well both inside and out. And in the morning our merchant and the priest mounted to drive off; but slip went the priest wherever he laid his hand or foot! And he had many a time nearly broken his neck as they drove along. "What the deuce," he cried, "can it be that it is so thick and greasy?"

So they stopped and called Howleglass in a great passion, inquiring what vile work he had been doing, and swore and threatened dreadfully. Just then a wagon-load of straw luckily went by, and the unhappy party purchased a small quantity, with which to purify the well-bedizened chariot. Quite enraged, the merchant cried out, "Off to the gallows, you rascal!" and soon after Howleglass saw one not far from the roadside, and driving the chariot right underneath it, he was proceeding very leisurely to unharness the horses. "What is it that you are about, villain?" said his master. "Why," replied Howleglass, "did not you order me to drive off to the gallows? where I thought I was to set you down." On looking up, the priest and the merchant sure enough saw the gibbet; upon which his master, being seized with a panic, commanded him to back, and drive right away as hard as he could flog. Hearing this, Howleglass dashed neck and nothing through the mud, so that by the horrible pulling and tearing, the vehicle came straight in two, the hinder part remaining with the merchant and the priest stuck in the mud, and the other proceeding with Howleglass and the horses just as if nothing had happened. At length with much shouting and running the merchant overtook his driver, and was beginning to inflict summary vengeance upon him, when the priest came up and prevented him; and in this fashion they contrived to accomplish their journey, and so home again. Well!

his wife inquired how the merchant had enjoyed his journey? "Oh, delightful," cried the merchant, "now that we are safely returned." Then he called Howleglass, saying, "To-night eat and drink to your heart's content, for to-morrow you quit this house. I cannot keep you, you are too great a malicious rascal for me." "All right, master," said Howleglass. And in the morning when the merchant went out, he again said, "Eat and drink, take as much as you like, but do not let me find you here when I come home from church." So while the family was at church, Howleglass proceeded as he had been ordered to take what he liked; and very shortly he had almost completely gutted the house. In short, the merchant met him with a whole load of his goods in the street as he was coming from church. "Ha! my honest cook," he cried, "what are you dressing now?" "What you commanded me to do," replied Howleglass: "you informed me that I might take what I liked, and rid the house of me." "Leave these things where they are," exclaimed the merchant, "and go to the devil if you please." Howleglass said, "I do everything that my masters order me, and yet I cannot live in peace." So he quitted the merchant in a huff, whom he was sorry again to have met with, while the former had his goods conveyed back to the house.

DOCTOR FAUST AND THE USURER

(Anonymous: Late 16th Century)

THE author of the so-called Chapbook of Dr. Faust was in all probability a Lutheran pastor. The first known edition appeared in 1587. It is a loosely constructed collection of incidents more or less remotely centred in the actual career of Dr. Faust, who died some fifty years before. It is a "curious patchwork of genuine folk tales that were really current about Doctor Faust . . . and learned demonological rubbish taken from preexistent treatises." A version of this chapbook fell into the hands of Christopher Marlowe; to this we owe *Dr. Faustus*, as well as the *Faust* of Goethe.

The present version, translated by Thomas Roscoe, is reprinted from Roscoe's *German Novelists*, London, no date. It is one of the separate incidents in the *Life*. It bears only a long description by way of title.

DOCTOR FAUST AND THE USURER

(From *The History of Dr. J. Faust . . .*, etc.)

IT used to be an old saying that the conjuror, "charm he never so wisely," for the year together, was never half a stiver richer in the world for his pains. Now Doctor Faustus began to experience the truth of this, inasmuch as the grand promises made by his demon in their first contract were mere bubbles, well worthy of their proprietor—a liar and the father of lies. For he had led the Doctor to believe that he was compelled into the service and overreached by him, so that vast riches would flow in upon him. Four years of his demon's apprenticeship had yet to run, though he was still not a whit the richer, either in gold or goods, for all that Mephistopheles had done. It was agreed likewise he was to partake only of the best fare that could be obtained at princes' courts wheresoever he should travel, as we have already seen. On this account he had held a variety of disputations with his familiar demon, which generally ended, however, by his inviting some boon companions to come and banquet with him. At length, finding himself in want of ready cash, he was compelled to apply to a certain Jew, with whom in the first instance he agreed for sixty dollars, which he promised to return in the space of one month. This being expired, the Jew went to demand his dollars with the interest which was become due, when the Doctor replied to his application as follows: "Jew, I have no money; and I have no means, just now, of procuring any. However, if you are willing to accept good security, I think we can come to terms. I will give you either an arm or a leg, whichever shall best please you, and which shall be made over to you as a pledge of mortgage; though under this one condition: that as soon as I shall have the money forthcoming, you will be prepared to restore to me my leg." Now, the Jew, being naturally every good Christian's enemy, thought to himself, I am glad of this, but he must be a most singular genius to think of pawning me his life and blood for the sake of money. What can I do with such security as this? But meanwhile Doctor Faustus, taking out a saw, was very leisurely sawing off his leg, which he handed to the Jew (though it was all mere illusion), repeating the same condition that he was to return it the moment he should obtain the money, as he (the Doctor) knew how to set it in its place again. So the Jew, not a little pleased with his contract, marched off with the Doctor's leg. When he had kept it, however, a short time, he began to think, What shall I do with this rogue of a Christian's limb? If I carry it about with me I shall be poisoned with the stench, besides its being of no further use to him when he shall want it, however good a security, for what more could he give? Being at length quite puzzled in which way to act for the best, one day as he was crossing over a bridge, weary with calculating *pro et contra*, he threw the Doctor's leg into the water, and thought himself well rid of it. Doctor Faustus, fully aware of what had passed, sent notice to the Jew three days afterwards that he was ready to repay him the money. The latter repented now that he had been so hasty, but he went. The first question put by the Doctor was what he had done with his pledge. "What have I done!" replied the Jew. "What could I do with it? It was of no use, and I threw it away." The Doctor on hearing this took the Jew roundly to task, declaring that he must have his leg again, come what would, or that he (the Jew) must look for the consequences. Alarmed at the violence of the Doctor's threats, the unlucky Israelite at length consented to adjust the matter by further advancing sixty dollars, in order to avoid the terrors of the law.

CHRISTIAN GELLERT

(1715–1769)

The son of a Saxon clergyman, Christian Fürchtegott (meaning Christian Fear-God) Gellert is said to have exemplified by his life the meaning of his names. For years a victim of ill-health and a hypochondriac, he spent the last part of his life lecturing on poetry at the University of Leipzig. He wrote plays, novels, fables and tales, but is to-day remembered only for his *Fables and Tales* in verse (1746-1748). These are written in a sprightly manner, and are conceived and executed with a delicacy that was rare among the German writers of Gellert's day.

The Sick Wife, one of the *Fables and Tales*, is translated especially for this volume, by Barrett H. Clark.

THE SICK WIFE

WHO can estimate the innumerable evils that constantly threaten the health and well-being of mankind? It is needful that we inquire into their causes, for the more we know of the dangers the better able are we to avoid trouble.

The fair young Sulpicia, dearly beloved of her husband, went off one day to visit a friend. Though she left home in the best of health, she returned half dead, it seemed, and at once threw herself down upon her bed. Could it be that her circulation had suddenly stopped? Her clothes were loosened, and three pairs of hands made busy to assist her. None too many, forsooth!

The poor young husband dissolved in a flood of tears: who could fail to be affected by so serious a situation? It was still too early, after but a single year of marriage, to wish to be rid of his wife! So he sent immediately for a physician. The youthful Æsculapius appeared on the scene in full regalia. Seating himself on the edge of the patient's bed, he assumed an expression as much as to say he had precisely the right remedy. He felt the wife's pulse, and wondered to himself what his medical books recommended in a case of this sort. But he ordered pen and ink to be brought him at once, and sat down to write. A servant was sent post-haste, and meantime the husband inquired what could be the trouble with his wife? The physician looked at him and smiled:

"You ask me what is the matter? There is really no need to tell you that. You know, it is a very good sign when young wives fret and complain!"

At this news the husband was overjoyed.

The night passed. The patient drank her potion, but it had no effect upon her at all. Another physician had to be summoned.

Patience! At last they were about to discover what really ailed the woman. The second physician was in no doubt: she was coming down with the smallpox!

Well, first she was going to become a mother, and then it was a case of smallpox!

Say no more, Doctors, and prescribe nothing further, for one of you at least is entirely in the wrong! Rather leave her in the hands of Nature and to the mercies of her own comfortable bed. No matter how dangerous the disease, it is not half so dangerous as the Doctors' cures.

Patience! Perhaps she will recover to-day.

Her good husband never left her side, and not a half-hour passed but he asked her a hundred times if she didn't feel a little better? My good fellow, what use is that? Will your talk not make her worse?

She spoke in gasps. It was easy to see by her speech that the pain was increasing. Alas, poor woman! Death seemed at hand. It would be a blessed release from her agony.

But hark! Who knocks? It must be the Doctor? No.

It was a tailor, bringing a dress. Ha, he comes in good time!

"Is it," asks the wife with great difficulty, "my funeral dress? Alas, I will look quite as pale. Had Heaven permitted me to live, I would have ordered a dress like that, of the same kind of material. The tailor would know just how to make it. He made one for my friend. It's the loveliest dress in the whole world. Last time I called on her she wore it. Ah, how short is life. All is vanity!"

Take courage, grief-stricken husband! You hear, do you not, that your wife can at last speak with considerable ease? Don't lose hope. The breath has not yet left her body.

The tailor left the room, and the husband went out with him, and the two spoke secretly together behind the closed door. The tailor swore mighty oaths, and went off to do what he promised. He returned before evening, and went in to Sulpicia who, still in bed, thanked him heartily for coming.

What did the tailor bring with him?

He proceeded at once to unroll something that was wrapped in cloth. What a wonderful sight to behold! The selfsame cloth, the rich and marvelous dress! But what was it doing there? Surely the young wife could not hope to wear it?

"My dearest angel," said her husband, "I would give everything I possess to see you well again and wearing this dress!"

"Oh, I am so ill," began the wife, "I am not even strong enough to deny you anything. I will get up from this bed, so that you may see this very day how the dress becomes me."

The screen was brought, and the poor woman, as weak as though she had lain in bed a whole year, got up. After she was completely dressed out in her finery, she sat down and drank coffee. Well at last! There was no trace of any illness.

A dress was what had ailed her, and a dress was the only effective remedy. A tailor had cured what no physician could so much as diagnose.

JAKOB GRIMM

(1775–1863)

WILHELM GRIMM

(1776–1859)

The Brothers Grimm, as they are still affectionately called, were both scholars of high repute, and both professors at the University of Berlin. Though they contributed a great deal to the science of philology and the history of literature, their fame rests chiefly on their collections of folk-tales, issued under the title *Children's and Household Stories*, in 1812 and 1814. These were the result of personal investigation and travel. *Little Briar-Rose* is only one of their many charming tales. It is to be observed that in the work of the Brothers Grimm the writers have moulded each story with a conscious art: they are not to be classified as scientists, but artists.

The present version, anonymously translated, is reprinted from an undated London edition of the *Tales of the Brothers Grimm.*

LITTLE BRIAR-ROSE

(From *Children's and Household Stories*)

LONG ago there was a king and a queen. They said every day, "Oh, if we only had a child!" and still they never got one. Then it happened, when once the queen was bathing, that a frog crept ashore out of the water, and said to her, "Your wish shall be fulfilled. Before a year passes you shall bring a daughter into the world."

What the frog said, happened, and the queen had a little girl that was so beautiful that the king could not contain himself for joy, and made a great feast. He invited not only his relatives, friends, and acquaintances, but also the wise women, that they might be gracious and kind to the child. Now, there were thirteen of them in his kingdom; but because he had only twelve gold plates for them to eat from, one of them had to stay at home. The feast was splendidly celebrated, and when it was over the wise women gave the child their wonderful gifts. One gave her virtue, another beauty, another wealth, and so with everything that people want in the world. But when eleven had spoken, suddenly the thirteenth came in. She wished to avenge herself, because she had not been asked; and without greeting or looking at anyone, she cried out, "In her fifteenth year the king's daughter shall wound herself on a spindle, and fall down dead." And without saying another word, she turned around and left the hall. All were frightened. When the twelfth came up, who had her wish still to give, since she could not remove the sentence, but only soften it, she said, "Yet it shall not be a real death, but only a hundred years' deep sleep, into which the king's daughter shall fall."

The king, who wanted to save his dear child from harm, sent out an order that all the spindles in the kingdom should be burned. But in the girl the gifts of the wise women were all fulfilled; for she was so beautiful, good, kind, and sensible, that nobody who saw her could help loving her. It happened that just on the day when she was fifteen years old the king and queen were not at home, and the little girl was left quite alone in the castle. Then she went wherever she pleased, looked in the rooms and chambers, and at last she got to an old tower. She went up the narrow winding stairs, and came to a little door. In the keyhole was a rusty key, and when she turned it the door sprang open, and there in a little room sat an old woman with a spindle, and spun busily her flax. "Good-day, Aunty," said the king's daughter; "what are you doing there?" "I am spinning," said the old woman, and nodded. "What sort of a thing is that that jumps about so gaily?" said the girl. She took the spindle and wanted to spin, too. But she had hardly touched the spindle before the spell was fulfilled, and she pricked her finger with it.

At the instant she felt the prick she fell down on the bed that stood there, and lay in a deep sleep. And this sleep spread over all the castle. The king and queen, who had just come home and entered the hall, began to go to sleep, and all the courtiers with them. The horses went to sleep in the stalls, the dogs in the yard, the doves on the roof, the flies on the wall, yes, the fire that was flickering on the hearth grew still and went to sleep. And the roast meat stopped sputtering, and the cook, who was going to take the cook-boy by the hair because he had forgotten something, let him go and slept. And the wind was still, and no leaf stirred in the trees by the castle.

But all around the castle a hedge of briars grew, that got higher every year and at last surrounded the whole castle and grew up over it, so that nothing more could be seen of it, not even the flag on the roof. But the story went about in the country of the beautiful sleeping Briar-Rose (for so the king's daughter was called); so that from time to time kings' sons came and tried to get through the hedge into the castle. But they could not; for the briars, as though they had hands, clung fast together, and the young men stuck fast in them, could not get out again, and died a wretched death. After long, long years, there came again a king's son to that country, and heard how an old man told about the briar hedge; that there was a castle behind it, in which a wonderfully beautiful king's daughter called Briar-Rose had been sleeping for a hundred years, and that the king and the queen and all the court were sleeping with her. He knew, too, from his grandfather that many kings' sons had already come and tried to get through the briar hedge, but had all been caught in it and died a sad death. Then the young man said, "I am not afraid. I will go and see the beautiful Briar-Rose." The good old man might warn him as much as he pleased; he did not listen to his words.

But now the hundred years were just passed, and the day was come when Briar-Rose was to wake again. So when the king's son went up to the briars, they were just great beautiful flowers that opened of their own accord and let him through unhurt; and behind him they closed together as a hedge again. In the yard he saw the horses and the mottled hounds lying and sleeping; on the roof perched the doves, their heads stuck under their wings; and when he came into the house the flies were sleeping on the wall, in the kitchen the cook still held up his hand as though to grab the boy, and the maid was sitting before the black hen that was to be plucked. Then he went further, and in the hall saw all the courtiers lying and sleeping, and upon their throne lay the king and the queen. Then he went further, and all was so still that you could hear yourself breathe; and at last he came to the tower and opened the door of the little room where Briar-Rose was sleeping. There she lay, and she was so beautiful that he could not take his eyes off her; and he bent down and gave her a kiss. But just as he touched her with the kiss,

Briar-Rose opened her eyes, awoke, and looked at him very kindly. Then they went downstairs together; and the king awoke, and the queen, and all the courtiers, and made great eyes at one another. And the horses in the yard got up and shook themselves, the hounds sprang about and wagged their tails, the doves on the roof pulled out their heads from under their wings, looked around and flew into the field, the flies on the wall went on crawling, the fire in the kitchen started up and blazed and cooked the dinner, the roast began to sputter again, and the cook gave the boy such a box on the ear that he screamed, and the maid finished plucking the hen. Then the wedding of the king's son with Briar-Rose was splendidly celebrated, and they lived happy till their lives' end.

E. T. A. HOFFMANN

(1776–1822)

ERNST THEODOR AMADEUS HOFFMANN was a master of one particular type of short story, which was to a great extent a product of the romantic tendencies of his times. His earliest collection of tales, *Fantasy Pieces in the Manner of Callot*, are characterized by those qualities of fantasy and mystery with which his name is always associated. The collection under the title of *The Serapion Brethren*, is set within a "frame-narrative of the story-telling club in Berlin, where Hoffmann spent the last six years of his life as judge of a criminal court."[1] Poe was especially indebted to Hoffmann in the composition of his stories, as were several of the most important Nineteenth Century fiction writers all over Europe.

The present translation, by Alexander Ewing, is reprinted from *The Serapion Brethren*, Bohn Library, London, by permission of the publishers, G. Bell and Sons.

THE STORY OF SERAPION

(From *The Serapion Brethren*)

"YOU know that some years ago I spent a considerable time in B——, a place in one of the pleasantest districts of the South of Germany. As my habit is, I used to take long walks in the surrounding country by myself, without any guide, though I should often have been the better for one. On one of these occasions I got into a piece of thickly wooded country and lost my way; the farther I went, the less could I discover the smallest vestige of a human footstep. At last the wood grew less thick, and I saw, not far from me, a man in a hermit's brown robe, with a broad straw hat on his head, and a long, wild black beard, sitting on a rock by the side of a deep ravine, gazing, with folded hands, thoughtfully into the distance. This sight had something so strange, unexpected, and out of the common about it that I felt a shiver of eeriness and awe. One can scarcely help such a feeling when what one has only heretofore seen in pictures, or read of in books, suddenly appears before one's eyes in actual, everyday life. Here was an anchorite of the early ages of Christianity, in the body, seated in one of Salvator Rosa's wild mountain scenes. But it soon occurred to me that probably a monk on his peregrinations was nothing uncommon in that part of the country. So I walked up to him, and asked if he could tell me the shortest way out of the wood to the high road leading to B——. He looked at me from head to foot with a gloomy glance, and said, in a hollow and solemn voice:

" 'I know well that it is merely an idle curiosity to see me, and to hear me speak which has led you to this desert. But you must perceive that I have no time to talk with you now. My friend Ambrosius of Camaldoli is returning to Alexandria. Travel with him.'

"With which he arose and walked down into the ravine.

"I felt as if I must be in a dream. Presently I heard the sound of wheels close by. I made my way through the thickets, and found myself in a forest track, where I saw a countryman going along in a cart. I overtook him, and he shortly brought me to the high road leading to B——. As we went along I told him my adventure, and asked if he knew who the extraordinary man in the forest was.

" 'Oh, sir,' he said, 'that was the worthy man who calls himself Priest Serapion, and who has been living in these woods for some years, in a little hut which he built himself. People say he's not quite right in his head, but he is a nice, good gentleman, never does any harm, and edifies us of the village with pious discourses, giving us all the good advice that he can.'

"I had come across the anchorite some six or eight miles from B——, so I concluded that something must be known of him there, and this proved to be the case. Dr. S—— told me all the story. This hermit had once been one of the most brilliant intellects, one of the most universally accomplished men in M——; and belonging, as he did, to a very distinguished family, he was naturally appointed to an important diplomatic post as soon as he had completed his studies: the duties of this office he discharged with great ability and energy. Moreover, he had remarkable poetical gifts, and everything he wrote was inspired by a most brilliant fancy, a mind and imagination which sounded the profoundest depths of all subjects. His incomparable humor, and the unusual charm of his character made him the most delightful of companions imaginable. He had risen from step to step of his career, and was on the point of being despatched on an important diplomatic mission, when he disappeared, in the most incomprehensible fashion, from M——. All search for him was fruitless, and conjecture and inquiry were baffled by a combination of circumstances.

"After a time there appeared amongst the villages, in the depths of the Tyrolese mountains, a man in a brown robe, who preached in these hamlets, and then went away into the wildest parts of the forests, where he lived the life of a hermit. It chanced one day that Count P—— saw this man (who called himself Priest Serapion), and at once recognized him as his unfortunate nephew, who had disappeared from M——. He was taken into custody, became violent, and all the skill of the best doctors in M—— could do nothing to alleviate his terrible condition. He was taken to the lunatic asylum at B——, and there the methodical system, based upon profound psychological knowledge, pursued by the medical man then in charge of that institution, succeeded in bringing about a condition of much less excitement, and greater quietness in the form of his malady. Whether this doctor, true to his theory, gave the patient an opportunity of escaping, or whether he himself found the means of doing so, escape he did, and was lost sight of for a considerable time.

"Serapion appeared, ultimately, in the country some eight miles from B——, where I had seen him; and the doctor declared that if any true compassion was to be shown him, he should not be again driven into a condition of wild excitement; but that, if he was to be at peace, and, after his fashion, happy, he should be left in these woods in perfect freedom, to do just as he liked; in which case he, the said doctor, would be responsible for the consequences. Accordingly, the police authorities were content to leave him to a distant and imperceptible supervision by the officials of the nearest village, and the result bore out what the doctor had said. Serapion built himself a little hut, pretty, and, under the circumstances, comfortable. He made chairs and tables, wove mats of rushes to lie upon, and laid out a garden where he grew flowers and vegetables. In all that did not touch the idea that he was the hermit Serapion who fled into the Theban desert in the days of the Emperor Decius, and suffered martyrdom in Alexandria, his mind was completely unaffected. He could carry on the most intellectual conversation, and often showed traces of the brilliant humor and charming individuality of character for which he had been remarkable in his former life. The aforesaid doctor declared him to be completely incurable, and strongly deprecated all attempts to restore him to the world and to his former pursuits and duties.

"You will readily understand that I could not drive this anchorite of mine out of my thoughts, and that I experienced an irresistible longing to see him again. But just picture to yourselves the excess of my folly!

I had no less an undertaking in my mind than that of attacking Serapion's fixed idea at its very roots. I read Pinel, Reil, every conceivable book on insanity which I could lay my hands on. I fondly believed that it might be reserved for *me*, an amateur psychologist and doctor, to cast some rays of light into Serapion's darkened intelligence. And I did not omit, either, to make myself acquainted with the stories of all the Serapions (there were no fewer than eight of them) treated of in the histories of saints and martyrs.

"Thus equipped, I set out one fine morning in search of my anchorite.

"I found him working in his garden with hoe and spade, singing a devotional song. Wild pigeons, for which he had strewed an abundant supply of food, were fluttering and cooing round him, and a young deer was peeping through the leaves on the trellis. He was evidently living in the closest intimacy with the woodland creatures. Not the faintest trace of insanity was visible in his face; it bore a quiet expression of remarkable serenity and happiness; and all this confirmed what Dr. S—— in B—— had told me. When he heard of my projected visit to the anchorite, he advised me to go some fine, bright, pleasant morning, because he said, his mind would be less troubled then and he would be more inclined to talk to a stranger, whereas at evening he would shun all intercourse with mankind.

"As soon as he saw me he laid down his spade, and came towards me in a kind and friendly manner. I said that, being weary with a longish journey, I should be glad if he would allow me to rest with him for a little while.

" 'You are heartily welcome,' he said. 'The little which I can offer you in the shape of refreshment is at your service.'

"And he took me to a seat of moss in front of his hut, brought out a little table, set on bread, magnificent grapes, and a can of wine, and hospitably begged me to eat and drink. He sat down opposite to me, and ate bread with much appetite, washing it down with draughts of water.

"In good sooth I did not see how I was to lead the conversation to my subject—how I was to bring my psychological science to bear upon this peaceful, happy man. At last I pulled myself together and began:

" 'You style yourself Serapion, reverend sir?'

" 'Yes, certainly,' he answered. 'The Church has given me that name.'

" 'Ancient ecclesiastical history,' I continued, 'mentions several celebrated holy men of that name. An abbot Serapion, known for his good works—the learned Bishop Serapion alluded to by Hieronimus in his book *De Viris Illustribus*. There was also a monk Serapion, who (as Heraclides relates in his *Paradise*) on one occasion, coming from the Theban desert to Rome, ordered a virgin, who had joined him—saying she had renounced the world and its pleasures—to prove this by walking with him naked in the streets of Rome, and repulsed her when she hesitated, saying, "You still live the life of Nature, and are careful for the opinions of mankind. Think not that you are anything great or have overcome the world." If I am not mistaken, reverend sir, this was the "filthy monk" (Heraclides himself so styles him) who suffered a terrible martyrdom under the Emperor Decius—his limbs being torn asunder at the joints, and his body thrown down from a lofty rock.'

" 'That was so,' said Serapion, turning pale, and his eyes glowing with a somber fire. 'But Serapion the martyr, had no connection with that monk, who, in the fury of his asceticism, did battle against human nature. *I* am Serapion the martyr, to whom you allude.'

" 'What?' I cried, with feigned surprise. '*You* believe that you are that Serapion who suffered such a hideous martyrdom so many hundred years ago?'

" 'That,' said Serapion with much calmness, 'may appear incredible to you, and I admit that it must sound very wonderful to many who cannot see further than the points of their own noses. However, it is as I tell you. God's omnipotence permitted me to survive my martyrdom, and to recover from its effects, because it was ordained, in His mysterious providence, that I had still to pass a certain period of my existence, to His praise and glory, here in the Theban desert. There is nothing now to remind me of the tortures which I suffered except sometimes a severe headache, and occasional violent cramps and twitchings in my limbs.'

" 'Now,' thought I, 'is the time to commence my cure.'

"I made a wide circumbendibus, and talked in an erudite style concerning the malady of 'Fixed Idea,' which attacks people, marring, like one single discord, the otherwise harmonious organisms. I spoke of the scientific man who could not be induced to rise from his chair for fear he would break the windows across the street with his nose. I mentioned the Abbot Molanus, who conversed most rationally upon every subject, but would not leave his room because he thought he was a barleycorn, and the hens would swallow him. I came to the fact that to confound oneself with some historical character was a frequent form of Fixed Idea. 'Nothing more absurd and preposterous,' I said, 'could possibly be imagined than that a little bit of woodland country eight miles from B——, daily frequented by country folk, sportsmen, and people walking for exercise was the Theban desert, and he himself that ascetic who suffered martyrdom many centuries ago.'

"Serapion listened in silence. He seemed to feel what I said, and to be struggling with himself in deep reflection. So that I thought it was time to strike my decisive blow. I stood up, took him by both hands, and cried, loudly and emphatically:

" 'Count P——, awake from the pernicious dream which is enthralling you; throw off that abominable dress, and come back to your family, which mourns your loss, and to the world where you have such important duties to discharge.'

"Serapion gazed at me with a somber, penetrating gaze. Then a sarcastic smile played about his lips and cheeks, and he said, slowly and solemnly:

" 'You have spoken, sir, long, and, as *you* consider, wisely and well. Allow *me*, in turn, to say a few words in reply. Saint Anthony, and all the men of the Church who have withdrawn from the world into solitude, were often visited by vexing spirits, who, envying the inward peace and contentment of their souls, carried on with them lengthy contests, until they had to lie down conquered in the dust. And such is *my* fortune also. Every now and then there appear to me emissaries, sent by Satan, who try to persuade me that I am Count P—— of M——, and that I ought to betake myself to the life of Courts, and all sorts of unholiness. Were it not for the efficacy of prayer, I should take these people by the shoulders, turn them out of my little garden, and carefully barricade it against them. But I need not do so in your case; for *you* are, most unmistakably, the very feeblest of all the adversaries who have ever come to me, and I can vanquish *you* with your own weapons—those of ratiocination. It is insanity that is in question between us. But if one of us two is suffering from that sad malady, it is evident that *you* are so in a much greater degree than I. You maintain that it is a case of Fixed Idea that I believe myself to be Serapion the martyr—and I am quite aware that many persons hold the same opinion, or pretend that they do. Now, if I am really insane, none but a lunatic can think that he could *argue* me out of the Fixed Idea which insanity has engendered in me. Were such a proceeding possible, there would soon be no madmen on the face of the earth, for men would be able to rule, and command, their mental power, which is not their own, but merely lent to them for a time by that Higher Power which disposes of them. But if I am *not* mad, and if I am really Serapion the martyr, it is insane to set about arguing me out of that, and leading me to adopt the Fixed Idea that I am Count P—— of M——. You say that Serapion the martyr lived several centuries ago, and that, consequently, I cannot be that martyr, presumably for the reason that human beings cannot remain so long on this earth. Well, as regards this, the notion of time is just as *relative* a notion as that of number; and I may say to you that, according to the notion of time which I have in *me*, it is scarcely three *hours* (or whatever appellation you may choose to give to the divisions of time) since I was put to martyrdom by the Emperor Decius. But, leaving this on one side, can you assert, in opposition to me, that a life of such length as I say I have lived, is unexampled and contrary to human nature? Have you cognizance of the precise length of the life of every human being who has existed in all this wide world, that you can employ the expression 'unexampled' in this pert and decisive manner? Do you compare God's omnipotence to the wretched art of the clockmaker, who can't save his lifeless machinery from destruction? You say this place where we are is not the Theban desert, but a little woodland district eight miles from B——, daily frequented by country folk, sportsmen and others. *Prove* that to me.'

"Here I thought I had my man.

" 'Come with me,' said I, 'and in a couple of hours we shall be in B——, and what I assert will be proved.'

" 'Poor blinded fool,' said Serapion. 'What a wide distance lies between us and B——! But put the case that I went with you to some town which you call B——; would you be able to convince me that we had been traveling for two hours only, and the place we had arrived at was really B——? If I were to assert that you were insane, and suppose the Theban desert is a little bit of wooded country, and far-away Alexandria the town of B—— in the south of Germany, what would you say in reply? Our old discussion would go on forever. Then there is another point which you ought seriously to consider. You must, I should suppose, perceive that I, who am talking with you, am leading the peaceful and happy life of a man reconciled with God. It is only after having passed through martyrdom that such a life dawns upon the soul. And if it has pleased the Almighty to cast a veil over what happened before my martyrdom, is it not a terrible and diabolical action to try to tear that veil away?'

"With all my wisdom, I stood confounded and silenced in the presence of this insane man! With the very rationality of his irrationality he had beaten me completely out of the field, and I saw the folly of my undertaking in all its fulness. Still more than that, I felt the reproach contained in what he had last said as deeply as I was astounded at the dim remembrance of his previous life which shone through it like some lofty, invulnerable higher spirit.

"Serapion seemed to be reading my thoughts, and, looking me full in the face with an expression of the greatest kindliness, he said:

" 'I never took you for an evil-disposed adversary, and I see I was not mistaken. You may have been instigated by somebody—perhaps by the Evil One himself—to come here to vex and try me, but I am sure it was not a spontaneous act of yours. And perhaps the fact that you found me other than you expected, may have strengthened you in your expression of the doubts which you have suggested. Although I in no sense deviate from the devoutness beseeming him who has given up his life to God and the Church, that cynicism of asceticism into which many of my brethren have fallen—thereby giving proof of the weakness, nay, utter destruction of their mental vigor, instead of its boasted strength—is utterly foreign to me! You expected to find the Monk Serapion pale and haggard, wasted with fast and vigil, all the horror of visions, terrible as those which drove even St. Anthony to despair, in his somber face, with quivering knees scarce able to support him, in a filthy robe, stained with his blood. You find a placid, cheerful man. But I, too, have passed through those tortures, and have overcome them and survived. And when I awoke with shattered limbs and fractured skull, the spirit dawned, and shone bright within me, restoring my mind and my body to health. May it please Heaven speedily to grant to *you* also, my brother, even here on earth, a peace and happiness such as those which daily refresh and strengthen *me*. Have no dread of the terror of the deepest solitude. It is only there that a life like this can dawn upon the pious soul.'

"Serapion, who had spoken with genuine priestly unction, raised, in silence, his eyes to Heaven with an expression of blissful gratitude. How could I feel otherwise than awe-struck! A madman, congratulating himself on his condition, looking upon it as a priceless gift from Heaven, and, from the depths of his heart, wishing me a similar fate!

"I was on the point of leaving him, but he began in an altered tone, saying:

" 'You would, probably, scarcely suppose that this wild inhospitable desert is often almost too full of the noise and bustle of life to be suitable for my silent meditations. Every day I receive visits from the most remarkable people of the most diverse kinds. Ariosto was here yesterday, and Dante and Petrarch afterwards. And this evening I expect Evagrus, the celebrated father, with whom I shall discuss the most recent ecclesiastical affairs, as I did poetry yesterday. I often go up to the top of that hill there, whence the towers of Alexandria are to be seen distinctly in clear weather, and the most wonderful and interesting events happen before my eyes. Many people have thought *that* incredible, too, and considered that I only *fancy* I see before me, in actual life, what is merely born in my mind and imagination. Now *I* say *that* is the most incomprehensible piece of folly that can exist. What is it, except the mind, which takes cognizance of what happens around us in time and space? What is it that hears, and feels, and sees? Is it the lifeless mechanism which we call eyes, ears, hands, etc., and not the mind? Does the mind give form and shape to that peculiar world of its own which has space and time for its conditions of existence, and *then* hand over the functions of seeing, hearing, etc., to some *other* principle inherent in us? How illogical! Therefore, if it is the mind only which takes cognizance of events around us, it follows that that which it has taken cognizance of *has* actually occurred. Last evening only, Ariosto was speaking of the images of his fancy, and saying he had created in his brain forms and events which had never existed in time and space. I at once denied the possibility of this, and he was obliged to allow that it was only from lack of a higher knowledge that a poet would box up within the narrow limits of his brain that which, by virtue of his peculiar seer gift, he was enabled to see in full life before him. But the complete acquirement of this higher knowledge only comes after martyrdom, and is strengthened by the life in profound solitude. You don't appear to agree with me; probably you don't understand me here. Indeed how could a child of this world, however well disposed, understand an anchorite consecrated in all his works and ways to God. Let me tell you what happened before my eyes, as I was standing this morning at sunrise at the top of that hill.'

"He then related a regular romance, with a plot and incidents such as only the most imaginative poet could have constructed. The characters and events stood out with such a vivid, plastic relief, that it was impossible—carried away as one was by the magic spell of them—to help believing, as if in a species of dream, that Serapion had actually witnessed them from the hilltop. This romance was succeeded by another, and that by another, by which time the sun stood high above us in the noontide sky. Serapion then rose from his seat, and looking into the distance, said: 'Yonder comes my brother Hilarion, who, in his overstrictness, always blames me for being too much given to the society of strangers.'

"I understood the hint, and took my leave, asking if I should be allowed to pay him another visit. Serapion answered with a gentle smile, 'My friend, I thought you would be eager to get away from this wilderness, so little adapted to your mode of life. But if it is your pleasure to take up your abode for a time in my neighborhood, you will always be welcome to my cottage and my little garden. Perhaps it may be granted to me to convert him who came to me as an adversary. Farewell, my friend.'

"I am wholly unable to characterize the impression which my visit to him had made upon me. Whilst his condition, his methodical madness in which he found the joy of his life, produced the weirdest effect upon me, his extraordinary poetical genius filled me with amazement, and his kindly, peaceful happiness, instinct with the quietest resignation of the purest mind, touched me unspeakably. I thought of Ophelia's sorrowful words:

> " 'O what a noble mind is here o'erthrown! etc.'

Yet I could not make plaint against the Omnipotence, which probably had, in this mysterious fashion, steered his bark away from reefs, which might have wrecked it, into this secure haven.

"The oftener I went to see him, the more attached to him I became. I always found him happy, and disposed to converse, and I took great care never again to essay my rôle of the psychological doctor. It was wonderful with what acuteness and penetration he spoke of life in all its aspects, and most remarkable of all, how he deduced historical events from causes wholly remote from all ordinary theories on the subject. When sometimes—notwithstanding the striking acuteness of those divinations of his—I took it upon me to object that no work on history made any mention of the circumstances which he alluded to, he would answer, with his quiet smile, that probably no historian in the world knew as much about them as he did, seeing that he had them from the very lips of the people concerned, when they came to see him.

"I was obliged to leave B—— and it was three years before I could go back there. It was late in Autumn, about the middle of November —the 14th, if I do not mistake—when I set out to pay my anchorite a visit. Whilst I was still at a distance, I heard the sound of the little bell which hung above his hut, and was filled with gloomy forebodings, without apparent cause. At last I reached the cottage and went in.

"Serapion was lying on his mat, with his hands folded on his breast. I thought he was sleeping, and went softly up to him. Then I saw that he was dead."

GOTTFRIED KELLER

(1819–1890)

KELLER, one of the most distinguished writers of Switzerland, is claimed by the Germans because he wrote in their language. The son of a Swiss mechanic, he spent a dreamy and aimless youth. He lived a great part of his life in Zürich. It was not until after his death that he was recognized as one of the masters of German literature. Professor Thomas declares that his "books are on the whole the very best reading to be found in the whole range of Nineteenth Century German fiction." He wrote almost entirely of his beloved Switzerland. His *Seven Legends* (1872), in which *A Legend of the Dance* first appeared, is one of his most beautiful books.

The present version, translated by Martin Wyness, is reprinted, by permission of the publishers, from *Seven Legends*, Gowans & Gray, Glasgow, 1911.

A LEGEND OF THE DANCE

ACCORDING to Saint Gregory, Musa was the dancer among the saints. The child of good people, she was a bright young lady, a diligent servant of the Mother of God, and subject only to one weakness, such an uncontrollable passion for the dance that when the child was not praying she was dancing, and that on all imaginable occasions. Musa danced with her playmates, with children, with the young men, and even by herself. She danced in her own room and every other room in the house, in the garden, in the meadows. Even when she went to the altar it was to a gracious measure rather than a walk, and even on the smooth marble flags before the church door, she did not scruple to practice a few hasty steps.

In fact, one day when she found herself alone in the church, she could not refrain from executing some figures before the altar, and, so to speak, dancing a pretty prayer to the Virgin Mary. She became so oblivious of all else that she fancied she was merely dreaming when she saw an oldish but handsome gentleman dancing opposite her and supplementing her figures so skilfully that the pair got into the most elaborate dance imaginable. The gentleman had a royal purple robe, a golden crown on his head, and a glossy black curled beard, which age had touched as with streaks of starlight. At the same time music sounded from the choir where half a dozen small angels stood, or sat with their chubby little legs hanging over the screen, and fingered or blew their various instruments. The urchins were very pleasant and skilful. Each rested his music on one of the stone angels with which the choir screen was adorned, except the smallest, a puffy-cheeked piper who sat cross-legged and contrived to hold his music with his pink toes. He was the most diligent of them all. The others dangled their feet, kept spreading their pinions, one or other of them, with a rustle, so that their colors shimmered like doves' breasts, and they teased each other as they played.

Musa found no time to wonder at all this until the dance, which lasted a pretty long time, was over; for the merry gentleman seemed to enjoy himself as much as the maid, who felt as if she were dancing about in heaven. But when the music ceased and Musa stood there panting, she began to be frightened in good earnest, and looked in astonishment at the ancient, who was neither out of breath nor warm, and who now began to speak. He introduced himself as David, the Virgin Mary's royal ancestor, and her ambassador. He asked if she would like to pass eternal bliss in an unending pleasure dance, compared with which the dance they had just finished could only be called a miserable crawl.

To this she promptly answered that she would like nothing better. Whereupon the blessed King David said again that in that case she had nothing more to do than to renounce all pleasure and all dancing for the rest of her days on earth and devote herself wholly to penance and spiritual exercises, and that without hesitation or relapse. The maiden was taken aback at these conditions, and asked whether she must really give up dancing altogether. She questioned indeed whether there was any dancing in Heaven; for there was a time for everything. This earth looked very fit and proper for dancing; it stood to reason that Heaven must have very different attractions, else death were a superfluity.

But David explained to her that her notions on the subject were erroneous, and proved from many Bible texts, and from his own example that dancing was assuredly a sanctified occupation for the blessed. But what was wanted just now was an immediate decision, Yes or No, whether she wished to enter into eternal joy by way of temporal self-denial, or not. If she did not, then he would go farther on; for they wanted some dancers in Heaven.

Musa stood, still doubtful and undecided, and fumbled anxiously with her finger-tips in her mouth. It seemed too hard never to dance again from that moment, all for the sake of an unknown reward. At that, David gave a signal, and suddenly the musicians struck up some bars of a dance of such unheard-of bliss and unearthliness that the girl's soul leaped in her body, and her limbs twitched; but she could not get one of them to dance, and she noticed that her body was far too heavy and stiff for the tune. Full of longing, she thrust her hand into the King's and made the promise which he demanded.

Forthwith he was no more to be seen, and the angel-musicians whirred and fluttered and crowded out and away through an open window. But, in mischievous childish fashion, before going they dealt the patient stone angels a sounding slap on the cheeks with their rolled-up music.

Musa went home with devout step, carrying that celestial melody in her ears; and having laid all her dainty raiment aside, she got a coarse gown made and put it on. At the same time she built herself a cell at the end of her parents' garden, where the deep shade of the trees lingered, made a scant bed of moss and from that day onward separated herself from all her kindred, and took up her abode there as a penitent and saint. She spent all her time in prayer, and often disciplined herself with a scourge. But her severest penance consisted in holding her limbs stiff and immovable, for whenever she heard a sound, the twitter of a bird or the rustling of the leaves in the wind, her feet twitched as much as to tell her they must dance.

As this involuntary twitching would not forsake her, and often seduced her to a little skip before she was aware, she caused her tender feet to be fastened together by a light chain. Her relatives and friends marveled day and night at the transformation, rejoiced to possess such a saint, and guarded the hermitage under the trees as the apple of their eye. Many came for her counsel and intercession. In particular, they used to bring young girls to her who were rather clumsy on their feet, for it was observed that everyone whom she touched at once became light and graceful in gait.

So she spent three years in her cell, but by the end of the third year Musa had become almost as thin and transparent as a summer cloud.

She lay continually on her bed of moss, gazed wistfully into Heaven, and was convinced that she could already see the golden sandals of the blessed, dancing and gliding about through the azure.

At last one harsh autumn day the tidings spread that the saint lay on her death-bed. She had taken off her dark penitential robe, and caused herself to be arrayed in bridal garments of dazzling white. So she lay with folded hands and smilingly awaited the hour of death. The garden was all filled with devout persons, the breezes murmured, and the leaves were falling from the trees on all sides. But suddenly the sighing of the wind changed into music, which appeared to be playing in the tree-tops, and as the people looked up, lo, all the branches were clad in fresh green, the myrtles and pomegranates put out blossom and fragrance, the earth decked itself with flowers, and a rosy glow settled upon the white, frail form of the dying saint.

That same instant she yielded up her spirit. The train about her feet sprang asunder with a sharp twang, Heaven opened wide all around, full of unbounded radiance so that all could see in. Then they saw many thousands of beautiful young men and maidens in the utmost splendor, dancing circle upon circle farther than the eye could reach. A magnificent King enthroned on a cloud, with a special band of small angels seated on its edge, bore down a little way towards earth, and received the form of the sainted Musa from before the eyes of all the beholders who filled the garden. They saw, too, how she sprang into the open Heaven and immediately danced out of sight among the jubilant radiant circle.

That was a high feast-day in Heaven. Now the custom (to be sure, it is denied by Saint Gregory of Nyssa, but stoutly maintained by his namesake of Nazianza) on feast-days was to invite the nine Muses, who sat for the rest of their time in Hell and to admit them to Heaven that they might be of assistance. They were well entertained, but once the feast was over had to go back to the other place.

When, now, the dances and songs and all the ceremonies had come to an end and the heavenly company sat down, Musa was taken to a table where the nine Muses were being served. They sat huddled together half scared, glancing about with their fiery black or dark-blue eyes. The busy Martha of the Gospels was caring for them in person. She had on her finest kitchen-apron and a tiny little smudge on her white chin and was pressing all manner of good things on the Muses in the friendliest possible way, but when Musa and Saint Cecilia and some other artistic women arrived and greeted the shy Pierians cheerfully, and joined their company, they began to thaw, grew confidential, and the feminine circle became quite pleasant and happy. Musa sat beside Terpsichore, and Cecilia between Polyhymnia and Euterpe, and all took one another's hands. Next came the little minstrel urchins and made up to the beautiful women with an eye to the bright fruit which shone on the ambrosial table. King David himself came and brought a golden cup, out of which all drank, so that gracious joy warmed them. He went round the table, not omitting as he passed to chuck pretty Erato under the chin. While things were going on so favorably at the Muses' table, Our Gracious Lady herself appeared in all her beauty and goodness, sat down a few minutes beside the Muses, and kissed the august Urania with the starry coronet tenderly upon the lips, when she took her departure, whispering to her that she would not rest until the Muses could remain in Paradise forever.

But that never came about. To declare their gratitude for the kindness and friendliness which had been shown them, and to prove their good-will, the Muses took counsel together and practised a hymn of praise in a retired corner of the Underworld. They tried to give it the form of the solemn chorals which were the fashion in Heaven. They arranged it in two parts of four voices each, with a sort of principal part, which Urania took, and they thus produced a remarkable piece of vocal music.

The next time a feast-day was celebrated in Heaven, and the Muses again rendered their assistance, they seized what appeared to be a favorable moment for their purpose, took their places, and began their song. It began softly, but soon swelled out mightily, but in those regions it sounded so dismal, almost defiant and harsh, yet so wistful and mournful that first of all a horrified silence prevailed, and next the whole assembly was seized with a sad longing for earth and home, and broke into universal weeping.

A sigh without end throbbed throughout Heaven. All the Elders and Prophets started up in dismay while the Muses, with the best of intentions, sang louder and more mournfully, and all Paradise, with the Patriarchs and Elders and Prophets and all who ever walked or lay in green pastures, lost all command of themselves. Until at last, the High and Mighty Trinity Himself came to put things right, and reduced the too zealous Muses to silence with a long reverberating peal of thunder.

Then quiet and composure were restored to Heaven, but the poor nine Sisters had to depart and never dared enter it again from that day onward.

PAUL HEYSE

(1830—)

Heyse is one of the most distinguished and highly respected German writers of the past century. Poet, novelist, dramatist, critic, he "created a new standard of style and artistic finish for the novelette." *The Fury* appeared in Heyse's first collection of stories, which was published in 1855. It is generally regarded as one of the very best stories in the German language.

Reprinted from the volume *Tales from the German of Paul Heyse,* New York, 1878, D. Appleton & Co., publishers, by whose permission it is here used. The original title is *L'Arrabbiata.*

THE FURY

THE day had scarcely dawned. Over Vesuvius hung one broad gray stripe of mist, stretching across as far as Naples, and darkening all the small towns along the coast. The sea lay calm. Along the shore of the narrow creek that lies beneath the Sorrento cliffs, fishermen and their wives were at work already, some with giant cables drawing their boats to land, with the nets that had been cast the night before, while others were rigging their craft, trimming the sails, or fetching out oars and masts from the great grated vaults that have been built deep into the rocks for shelter to the tackle overnight. Nowhere an idle hand; even the very aged, who had long given up going to sea, fell into the long chain of those who were hauling in the nets. Here and there, on some flat housetop, an old woman stood and spun, or busied herself about her grand-children, whom their mother had left to help her husband.

"Do you see, Rachela? yonder is our padre curato," said one to a little thing of ten, who brandished a small spindle by her side; "Antonio is to row him over to Capri. Madre Santissima! but the reverend signore's eyes are dull with sleep!" and she waved her hand to a benevolent-looking little priest, who was settling himself in the boat, and spreading out upon the bench his carefully tucked-up skirts.

The men upon the quay had dropped their work to see their pastor off, who bowed and nodded kindly, right and left.

"What for must he go to Capri, granny?" asked the child. "Have the people there no priest of their own, that they must borrow ours?"

"Silly thing!" returned the granny. "Priests they have in plenty—and the most beautiful of churches, and a hermit too, which is more than we have. But there lives a great signora, who once lived here; she was so very ill! Many's the time our padre had to go and take the Most Holy to her, when they thought she could not live the night. But with the Blessed Virgin's help she got strong and well, and was able to bathe every day in the sea. When she went away, she left a fine heap of ducats behind her for our church, and for the poor; and she would not go, they say, until our padre promised to go and see her over there, that she might confess to him as before. It is quite wonderful, the store she lays by him! Indeed, and we have cause to bless ourselves for having a curato who has gifts enough for an archbishop, and is in such request with all the great folks. The Madonna be with him!" she cried, and waved her hand again, as the boat was about to put from shore.

"Are we to have fair weather, my son?" inquired the little priest, with an anxious look toward Naples.

"The sun is not yet up," the young man answered; "when he comes, he will easily do for that small trifle of mist."

"Off with you, then! that we may arrive before the heat."

Antonio was just reaching for his long oar to shove away the boat, when suddenly he paused, and fixed his eyes upon the summit of the steep path that leads down from Sorrento to the water. A tall and slender girlish figure had become visible upon the heights, and was now hastily stepping down the stones, waving her handkerchief. She had a small bundle under her arm, and her dress was mean and poor. Yet she had a distinguished if somewhat savage way of throwing back her head, and the dark tress wreathed around it was like a diadem.

"What have we to wait for?" inquired the curato.

"There is someone coming who wants to go to Capri—with your permission, padre. We shall not go a whit the slower. It is a slight young thing, but just eighteen."

At that moment the young girl appeared from behind the wall that bounds the winding path.

"Laurella!" cried the priest. "And what has she to do in Capri?"

Antonio shrugged his shoulders. She came up with hasty steps, her eyes fixed straight before her.

"Ha! l'Arrabiata! good-morning!" shouted one or two of the young boatmen. But for the curato's presence, they might have added more; the look of mute defiance with which the young girl received their welcome appeared to tempt the more mischievous among them.

"Good-day, Laurella!" now said the priest. "How are you? Are you coming with us to Capri?"

"If I may, padre."

"Ask Antonio there; the boat is his. Every man is master of his own, I say, as God is master of us all."

"There is half a carlino, if I may go for that?" said Laurella, without looking at the young boatman.

"You need it more than I," he muttered, and pushed aside some orange-baskets to make room. He was to sell the oranges in Capri, which little isle of rocks has never been able to grow enough for all its visitors.

"I do not choose to go for nothing," said the girl, with a slight frown of her dark eyebrows.

"Come, child," said the priest; "he is a good lad, and had rather not enrich himself with that little morsel of your poverty. Come now, and step in," and he stretched out his hand to help her, "and sit you down by me. See, now, he has spread his jacket for you, that you may sit the softer. Young folks are all alike; for one little maiden of eighteen they will do more than for ten of us reverend fathers. Nay, no excuse, Tonino. It is the Lord's own doing, that like and like should hold together."

Meantime Laurella had stepped in, and seated herself beside the padre, first putting away Antonio's jacket without a word. The young fellow let it lie, and, muttering between his teeth, he gave one vigorous push against the pier, and the little boat flew out into the open bay.

"What are you carrying there in that little bundle?" inquired the padre, as they were floating on over a calm sea, now just beginning to be lighted up with the earliest rays of the rising sun.

"Silk, thread, and a loaf, padre. The silk is to be sold at Anacapri, to a woman who makes ribbons, and the thread to another."

"Spun by yourself?"

"Yes, sir."

"You once learned to weave ribbons yourself, if I remember right?"

"I did, sir; but mother has been much worse, and I cannot stay so long from home; and a loom to ourselves we are not rich enough to buy."

"Worse, is she? Ah! dear, dear! when I was with you last, at Easter, she was up."

"The spring is always her worst time. Ever since those last great storms, and the earthquakes she has been forced to keep her bed from pain."

"Pray, my child. Never slacken your prayers and petitions that the Blessed Virgin may intercede for you; and be industrious and good, that your prayers may find a hearing."

After a pause: "When you were coming toward the shore, I heard them calling after you. 'Good-morning, l'Arrabiata!' they said. What made them call you so? It is not a nice name for a young Christian maiden, who should be meek and mild."

The young girl's brown face glowed all over, while her eyes flashed fire.

"They always mock me so, because I do not dance and sing, and stand about to chatter, as other girls do. I might be left in peace, I think; I do *them* no harm."

"Nay, but you might be civil. Let others dance and sing, on whom this life sits lighter; but a kind word now and then is seemly even from the most afflicted."

Her dark eyes fell, and she drew her eyebrows closer over them, as if she would have hidden them.

They went on a while in silence. The sun now stood resplendent above the mountain chain; only the tip of Mount Vesuvius towered beyond the group of clouds that had gathered about its base; and on the Sorrento plains the houses were gleaming white from the dark green of their orange-gardens.

"Have you heard no more of that painter, Laurella?" asked the curato—"that Neapolitan, who wished so much to marry you?" She shook her head. "He came to make a picture of you. Why would you not let him?"

"What did he want it for? There are handsomer girls than I. Who knows what he would have done with it? He might have bewitched me with it, or hurt my soul, or even killed me, mother says."

"Never believe such sinful things!" said the little curato very earnestly. "Are not you ever in God's keeping, without whose will not one hair of your head can fall? and is one poor mortal with an image in his hand to prevail against the Lord? Besides, you might have seen that he was fond of you; else why should he want to marry you?"

She said nothing.

"And wherefore did you refuse him? He was an honest man, they say, and comely; and he would have kept you and your mother far better than you ever can yourself, for all your spinning and silk-winding."

"We are so poor!" she said passionately; "and mother has been ill so long, we should have become a burden to him. And then I never should have done for a signora. When his friends came to see him, he would only have been ashamed of me."

"How can you say so? I tell you the man was good and kind; he would even have been willing to settle in Sorrento. It will not be so easy to find another, sent straight from heaven to be the saving of you, as this man, indeed, appeared to be."

"I want no husband—I never shall," she said, very stubbornly, half to herself.

"Is this a vow? or do you mean to be a nun?"

She shook her head.

"The people are not so wrong who call you wilful, although the name they give you is not kind. Have you ever considered that you stand alone in the world, and that your perverseness must make your sick mother's illness worse to bear, her life more bitter? And what sound reason can you have to give for rejecting an honest hand, stretched out to help you and your mother? Answer me, Laurella."

"I have a reason," she said reluctantly, and speaking low; "but it is one I cannot give."

"Not give! not give to me? not to your confessor, whom you surely know to be your friend—or is he not?"

Laurella nodded.

"Then, child, unburden your heart. If your reason be a good one, I shall be the very first to uphold you in it. Only you are young, and know so little of the world. A time may come when you will find cause to regret a chance of happiness thrown away for some foolish fancy now."

Shyly she threw a furtive glance over to the other end of the boat, where the young boatman sat, rowing fast. His woolen cap was pulled deep down over his eyes; he was gazing far across the water, with averted head, sunk, as it appeared, in his own meditations.

The priest observed her look, and bent his ear down closer.

"You did not know my father?" she whispered, while a dark look gathered in her eyes.

"Your father, child! Why, your father died when you were ten years old. What can your father (Heaven rest his soul in paradise!) have to do with this present perversity of yours?"

"You did not know him, padre; you did not know that mother's illness was caused by him alone."

"And how?"

"By his ill-treatment of her; he beat her and trampled upon her. I well remember the nights when he came home in his fits of frenzy. She never said a word, and did everything he bade her. Yet he would beat her so, my heart felt ready to break. I used to cover up my head and pretend to be asleep, but I cried all night. And then, when he saw her lying on the floor, quite suddenly he would change, and lift her up and kiss her till she screamed and said he smothered her. Mother forbade me ever to say a word of this; but it wore her out. And in all these long years since father died, she has never been able to get well again. And if she should soon die—which God forbid!—I know who it was that killed her."

The little curato's head wagged slowly to and fro; he seemed uncertain how far to acquiesce in the young girl's reasons. At length he said: "Forgive him, as your mother has forgiven! And turn your thoughts from such distressing pictures, Laurella; there may be better days in store for you, which will make you forget the past."

"Never shall I forget that!" she said, and shuddered. "And you must know, padre, it is the reason why I have resolved to remain unmarried. I never will be subject to a man, who may beat and then caress me. Were a man now to want to beat or kiss me, I could defend myself; but mother could not—neither from his blows nor kisses—because she loved him. Now, I will never so love a man as to be made ill and wretched by him."

"You are but a child, and you talk like one who knows nothing at all of life. Are all men like that poor father of yours? Do all ill-treat their wives, and give vent to every whim and gust of passion? Have you never seen a good man yet? or known good wives, who live in peace and harmony with their husbands?"

"But nobody ever knew how father was to mother; she would have died sooner than complain or tell of him, and all because she loved him.

If this be love—if love can close our lips when they should cry out for help—if it is to make us suffer without resistance, worse than even our worst enemy could make us suffer—then, I say, I never will be fond of mortal man."

"I tell you you are childish; you know not what you are saying. When your time comes, you are not likely to be consulted whether you choose to fall in love or not." After a pause, he added, "And that painter: did you think he could have been cruel?"

"He made those eyes I have seen my father make, when he begged my mother's pardon and took her in his arms to make it up. I know those eyes. A man may make such eyes, and yet find it in his heart to beat a wife who never did a thing to vex him! It made my flesh creep to see those eyes again."

After this she would not say another word. The curato also remained silent. He bethought himself of more than one wise saying, wherewith the maiden might have been admonished; but he refrained, in consideration of the young boatman, who had been growing rather restless toward the close of this confession.

When, after two hours' rowing, they reached the little bay of Capri, Antonio took the padre in his arms, and carried him through the last few ripples of shallow water, to set him reverently down upon his legs on dry land. But Laurella did not wait for him to wade back and fetch her. Gathering up her little petticoat, holding in one hand her wooden shoes and in the other her little bundle, with one splashing step or two she had reached the shore. "I have some time to stay at Capri," said the priest. "You need not wait—I may not perhaps return before to-morrow. When you get home, Laurella, remember me to your mother; I will come and see her within the week. You mean to go back before it gets dark?"

"If I find an opportunity," answered the girl, turning all her attention to her skirts.

"I must return, you know," said Antonio, in a tone which he believed to be one of great indifference. "I shall wait here till the Ave Maria. If you should not come, it is the same to me."

"You must come," interposed the little priest; "you never can leave your mother all alone at night. Is it far you have to go?"

"To a vineyard by Anacapri."

"And I to Capri. So now God bless you, child—and you, my son."

Laurella kissed his hand, and let one farewell drop, for the padre and Antonio to divide between them. Antonio, however, appropriated no part of it to himself; he pulled off his cap exclusively to the padre, without even looking at Laurella. But after they had turned their backs, he let his eyes travel but a short way with the padre, as he went toiling over the deep bed of small, loose stones; he soon sent them after the maiden, who, turning to the right, had begun to climb the heights, holding one hand above her eyes to protect them from the scorching sun. Just before the path disappeared behind high walls, she stopped, as if to gather breath, and looked behind her. At her feet lay the marina; the rugged rocks rose high around her; the sea was shining in the rarest of its deep-blue splendor. The scene was surely worth a moment's pause. But, as chance would have it, her eyes, in glancing past Antonio's boat, met Antonio's own, which had been following her as she climbed.

Each made a slight movement, as persons do who would excuse themselves for some mistake; and then, with her darkest look, the maiden went her way.

Hardly one hour had passed since noon, and yet for the last two Antonio had been sitting waiting on the bench before the fishers' tavern. He must have been very much preoccupied with something, for he jumped up every moment to step out into the sunshine, and look carefully up and down the roads, which, parting right and left, lead to the only two little towns upon the island. He did not altogether trust the weather, he then said to the hostess of the osteria; to be sure, it was clear enough, but he did not quite like that tint of sea and sky. Just so it had looked, he said, before the last awful storm, when the English family had been so nearly lost; surely she must remember it?

No, indeed, she said, she didn't.

Well, if the weather should happen to change before night, she was to think of him, he said.

"Have you many fine folk over there?" she asked him, after a while.

"They are only just beginning; as yet, the season has been bad enough; those who came to bathe, came late."

"The spring came late. Have you not been earning more than we at Capri?"

"Not enough to give me macaroni twice a week, if I had had nothing but the boat—only a letter now and then to take to Naples, or a gentleman to row out into the open sea, that he might fish. But you know I have an uncle who is rich; he owns more than one fine orange-garden; and, 'Tonino,' says he to me, 'while I live you shall not suffer want; and when I am gone you will find that I have taken care of you.' And so, with God's help, I got through the winter."

"Has he children, this uncle who is rich?"

"No, he never married; he was long in foreign parts, and many a good piastre he has laid together. He is going to set up a great fishing business, and set me over it, to see the rights of it."

"Why, then you are a made man, Tonino!"

The young boatman shrugged his shoulders. "Every man has his own burden," said he, starting up again to have another look at the weather, turning his eyes right and left, although he must have known that there can be no weather side but one.

"Let me fetch you another bottle," said the hostess; "your uncle can well afford to pay for it."

"Not more than one glass; it is a fiery wine you have in Capri, and my head is hot already."

"It does not heat the blood; you may drink as much of it as you like. And here is my husband coming; so you must sit a while, and talk to him."

And in fact, with his nets over his shoulder, and his red cap upon his curly head, down came the comely padrone of the osteria. He had been taking a dish of fish to that great lady, to set before the little curato. As soon as he caught sight of the young boatman, he began waving him a most cordial welcome; and he came to sit beside him on the bench, chattering and asking questions. Just as his wife was bringing her second bottle of pure unadulterated Capri, they heard the crisp sand crunch, and Laurella was seen approaching from the left-hand road to Anacapri. She nodded slightly in salutation; then stopped, and hesitated.

Antonio sprang from his seat. "I must go," he said. "It is a young Sorrento girl, who came over with the signor curato in the morning. She has to get back to her sick mother before night."

"Well, well, time enough yet before night," observed the fisherman; "time enough to take a glass of wine. Wife, I say, another glass!"

"I thank you; I had rather not"; and Laurella kept her distance.

"Fill the glasses, wife; fill them both, I say; she only wants a little pressing."

"Don't," interposed the lad. "It is a wilful head of her own she has; a saint could not persuade her to do what she does not choose." And, taking a hasty leave, he ran down to the boat, loosened the rope, and stood waiting for Laurella. Again she bent her head to the hostess, and slowly approached the water, with lingering steps. She looked around on every side, as if in hopes of seeing some other passenger. But the marina was deserted. The fishermen were asleep, or rowing about the coast with rods or nets; a few women and children sat before their doors, spinning or sleeping; such strangers as had come over in the morning were waiting for the cool of the evening to return. She had not time to look about her long; before she could prevent him, Antonio had seized her in his arms and carried her to the boat, as if she had been an infant. He leaped in after her, and with a stroke or two of his oar they were in deep water.

She had seated herself at the end of the boat, half turning her back to him, so that he could only see her profile. She wore a sterner look than ever; the low, straight brow was shaded by her hair; the rounded lips were firmly closed; only the delicate nostril occasionally gave a wilful quiver. After they had gone on a while in silence, she began to feel the scorching of the sun; and, unloosening her bundle, she threw the handkerchief over her head, and began to make her dinner of the bread; for in Capri she had eaten nothing.

Antonio did not stand this long; he fetched out a couple of the oranges with which the baskets had been filled in the morning. "Here is something to eat to your bread, Laurella," he said. "Don't think I kept them for you; they had rolled out of the basket, and I only found them when I brought the baskets back to the boat."

"Eat them yourself; bread is enough for me."

"They are refreshing in this heat, and you have had to walk so far."

"They gave me a drink of water, and that refreshed me."

"As you please," he said, and let them drop into the basket.

Silence again. The sea was smooth as glass. Not a ripple was heard against the prow. Even the white sea-birds that roost among the caves of Capri pursued their prey with soundless flight.

"You might take the oranges to your mother," again commenced Tonino.

"We have oranges at home; and when they are gone, I can go and buy some more."

"Nay, take these to her, and give them to her with my compliments."

"She does not know you."

"You could tell her who I am."

"I do not know you either."

It was not the first time that she had denied him thus. One Sunday of last year, when that painter had first come to Sorrento, Antonio had chanced to be playing *boccia* with some other young fellows in the little piazza by the chief street.

There, for the first time, had the painter caught sight of Laurella, who, with her pitcher on her head, had passed by without taking any notice of him. The Neapolitan, struck by her appearance, stood still and gazed after her, not heeding that he was standing in the very midst of the game, which, with two steps, he might have cleared. A very ungentle ball came knocking against his shins, as a reminder that this was not the spot to choose for meditation. He looked round, as if in expectation of some excuse. But the young boatman who had thrown the ball stood silent among his friends, in such an attitude of defiance that the stranger had found it more advisable to go his ways and avoid discussion. Still, this little encounter had been spoken of, particularly at the time when the painter had been pressing his suit to Laurella. "I do not even know him," she said indignantly, when the painter asked her whether it was for the sake of that uncourteous lad she now refused him. But she had heard that piece of gossip, and known Antonio well enough when she had met him since.

And now they sat together in this boat, like two most deadly enemies, while their hearts were beating fit to kill them. Antonio's usually so good-humored face was heated to scarlet; he struck the oars so sharply that the foam flew over to where Laurella sat, while his lips moved as if muttering angry words. She pretended not to notice, wearing her most unconscious look, bending over the edge of the boat, and letting the cool water pass between her fingers. Then she threw off her handkerchief again, and began to smooth her hair, as though she had been alone. Only her eyebrows twitched, and she held up her wet hands in vain attempts to cool her burning cheeks.

Now they were well out in the open sea. The island was far behind, and the coast before them lay yet distant in the hot haze. Not a sail was within sight, far or near—not even a passing gull to break the stillness. Antonio looked all round, evidently ripening some hasty resolution. The color faded suddenly from his cheek, and he dropped his oars. Laurella looked round involuntarily—fearless, yet attentive.

"I must make an end of this," the young fellow burst forth. "It has lasted too long already! I only wonder that it has not killed me! You say you do not know me? And all this time you must have seen me pass you like a madman, my whole heart full of what I had to tell you; and then you only made your crossest mouth, and turned your back upon me."

"What had I to say to you?" she curtly replied. "I may have seen that you were inclined to meddle with me, but I do not choose to be on people's wicked tongues for nothing. I do not mean to have you for a husband—neither you nor any other."

"Nor any other? So you will not always say! You say so now, because you would not have that painter. Bah, you were but a child! You will feel lonely enough yet, some day; and then, wild as you are, you will take the next best who comes to hand."

"Who knows? which of us can see the future? It may be that I will change my mind. What is that to you?"

"What is it to me?" he flew out, starting to his feet, while the small boat leaped and danced. "What is it to me, you say? You know well enough! I tell you, that man shall perish miserably to whom you shall prove kinder than you have been to me!"

"And to you, what did I ever promise? Am I to blame if you be mad? What right have you to me?"

"Ah! I know," he cried, "my right is written nowhere. It has not been put in Latin by any lawyer, nor stamped with any seal. But this I feel: I have just the right to you that I have to heaven, if I die an honest Christian. Do you think I could look on and see you go to church with another man, and see the girls go by and shrug their shoulders at me?"

"You can do as you please. I am not going to let myself be frightened by all those threats. I also mean to do as I please."

"You shall not say so long!" and his whole frame shook with passion. "I am not the man to let my whole life be spoiled by a stubborn wench like you! You are in my power here, remember, and may be made to do my bidding."

She could not repress a start, but her eyes flashed bravely on him.

"You may kill me if you dare," she said slowly.

"I do nothing by halves," he said, and his voice sounded choked and hoarse. "There is room for us both in the sea. I cannot help thee, child"—he spoke the last words dreamily, almost pitifully—"but we must both go down together—both at once—and now!" he shouted, and snatched her in his arms. But at the same moment he drew back his right hand; the blood gushed out; she had bitten him fiercely.

"Ha! can I be made to do your bidding?" she cried, and thrust him from her, with one sudden movement. "Am I here in your power?" and she leaped into the sea, and sank.

She rose again directly; her scanty skirts clung close; her long hair, loosened by the waves, hung heavy about her neck. She struck out valiantly, and, without uttering a sound, she began to swim steadily from the boat toward the shore.

With senses benumbed by sudden terror, he stood, with outstretched neck, looking after her, his eyes fixed as though they had just been witness to a miracle. Then, giving himself a shake, he seized his oars, and began rowing after her with all the strength he had, while all the time the bottom of the boat was reddening fast with the blood that kept streaming from his hand.

Rapidly as she swam, he was at her side in a moment. "For the love of our most Holy Virgin," he cried, "get into the boat! I have been a madman! God alone can tell what so suddenly darkened my brain. It came upon me like a flash of lightning and set me all on fire. I knew not what I did or said. I do not even ask you to forgive me, Laurella, only to come into the boat again and not to risk your life!"

She swam on as though she had not heard him.

"You can never swim to land. I tell you it is two miles off. Think of your mother! If you should come to grief, I should die of horror."

She measured the distance with her eye, and then, without answering him one word, she swam up to the boat, and laid her hands upon the edge; he rose to help her in. As the boat tilted over to one side with the girl's weight, his jacket that was lying on the bench slipped into the water. Agile as she was, she swung herself on board without assistance, and gained her former seat. As soon as he saw that she was safe, he took to his oars again, while she began quietly wringing out her dripping clothes, and shaking the water from her hair. As her eyes fell upon the bottom of the boat, and saw the blood, she gave a quick look at the hand, which held the oar as if it had been unhurt.

"Take this," she said, and held out her handkerchief. He shook his head, and went on rowing. After a time she rose, and, stepping up to him, bound the handkerchief firmly round the wound, which was very deep. Then, heedless of his endeavors to prevent her, she took an oar, and, seating herself opposite him, began to row with steady strokes, keeping her eyes from looking toward him—fixed upon the oar that was scarlet with his blood. Both were pale and silent. As they drew near land, such fishermen as they met began shouting after Antonio and gibing at Laurella; but neither of them moved an eyelid, or spoke one word.

The sun stood yet high over Procida when they landed at the marina. Laurella shook out her petticoat, now nearly dry, and jumped on shore. The old spinning woman, who in the morning had seen them start, was still upon her terrace. She called down, "What is that upon your hand, Tonino? Jesus Christ! the boat is full of blood!"

"It is nothing, comare," the young fellow replied. "I tore my hand against a nail that was sticking out too far; it will be well to-morrow. It is only this confounded ready blood of mine, that always makes a thing look worse than it is."

"Let me come and bind it up, comparello. Stop one moment; I will go and fetch the herbs, and come to you directly."

"Never trouble yourself, comare. It has been dressed already; to-morrow morning it will be all over and forgotten. I have a healthy skin, that heals directly."

"Addio!" said Laurella, turning to the path that goes winding up the cliffs. "Good-night!" he answered, without looking at her; and then taking his oars and baskets from the boat, and climbing up the small stone stairs, he went into his own hut.

He was alone in his two little rooms, and began to pace them up and down. Cooler than upon the dead calm sea, the breeze blew fresh through the small unglazed windows, which could only be closed with wooden shutters. The solitude was soothing to him. He stooped before the little image of the Virgin, devoutly gazing upon the glory round the head (made of stars cut out in silver paper). But he did not want to pray. What reason had he to pray, now that he had lost all he had ever hoped for?

And this day appeared to last forever. He did so long for night! for he was weary, and more exhausted by the loss of blood than he would have cared to own. His hand was very sore. Seating himself upon a little stool, he untied the handkerchief that bound it; the blood, so long repressed, gushed out again; all round the wound the hand was swollen high.

He washed it carefully, cooling it in the water; then he clearly saw the marks of Laurella's teeth.

"She was right," he said; "I was a brute, and deserved no better. I will send her back the handkerchief by Giuseppe to-morrow. Never shall she set eyes on me again." And he washed the handkerchief with the greatest care, and spread it out in the sun to dry.

And having bound up his hand again, as well as he could manage with his teeth and his left hand, he threw himself upon his bed, and closed his eyes.

He was soon waked up from a sort of slumber by the rays of the bright moonlight, and also by the pain of his hand; he had just risen for more cold water to soothe its throbbings, when he heard the sound of someone at the door. Laurella stood before him.

She came in without a question, took off the handkerchief she had tied over her head, and placed her little basket upon the table; then she drew a deep breath.

"You are come to fetch your handkerchief," he said. "You need not have taken that trouble. In the morning I would have asked Giuseppe to take it to you."

"It is not the handkerchief," she said quickly. "I have been up among the hills to gather herbs to stop the blood; see here." And she lifted the lid of her little basket.

"Too much trouble," he said, not in bitterness—"far too much trouble. I am better, much better; but if I were worse, it would be no more than I deserve. Why did you come at such a time? If any one should see you? You know how they talk, even when they don't know what they are saying."

"I care for no one's talk," she said, passionately. "I came to see your hand, and put the herbs upon it; you cannot do it with your left."

"It is not worth while, I tell you."

"Let me see it then, if I am to believe you."

She took his hand, that was not able to prevent her, and unbound the linen. When she saw the swelling, she shuddered, and gave a cry: "Jesus Maria!"

"It is a little swollen," he said; "it will be over in four-and-twenty hours."

She shook her head. "It will certainly be a week before you can go to sea."

"More likely a day or two; and if not, what matters?"

She had fetched a basin, and began carefully washing out the wound, which he suffered passively, like a child. She then laid on the healing leaves, which at once relieved the burning pain, and finally bound it up with the linen she had brought with her.

When it was done: "I thank you," he said. "And now, if you would do me one more kindness, forgive the madness that came over me; forget all I said and did. I cannot tell how it came to pass; certainly it was not your fault—not yours. And never shall you hear from me again one word to vex you."

She interrupted him. "It is I who have to beg your pardon. I should have spoken differently. I might have explained it better, and not enraged you with my sullen ways. And now that bite—"

"It was in self-defense; it was high time to bring me to my senses. As I said before, it is nothing at all to signify. Do not talk of being forgiven; you only did me good, and I thank you for it. And now, here is your handkerchief; take it with you."

He held it to her, but yet she lingered, hesitated, and appeared to have some inward struggle. At length she said: "You have lost your jacket, and by my fault; and I know that all the money for the oranges was in it. I did not think of this till afterward. I cannot replace it now; we have not so much at home—or if we had, it would be mother's. But this I have—this silver cross. That painter left it on the table the day he came for the last time. I have never looked at it all this while, and do not care to keep it in my box; if you were to sell it? It must be worth a few piastres, mother says. It might make up the money you have lost; and if not quite, I could earn the rest by spinning at night when mother is asleep."

"Nothing will make me take it," he said shortly, pushing away the bright new cross which she had taken from her pocket.

"You must," she said; "how can you tell how long your hand may keep you from your work? There it lies; and nothing can make me so much as look at it again."

"Drop it in the sea, then."

"It is no present I want to make you; it is no more than is your due; it is only fair."

"Nothing from you can be due to me; and hereafter when we chance to meet, if you would do me a kindness, I beg you not to look my way. It would make me feel you were thinking of what I have done. And now good-night; and let this be the last word said."

She laid the handkerchief in the basket, and also the cross, and closed the lid. But when he looked into her face, he started. Great heavy drops were rolling down her cheeks; she let them flow unheeded.

"Maria Santissima!" he cried. "Are you ill? You are trembling from head to foot!"

"It is nothing," she said; "I must go home"; and with unsteady steps she was moving to the door, when suddenly she leaned her brow against the wall, and gave way to a fit of bitter sobbing. Before he could go to her she turned upon him suddenly, and fell upon his neck.

"I cannot bear it!" she cried, clinging to him as a dying thing to life —"I cannot bear it! I cannot let you speak so kindly, and bid me go, with all this on my conscience. Beat me! trample on me! curse me! Or if it can be that you love me still, after all I have done to you, take me and keep me, and do with me as you please; only do not send me away so!" She could say no more for sobbing.

Speechless, he held her a while in his arms. "If I can love you still!" he cried at last. "Holy Mother of God! Do you think that all my best heart's blood has gone from me through that little wound? Don't you hear it hammering now, as though it would burst my breast and go to you? But if you say this to try me, or because you pity me, I can forget it. You are not to think you owe me this, because you know what I have suffered for you."

"No!" she said very resolutely, looking up from his shoulder into his face, with her tearful eyes; "it is because I love you; and let me tell you, it was because I always feared to love you that I was so cross. I will be so different now. I never could bear again to pass you in the street without one look! And lest you should ever feel a doubt, I will kiss you, that you may say, 'She kissed me'; and Laurella kisses no man but her husband."

She kissed him thrice, and, escaping from his arms: "And now good-night, amor mio, cara vita mia!" she said. "Lie down to sleep, and let your hand get well. Do not come with me; I am afraid of no man, save of you alone."

And so she slipped out, and soon disappeared in the shadow of the wall.

He remained standing by the window, gazing far out over the calm sea, while all the stars in heaven appeared to flit before his eyes.

The next time the little curato sat in his confessional, he sat smiling to himself. Laurella had just risen from her knees after a very long confession.

"Who would have thought it?" he said musingly—"that the Lord would so soon have taken pity upon that wayward little heart? And I had been reproaching myself for not having adjured more sternly that ill demon of perversity. Our eyes are but shortsighted to see the ways of Heaven! Well, may God bless her, I say, and let me live to go to sea with Laurella's eldest born rowing me in his father's place! Ah! well, indeed! l'Arrabiata!"

ARTHUR SCHNITZLER

(1862—)

ARTHUR SCHNITZLER, born at Vienna in 1862, is one of the most distinguished figures in contemporary Austrian literature, and a dramatist and fiction writer of international renown. His delicately written and finely conceived short stories are among the very best of their kind. *The Triple Warning* is a philosophical and metaphysical parable related in the author's best and most brilliant style.

The present version is translated especially for this collection by Barrett H. Clark, from the volume *Masks and Miracles*, by permission of the author.

THE TRIPLE WARNING

IN the morning mist, shot through with the blue of the heavens, a youth was making his way toward the beckoning mountains. His heart thrilled to the rhythmical beat of all the world. Without a care or worry he went on for hours over the level country when, on reaching the edge of a forest, a voice rang out, sounding at once near at hand and far-off, and very mysterious:

"Go not through this forest, youth, unless thou wouldst commit murder."

The youth stood still in astonishment, looked in every direction, and seeing nowhere any sign of a living being, concluded that it was a spirit that had addressed him. But his innate courage would not permit him to heed the strange call, and reducing his gait only a little, he proceeded on his way without misgiving, his senses keenly alert, in order that he might be prepared for a meeting with the unknown enemy that had warned him. But he met no one, nor heard any suspicious sound as, unchallenged, he emerged out of the deep shadows of the trees into the open. Under the last wide boughs he sank down for a short rest, allowing his eyes to wander out across a wide meadow toward the mountains, from among which one peak rose aloft, naked and sharply outlined. This was his ultimate goal.

But scarcely had he arisen again when for the second time the mysterious voice was heard, sounding at once near at hand and far-off, mysteriously, but more earnestly than before:

"Go not through this meadow, youth, unless thou wouldst bring ruin to thy Fatherland."

The youth's pride this time forbade his taking heed; he even smiled at the rigmarole, which was delivered with the air as of one concealing something very important, and hurried on, not knowing whether impatience or unrest hastened his steps. The damp mist of evening descended upon the plain as he at last stood facing the rocky wall below his goal. Hardly had he set foot upon the bare surface of the stone, when the voice rang out again, near at hand and far-off, mysteriously, but more threateningly than before:

"No farther, youth, else wilt thou suffer death."

The youth laughed loudly and, without haste or hesitation, went on his way. And the less clear the ascending path became, the more did his chest expand, and finally on the bravely conquered peak his head was illumined by the last light of day.

"Here I am!" he called out in a tone of triumph. "If this was a test, O good or evil spirit, then have I won! No murder weighs on my conscience, unharmed slumbers my Fatherland below, and I still live. Whosoever thou art, I am stronger than thou, for I did not believe thee, and I did right."

Whereupon came a great sound as of thunder from the mountain sides, and at the same time exceeding close at hand:

"Youth, thou errest!" And the overpowering weight of the words felled the wanderer. He stretched himself out on the edge of rock as though he intended to rest there, and with an ironical curl of the lips he said half to himself:

"So it appears that I have committed murder without knowing it!"

"Thy careless foot has crushed a worm," the answer thundered back. And the youth answered with indifference:

"I see: neither a good nor an evil spirit spoke to me, but a spirit with a sense of humor. I was not aware that such hovered about among us mortals."

And again the voice resounded in the fading twilight of the heights:

"Art thou then no longer the same youth whose heart only this morning thrilled to the rhythmical beat of all the world? Is thy soul so dead that thou art untouched by the happiness and sorrow of even a worm?"

"Is that thy meaning?" replied the youth, wrinkling his forehead. "In that event am I a hundred—a thousand times guilty, like other mortals, whose careless steps have innocently destroyed tiny creatures without number."

"Against this particular thing wast thou warned. Dost thou know to what purpose this worm was destined in the eternal scheme of things?"

With sunken head the youth made answer:

"Since I neither knew nor could know that, thou must humbly confess that in my wandering through the forest I have committed precisely the one of many possible murders that it was thy will to prevent. But how I have contrived in my way over the fields to bring ruin to my Fatherland, I am really most curious to learn."

"Sawest thou, youth, the bright-colored butterfly," came the whispered answer, "that fluttered once to the right of thee?"

"Many butterflies did I see, as well as the one thou mentionest."

"Many butterflies! Ah, many did the breath from thy lips drive far from their way; but the one I speak of was driven off to the east, winging its way far and wide until it flew over the golden fence that encloses the royal park. From that butterfly will be born the caterpillar which next year, one hot summer afternoon, will crawl over the white neck of the young queen, awakening her so suddenly from her sleep that her heart will stand still in her breast, and the fruit of her womb languish and die. Thus the king's brother will inherit the kingdom instead of the rightful heir, whom thou wilt have cheated of his life; vicious, malicious, and cruel, he will so rule as to bring his people to despair, madness, and finally, in a frantic effort to save himself, he will plunge his country into a terrible war, and thus bring thy dear Fatherland to ruin. And on no one but thou rests the blame for all this, thou whose breath drove the colored butterfly eastwards across the meadow until it flew over the golden fence of the king's park."

The youth shrugged his shoulders:

"How, O invisible spirit, can I deny that all this that thou prophesiest will come to pass, since on earth one thing always follows from another, and often the most terrible events are caused by the most trivial things, and the most trivial events by the most terrible things? And why should I believe this particular prophecy, since the other, threatening me with death should I mount these steps, has not come to pass?"

"He who mounts those steps," rang out the terrible voice, "must turn back and descend them, if he wishes to mix with mankind again. Hast thou pondered that?"

The youth stopped suddenly and for a moment it seemed as though he would take the safe path downwards, but fearing the impenetrable night that encircled him, he clearly perceived that for so hazardous an enterprise he would require the light of day, and in order to make sure that he would have all his wits at his command on the morrow, he lay down again on the narrow ledge, longing ardently for the sleep that strengthens. As he lay there motionless, his thoughts keeping him awake, he opened his tired eyelids, while anxious shudders ran through his heart and veins. The dizzy precipice was ever before his eyes: that way lay the only road back to life. He who until then had been always sure of his path, now felt in his soul a doubt he had never before experienced, that deepened and caused him ever greater agony, until he could no longer bear it. He therefore decided rather to attempt forthwith what could not be avoided than to await the light in a torment of incertitude. Again he arose, ready for the venture without the blessed light of day, to conquer with faltering steps the dangerous path. But hardly had he set foot into the darkness when he realized as though condemned by an irrevocable judgment, that his fate was to be fulfilled without delay. He called out into the emptiness in anger and sorrow:

"O Invisible Spirit, who hast three times warned me and whom I have thrice refused to believe, O Spirit to whom I now bow down as to one stronger than I, tell me, ere thou destroyest me, who thou art?"

Again the voice rang out, stiflingly close at hand and immeasurably far away:

"No mortal hath yet known me. Many names have I: the superstitious call me Destiny, fools call me Luck, and the pious call me God. To those who deem themselves wise I am that Power which was in the Beginning and continues without end through all Eternity."

"Then I curse thee in this my last moment," shouted the youth with the bitterness of death in his heart. "If thou art indeed the Power that was in the Beginning and continues without end through all Eternity, then was it fated that all should happen as it did—that I should go through the forest and commit murder, that I should cross the meadow and bring ruin upon my Fatherland, that I should climb this rock and here find death—all this despite thy warning. But why was I condemned to hear thee speak to me thrice, if thy warning was not to help me? And why, oh, irony of ironies! must I in this my last moment whimper my feeble question to thee?"

An answer was made to the youth, stern and terrible, in a peal of mysterious laughter that echoed to the utmost confines of the invisible heavens. As he tried to catch the words the earth moved and sank from under his feet. He fell, deeper than a million bottomless pits, amid all the lurking nights of time, that have been and will be, from the Beginning to the End of all things.

HERMANN SUDERMANN

(1857—)

SUDERMANN was born in East Prussia in 1857, and educated at the Universities of Königsberg and Berlin. He was one of the foremost leaders of the dramatic movement of the nineties, though to-day he is regarded as definitely belonging to the past. But his stories of East Prussian and Lithuanian life, and his novels, are written with a fine imaginative power, and are still read both in Germany and abroad.

The present version, translated by Grace I. Colbron, is reprinted by permission of the publisher, from *Short Story Classics*, published and copyright by P. F. Collier's Sons, New York, 1907.

A NEW-YEAR'S EVE CONFESSION

THANKS be to God, dear lady, that I may once more sit beside you for a peaceful chat. The holiday tumult is past, and you have a little leisure for me again.

Oh, this Christmas season! I believe that it was invented by some evil demon expressly to annoy us poor bachelors, to show us the more clearly all the desolation of our homeless existence. For others a source of joy, it is for us a torture. Of course, I know, we are not all entirely lonely—for us also the joy of making others happy may blossom, that joy upon which rests the whole secret of the blessed holiday mood. But the pleasure of joining in the happiness of others is tainted for us by a touch of self-irony partly, and also by that bitter longing to which—in contrast to homesickness—I would give the name of "marriage sickness."

Why didn't I come to pour out my heart to you? you ask, you pitying soul, you—you that can give of your sympathy in the same rich measure that others of your sex save for their dainty malices. There's a reason. You remember what Speidel says in his delightful *Lonely Sparrows*, which you sent me the day after Christmas, with a true perception of my state of mind? "The bachelor by instinct," he says, "does not desire comfort. Once he is unhappy, he wishes to have the full enjoyment of his unhappiness."

Besides the "lonely sparrow" whom Speidel portrays, there is another sort of bachelor, the so-called "friend of the family." By this I do not mean those professional wreckers of homes, in whose eyes the serpent glitters as they settle down comfortably at the hospitable hearthstone. I mean the good uncle, papa's former school friend, who rocks the baby on his knee while he reads the magazine essays to mamma, carefully omitting all the doubtful portions.

I know men who give up their entire lives to the service of some family whose friendship they have won—men who live on without desire by the side of a beautiful woman whom in their hearts they secretly adore.

You doubt me? Oh, it is the words "without desire" that disturb you? You are right, perhaps. In the depth of even the tamest heart some wild desire lies, but—understand me here—it lies bound in chains.

As an instance I would like to tell you about a conversation which took place day before yesterday, on New Year's Eve, between two old, two very old, gentlemen. It is my secret how I came to know of this conversation, and I ask you not to let it go any further. May I begin, then?

Picture to yourself, as a setting for my story, a high-ceilinged room, old-fashioned in furnishings, lighted by a green-shaded, impertinently bright hanging-lamp of the sort our parents had in use before the era of petroleum. The cone of light that goes out from the flame falls upon a round, white-clothed table, upon which stands the various ingredients for a New-Year's punch, while several drops of oil show out broadly in the center of the table.

My two old gentlemen sat half in the shadow of the green lamp-shade, moldering ruins both, from long-past days, bowed and trembling, gazing before them with the dull glance of the dimming eyes of age. One, the host, is evidently an old officer, as you would recognize at once from his carefully wound cravat, his pointed, sharply cut mustache, and his martial eyebrows. He sits holding the handle of his roller-chair like a crutch tightly clasped in both hands. He is motionless except for his jaws, which move up and down ceaselessly with the motion of chewing. The other, who sits near him on the sofa, a tall, spare figure, his narrow shoulders crowned by the high-domed head of a thinker, draws occasional thin puffs of smoke from a long pipe which is just about to go out. Among the myriad wrinkles of his smooth-shaven, dried-up face, framed in a wreath of snow-white curls, there lurked a quiet, gentle smile, a smile which the peace of resignation alone can bring to the face of age.

The two were silent. In the perfect stillness of the room the soft bubbling of the burning oil mingled with the soft bubbling of the tobacco juice. Then, from the darkness of the background, the hanging clock began to announce hoarsely the eleventh hour. "This is the hour when she would begin to make the punch," said the man with the domed forehead. His voice was soft, with a slight vibration.

"Yes, this is the time," repeated the other. The sound of his speech was hard, as if the rattle of command still lingered in it.

"I did not think it would be so desolate without her," said the first speaker again.

The host nodded, his jaws moving.

"She made the New-Year's punch for us four-and-forty times," continued his friend.

"Yes, it's as long as that since we moved to Berlin, and you became our friend," said the old soldier.

"Last year at this time we were all so jolly together," said the other. "She sat in the armchair there, knitting socks for Paul's eldest. She worked busily, saying she must finish it by twelve o'clock. And she did finish it. Then we drank our punch and spoke quite calmly of death. And two months later they carried her away. As you know, I have written a fat book on the 'Immortality of the Idea.' You never cared much about it—I don't care for it myself now that your wife is dead. The entire Idea of the Universe means nothing to me now."

"Yes, she was a good wife," said the husband of the dead woman; "she cared for me well. When I had to go out for service at five o'clock in the morning, she was always up before me to look after my coffee. Of course she had her faults. When she got into philosophizing with you—h'm."

"You never understood her," murmured the other, the corners of his mouth trembling in controlled resentment. But the glance that rested long on his friend's face was gentle and sad, as if a secret guilt pressed upon his soul.

After a renewed pause, he began:

"Franz, there is something I want to tell you, something that has long troubled me, something that I do not want to carry with me to my grave."

"Well, fire away," said the host, taking up the long pipe that stood beside his chair.

"There was once—something—between your wife and me."

The host let his pipe fall back again, and stared at his friend with wide-opened eyes.

"No jokes, please, doctor," he said finally.

"It is bitter earnest, Franz," replied the other. "I have carried it about with me these forty years, but now it is high time to have it out with you."

"Do you mean to say that the dead woman was untrue to me?" cried the husband angrily.

"For shame, Franz," said his friend with a soft, sad smile.

The old soldier murmured something and lit his pipe.

"No, she was as pure as God's angels," continued the other. "It is you and I who are the guilty ones. Listen to me. It is now forty-three years ago; you had just been ordered here as captain to Berlin, and I was teaching at the University. You were a gay bird then, as you know."

"H'm," remarked the host, raising his trembling old hand to his mustache.

"There was a beautiful actress with great black eyes and little white teeth—do you remember?"

"*Do* I? Bianca was her name," answered the other as a faded smile flashed over his weather-beaten, self-indulgent face. "Those little white teeth could bite, I can tell you."

"You deceived your wife, and she suspected it. But she said nothing and suffered in silence. She was the first woman who had come into my life since my mother's death. She came into it like a shining star, and I gazed up to her in adoration as one might adore a star. I found the courage to ask her about her trouble. She smiled and said that she was not feeling quite strong yet—you remember it was shortly after the birth of your Paul. Then came New-Year's Eve—forty-three years ago to-night. I came in at eight o'clock as usual. She sat over her embroidery and I read aloud to her while we waited for you. One hour after another passed and still you did not come. I saw that she grew more and more uneasy, and began to tremble. I trembled with her. I knew where you were, and I feared you might forget the hour of midnight in the arms of that woman. She had dropped her work, I read no longer. A terrible silence weighed upon us. Then I saw a tear gather under her eyelid and drop slowly down upon the embroidery in her lap. I sprang up to go out and look for you. I felt myself capable of tearing you away from that woman by force. But at the same moment she sprang up also from her seat—this very same place where I am sitting now.

" 'Where are you going?' she cried, terror in every feature. 'I am going to fetch Franz,' I said. And then she screamed aloud: 'For God's sake, *you* stay with me at least— don't *you* forsake me also.'

"And she hurried to me, laid both hands on my shoulders and buried her tear-bedewed face on my breast. I trembled in every fiber, no woman had ever stood so near me before. But I controlled myself, and soothed and comforted her—she was so sadly in need of comfort. You came in soon after. You did not notice my emotion, your cheeks were burning, your eyes heavy with the fatigue of love. Since that evening a change had come over me, a change that frightened me. When I had felt her soft arms around my neck, when I had felt the fragrance of her hair, the shining star fell from its heaven, and—a woman stood before me, beautiful, breathing love. I called myself a villain, a betrayer, and to sooth my conscience somewhat I set about separating you from your mistress. Fortunately I had some money at my disposal. She was satisfied with the sum I offered her, and—"

"The devil!" exclaimed the old soldier in surprise; "then you were the cause of that touching farewell letter that Bianca sent me—in which she declared that she must give me up—although her heart would break?"

"Yes, I was the cause of it," said his friend. "But listen, there is more to tell. I had thought to purchase peace with that money, but the peace did not come. The wild thoughts ran riot all the more madly in my brain. I buried myself in my work—it was just about that time that I was working out the plan of my book on the 'Immortality of the Idea'—but still could not find peace. And thus the year passed and New-Year's Eve came round again. Again we sat together here, she and I. You were at home this time, but you lay sleeping on the sofa in the next room. A merry Casino dinner had tired you. And as I sat beside her, and my eyes rested on her pale face, then memory came over me with irresistible power. Once more I would feel her head on my breast, once more I would kiss her—and then—the end, if need be. Our eyes met for an instant; I seemed to see a secret understanding, an answer in her glance. I could control myself no longer; I fell at her feet and buried my burning face in her lap.

"I lay there motionless for two seconds perhaps, then I felt her soft hand rest cool upon my head, and her voice, soft and gentle, spoke the words: 'Be brave, dear friend; yes, be brave—do not deceive the man sleeping so trustfully in the next room.' I sprang up and gazed about, bewildered. She took a book from the table and handed it to me. I understood, opened it at random, and began to read aloud. I do not know what it was I read, the letters danced before my eyes. But the storm within my soul began to abate, and when twelve o'clock struck, and you came in sleepily for the New-Year's wishes, it was as if that moment of sin lay far, far behind me, in days that had long passed.

"Since that day I have been calmer. I knew that she did not return my love, and that I had only pity to hope from her. Years passed, your children grew up and married, we three grew old together. You gave up your wild life, forgot the other women, and lived for one alone, as I did. It was not possible that I should ever cease to love her, but my love took on another shape; earthly desires faded, and a bond of the spirit grew up between us. You have often laughed when you heard us philosophizing together. But if you had known how close were our souls at such moments you would have been very jealous. And now she is dead, and before the next New-Year's Eve comes round we two may follow her. It is, therefore, high time that I rid myself of this secret and say to you, 'Franz, I sinned against you once, forgive me.'"

He held out an imploring hand toward his friend; but the other answered, grumbling: "Nonsense. There is nothing to forgive. What you told me there, I knew it long ago. She confessed it herself forty years ago. And now I will tell you why I ran after other women until I was an old man—because she told me then that you were the one and only love of her life."

The friend stared at him without speaking, and the hoarse clock began to strike—midnight.

France

INTRODUCTION

THERE are probably more short stories, as there is assuredly a longer and more continuous development of the form, in the French than in any other literature of the world. In the earliest efforts of native writers, long before the close of the Middle Ages, are to be found the seeds of those lively and often beautiful forms that flourished from the Twelfth to the Sixteenth Centuries—*Fabliaux*, *Lays*, devotional and miraculous tales. From the epic *Chansons de geste*, beginning with the *Song of Roland*, throughout the whole period in which these remarkable poems thrived, the *trouvères* and troubadours incorporated independent and unified anecdotes and episodes into their long romances of chivalry and gallantry. These were in effect romantic and religious stories, treating of war and love and wonder and pious devotion.

But the earliest examples of independent tales are found in the *Fabliaux*. Although these were written in verse, they were the delight of the middle and lower classes: the verse was scarcely poetry, it was only a medium for the telling of the story. Of the hundred and fifty examples that survive out of the many thousands written, the first *Fabliau* dates from 1159, and the last from 1340. Most of them were anonymous, but among the few names of writers that have come down to us is that of Bernier, which is still remembered, because he wrote the exquisite *Divided Horsecloth*. The famous poet Rutebœuf also wrote *Fabliaux*, but he is better known for his other productions. For several reasons—still a matter of dispute among literary historians—the *Fabliau* suddenly disappeared about the middle of the Fourteenth Century. The other more or less similar forms—like the *Lay*, the *Miracle* and the *Devotional Tale*—still continued sporadically up to the end of the Middle Ages.

The *trouvères* and troubadours and minstrels who went over into Sicily and Italy and were instrumental in establishing there a vernacular literature, took with them their stories, which reappeared in prose form and in a more skilful guise some centuries later in the work of Boccaccio and his followers. Many of them were again treated by later French writers, Rabelais and Marguerite de Navarre and Antoine de Saintré, editor of the French *Hundred New Tales*. Rabelais was followed by imitators, like Noël du Fail, Bonaventure des Périers and Béroalde de Verville, all of whom added their share to the development of the story form.

With the opening of the Seventeenth Century the short story was overshadowed by the drama and the long-winded sentimental romance, although such writers as D'Alcripé, Tallement des Réaux, Camus, and Sorel assiduously applied themselves to the form. Toward the end of the century a new form was developed through the art of La Fontaine and Charles Perrault, whose fables and fairy tales are unsurpassed.

The Eighteenth Century, with its new philosophy, its scepticism, and its preoccupation with literary form, saw the rise of the philosophical and the moral tale. Fénelon began the Oriental, a variety of the moral tale, in the late sixteen hundreds. In England the same type was employed with success by Addison in the *Spectator* papers, and later by Dr. Johnson and Goldsmith. In France Voltaire was the supreme master of the form. Marmontel developed his own type of moral tale, with its extreme sentimentality. It is toward the close of the century that, as in England and Germany and Italy, we detect the first symptoms of a radical change in subject-matter and method of treatment. The same spirit that affected Mrs. Radcliffe and Monk Lewis in England, operated upon certain French forerunners of the romantic-fantastic "school." Influences from England and Germany were strong in the work of such writers as Gérard de Nerval and Alfred de Musset.

With the dawn of the Nineteenth Century we come to the modern short story. The number of writers in France who assiduously applied themselves to the writing of short stories without ulterior motives or philosophical and moral purpose was enormous. In the hands of Balzac, Musset, Gautier, Vigny, Mérimée, Nodier, and a host of others, the short story became a pure work of art. To Balzac is due much of the credit for bringing about a complete break with the past in this respect. As the century progressed, the form was adopted by nearly all the great writers of fiction: Flaubert, George Sand, Adam, Anatole France Daudet, Zola, Coppée, Maupassant, Richepin, and the rest.

The modern short story is one of the most highly perfected branch of French literature. There is something in the language that seems make it a fit medium for the conveyance of this kind of fiction; at a rate the French short story at its best has never been surpassed.

BERNIER

(12th or 13th Century, A.D.)

Nothing is known of the author of this story except his name, which is signed on the MS. *The Divided Horsecloth* is one of the best examples of a type that flourished in France during the Twelfth and Thirteenth Centuries: the *Fabliau* is a short story in verse differing principally from the *Lay* and the *Pious* or *Devotional Tale* by its simple style and its appeal, which is directed rather to the middle classes than the nobility. This particular story has been very popular with later writers, among whom both Montaigne and Browning have made use of it.

The present version is translated by Eugene Mason, in the volume *Aucassin and Nicolette and Other Medieval Romances and Legends*. Published in Everyman's Library, J. M. Dent and Sons, by whose permission it is here reprinted.

THE DIVIDED HORSECLOTH

EACH owes it to his fellows to tell as best he may, or, better still, to write with fair enticing words, such deeds and adventures as are good and profitable for us to know. For as men come and go about their business in the world, many things are told them which it is seemly to keep in remembrance. Therefore, it becomes those who say and relate, diligently and with fair intent to keep such matters in thought and study, even as did our fathers before us. Theirs is the school to which we all should pass, and he who would prove an apt scholar, and live beyond his day, must not be idle at his task. But the world dims our fine gold: the minstrel is slothful, and singers forget to sing, because of the pain and travail which go to the finding of their songs. So without waiting for any to-morrow, I will bring before you a certain adventure which chanced, even as it was told to me.

Some seven years ago it befell that a rich burgess of Abbeville departed from the town, together with his wife, his only son, and all his wealth, his goods and plenishing. This he did like a prudent man, since he found himself at enmity with men who were stronger and of more substance than he. So, fearing lest a worse thing should bechance him, from Abbeville he went up to Paris. There he sought a shop and dwelling, and paying his service, made himself vassal and burgess of the King. The merchant was diligent and courteous, his wife smiling and gracious, and their son was not given over to folly, but went soberly, even as his parents taught him. Much were they praised of their neighbors, and those who lived in the same street often set foot in their dwelling. For very greatly are those loved and esteemed by their fellows who are courteous in speech and address. He who has fair words in his mouth receives again sweet words in his ear, and foul words and foul deeds bring naught but bitterness and railing. Thus was it with this prudent merchant. For more than seven years he went about his business, buying and selling, concerning himself with matters of which he had full knowledge, putting by of his earnings a little every day, like a wise and worthy citizen. So this wealthy merchant lived a happy blameless life, till, by the will of God, his wife was taken from him, who had been his companion for some thirty years. Now these parents had but one only child, a son, even as I have told you before. Very grievously did he mourn the death of her who had cherished him so softly, and lamented his mother with many tears, till he came nigh to swoon. Then, to put a little comfort in his heart, his father said to him:

"Fair son, thy mother is dead, and we will pray to God that He grant her mercy in that day. But dry now thine eyes and thy face, for tears can profit thee nothing. By that road we all must go, neither can any man pass Death upon the way, nor return to bring us any word. Fair son, for thee there is goodly comfort. Thou art a young bachelor, and it is time to take thee a wife. I am full of years, and so I may find thee a fair marriage in an honorable house I will endow thee with my substance. I will now seek a bride for thee of birth and breeding—one of family and descent, one come of ancient race, with relations and friends a gracious company, a wife from honest folk and from an honest home. There, where it is good and profitable to be, I will set thee gladly, nor of wealth and moneys shalt thou find a lack."

Now in that place were three brethren, knights of high lineage, cousins to mighty lords of peerage, bearing rich and honorable blazons on their shields. But these knights had no heritage, since they had pawned all that they owned of woods and houses and lands, the better to take their pleasure at the tourney. Passing heavy and tormented were these brethren because in no wise might they redeem their pledge. The eldest of these brothers had a daughter, but the mother of the maid was dead. Now this damsel owned in Paris a certain fair house, over against the mansion of the wealthy merchant. The house was not of her father's heritage, but came to her from her mother, who had put the maid in ward to guardians, so that the house was free from pledge. She received in rent therefrom the sum of twenty Paris pounds every year, and her dues were paid her right willingly. So the merchant, esteeming her a lady of family and estate, demanded her hand in marriage of her father and of all her friends. The knight inquired in his turn of the means and substance of the merchant, who answered very frankly:

"In merchandise and in moneys I have near upon fifteen hundred pounds. Should I tell you that I had more, I should lie, and speak not the truth. I have besides one hundred Paris pounds, which I have gained in honest dealings. Of all this I will give my son the half."

"Fair sir," made answer the knight, "in no wise can this be agreed to. Had you become a Templar, or a White or a Black monk you would have granted the whole of your wealth either to the Temple or your Abbey. By my faith, we cannot consent to so grudging an offer, certes, sir merchant, no."

"Tell me then what you would have me do."

"Very willingly, fair, dear sir. We would that you grant to your son the sum and total of your substance, so that he be seized of all your wealth, and this in such fashion that neither you, nor any in your name, may claim return of any part thereof. If you consent to this the marriage can be made, but otherwise he shall never wed our child and niece."

The merchant turned this over for a while, now looking upon his son, now deep in thought. But very badly he was served of all his thought and pondering. For at the last he made reply to him and said:

"Lord, it shall even be done according to your will. This is our covenant and bargain, that so your daughter is given to my son I will grant him all that I have of worth. I take this company as witness that here I strip myself of everything I own, so that naught is mine, but all is his, of what I once was seized and possessed."

Thus before the witnesses he divested himself utterly of all his wealth, and became naked as a peeled wand in the eyes of the world, for this merchant now had neither purse nor penny, nor wherewithal to break his fast, save it were given him by his son. So when the words were spoken and the merchant altogether spoiled, then the knight took his daughter by the hand and handfasted her with the bachelor, and she became his wife.

For two years after this marriage the husband and the dame lived a quiet and peaceful life. Then a fair son was born to the bachelor, and the lady cherished and guarded him fondly. With them dwelt the merchant in the same lodging, but very soon he perceived that he had given himself a mortal blow in despoiling himself of his substance to live on the charity of others. But perforce he remained of their household for more than twelve years, until the lad had grown up tall, and began to take notice, and to remember that which often he heard of the making of his father's marriage. And well he promised himself that it should never go from mind.

The merchant was full of years. He leaned upon his staff, and went bent with age, as one who searches for his lost youth. His son was weary of his presence, and would gladly have paid for the spinning of his shroud. The dame, who was proud and disdainful, held him in utter despite, for greatly he was against her heart. Never was she silent, but always was she saying to her lord:

"Husband, for love of me, send your father upon his business. I lose all appetite just for the sight of him about the house."

"Wife," answered he, "this shall be done according to your wish."

So because of his wife's anger and importunity, he sought out his father straightway, and said:

"Father, father, get you gone from here. I tell you that you must do the best you can, for we may no longer concern ourselves with you and your lodging. For twelve years and more we have given you food and raiment in our house. Now all is done, so rise and depart forthwith, and fend for yourself, as fend you must."

When the father heard these words he wept bitterly, and often he cursed the day and the hour in which he found he had lived too long.

"Ah, fair, sweet son, what is this thou sayest to me! For the love of God turn me not from thy door. I lie so close that thou canst not want my room. I require of thee neither seat in the chimney corner, nor soft bed of feathers, no, nor carpet on the floor; but only the attic, where I may bide on a little straw. Throw me not from thy house because I eat of thy bread, but feed me without grudging for the short while I have to live. In the eyes of God this charity will cover all thy sins better than if thou went in haircloth next the flesh."

"Fair father," replied the bachelor, "preach me no preachings, but get you forth at once, for reason that my wife would have you gone."

"Fair son, where then shall I go, who am esteemed of nothing worth?"

"Get you gone to the town, for amongst ten thousand others very easily you may light on good fortune. Very unlucky you will be if there you cannot find a way to live. Seek your fortune bravely. Perchance some of your friends and acquaintances will receive you into their houses."

"Son, how then shall men take me to their lodging, when you turn me from the house which I have given you? Why should the stranger welcome that guest whom the son chases from his door? Why should I be received gladly by him to whom I have given naught, when I am evilly entreated of the rich man for whose sake I go naked?"

"Father," said he, "right or wrong, I take the blame upon my own head; but go you must because it is according to my will."

Then the father grieved so bitterly that for a little his very heart would have broken. Weak as he was, he raised himself to his feet and went forth from the house, weeping.

"Son," said he, "I commend thee to God; but since thou wilt that I go, for the love of Him give me at least a portion of packing cloth to shelter me against the wind. I am asking no great matter; nothing but a little cloth to wrap about me, because I am but lightly clad, and fear to die for reason of the cold."

Then he who shrank from any grace of charity made reply:

"Father, I have no cloth, so neither can I bestow, nor have it taken from me."

"Fair, sweet son, my heart trembles within me, so greatly do I dread the cold. Give me, then, the cloth you spread upon your horse, so that I come to no evil."

So he, seeing that he might not rid himself of his father save by the granting of a gift, and being desirous above all that he should part, bade his son to fetch this horsecloth. When the lad heard his father's call he sprang to him, saying:

"Father, what is your pleasure?"

"Fair son," said he, "get you to the stable, and if you find it open give my father the covering that is upon my horse. Give him the best cloth in the stable, so that he may make himself a mantle or a habit, or any other sort of cloak that pleases him."

Then the lad, who was thoughtful beyond his years, made answer:

"Grandsire, come now with me."

So the merchant went with him to the stable, exceedingly heavy and wrathful. The lad chose the best horsecloth he might find in the stable, the newest, the largest, and the most fair; this he folded in two, and drawing forth his knife, divided the cloth in two portions. Then he bestowed on his grandfather one half of the sundered horsecloth.

"Fair child," said the old man, "what have you done? Why have you cut the cloth that your father has given me? Very cruelly have you treated me, for you were bidden to give me the horsecloth whole. I shall return and complain to my son thereof."

"Go where you will," replied the boy, "for certainly you shall have nothing more from me."

The merchant went forth from the stable.

"Son," said he, "chastise now thy child, since he counts thy word as nothing but an idle tale, and fears not to disobey thy commandment. Dost thou not see that he keeps one half of the horsecloth?"

"Plague take thee!" cried the father; "give him all the cloth."

"Certes," replied the boy, "that will I never do, for how then shall you be paid? Rather will I keep the half until I am grown a man, and then give it to you. For just as you have chased him from your house, so I will put you from my door. Even as he has bestowed on you all his wealth, so, in my turn, will I require of you all your substance. Naught from me shall you carry away, save that only which you have granted to him. If you leave him to die in his misery, I wait my day, and surely will leave you to perish in yours."

The father listened to these words, and at the end sighed heavily.

He repented him of the evil that he purposed, and from the parable that his child had spoken took heed and warning. Turning himself about towards the merchant, he said:

"Father, return to my house. Sin and the Enemy thought to have caught me in the snare, but, please God, I have escaped from the fowler. You are master and lord, and I render all that I have received into your hands. If my wife cannot live with you in quiet, then you shall be served and cherished elsewhere. Chimney corner, and carpet, pillow and bed of feathers, at your ease you shall have pleasure in them all. I take St. Martin to witness that never will I drink stoup of wine, never carve morsel from dish, but that yours shall be the richer portion. Henceforth you shall live softly in the ceiled chamber, near by a blazing fire, clad warmly in your furred robe, even as I. And all this is not of charity, but of your right, for, fair, sweet father, if I am rich it is because of your substance."

Thus the brave witness and the open remonstrance of a child freed his father from the bad thoughts that he harbored. And deeply should this adventure be considered of those who are about to marry their children. Let them not strip themselves so bare as to have nothing left. For he who gives all, and depends upon the charity of others, prepares a rod for his own back.

THE PRIEST AND THE MULBERRIES

(Anonymous: 12th or 13th Century)

PRACTICALLY nothing is known of the author of this pleasant little *Fabliau*. Compared with the great majority of surviving stories of its kind, it is remarkably free from the coarseness which characterizes the *Fabliau*, particularly when it deals with the clergy.

The present version is translated by Eugene Mason, in the volume *Aucassin and Nicolette and Other Medieval Romances and Legends*. Published in Everyman's Library, J. M. Dent and Sons, by whose permission it is here reprinted. The title of the story in the original is *The Priest Who Ate Mulberries.*

THE PRIEST AND THE MULBERRIES

A CERTAIN priest having need to go to market, caused his mare to be saddled and brought to his door. The mare had carried her master for two years, and was high and well nourished, for during these years never had she known thirst nor hunger, but of hay and of oats ever had she enough and to spare. The priest climbed to the saddle and set out upon his journey, and well I remember that it was the month of September, for in that season mulberries grow upon the bushes in great plenty and abundance. The priest rode upon his way repeating his hours, his matins and his vigils. As he drew near the gate of the town the path ran through a certain deep hollow, and raising his eyes from his book the priest marked a bush thick with mulberries, bigger, blacker and more ripe than any he had ever seen. Desire entered his heart, for very covetous was he of this fair fruit, and gradually checking the pace of his mare, he presently caused her to stand beside the bush. Yet one thing still was wanting to his delight. The mulberries near the ground were set about with spines and thorns, whilst the sweetest of all hung so high upon the tree that in no wise could he reach them from his seat. This thing the priest saw, so in a while he climbed up, and stood with his two feet upon the saddle, whence by leaning over a little he could pluck the fruit. Then he chose the fairest, the ripest, and the sweetest of all these mulberries, eating them as swiftly and greedily as he might, whilst the mare beneath him moved never a whit. Now, when this priest had eaten as many mulberries as he was able, he glanced downwards, and saw that the mare was standing still and coy, with her head turned towards the bank of that deep road. Thereat the priest rejoiced very greatly, for his two feet were yet upon the saddle, and the mare was very tall.

"God!" said he, "if any one now should cry 'Gee up!'" He thought and spoke the words at the same moment, whereat the mare was suddenly frighted, and springing forward on the instant tumbled the luckless priest into the bush where the thorns and briars grew sharpest and thickest. There he lay in that uneasy bed, nor might move from one side to the other, backwards or forwards, for all the money in the mint.

The mare galloped straight to her own stable, but when the priest's household saw her return in this fashion they were greatly discomforted. The servants cursed her for an evil and a luckless jade, whilst the cook maid swooned like any dame, for well she believed that her master was dead. When they were returned a little to themselves they ran to and fro, here and there, about the country searching for the priest, and presently on their way to the market town they drew near to that bush where their master yet lay in much misease. On hearing their words bewailing his piteous case, the priest raised a lamentable voice, and cried:

"Diva, Diva, do not pass me by. This bush is an uneasy bed, and here I lie very hurt and troubled and utterly cast down. Do you not see how my blood is staining these thorns and briars a vermeil red?"

The servants hurried to the bush, and stared upon the priest.

"Sir," said they, "who has flung you herein?"

"Alas," answered he, "'tis sin that has undone me. This morning when I rode this way reading in my Book of Hours, I desired over greatly to eat of the mulberries growing hereon, and so I fell into the sin of gluttony. Therefore this bush gat hold upon me. But help me forth from this place, for I wish now for no other thing but to have a surgeon for my hurts, and to rest in my own house."

Now by this little story we may learn that the prudent man does not cry aloud all he may think in his heart, since by so doing many an one has suffered loss and shame, as we may see by this fable of the Priest and the Mulberries.

MARIE DE FRANCE

(About 1150–1200)

All that is positively known of the author of this *Lay* is that she wrote in Norman French, that her name was Marie, and that she was "of France." It is even thought that she may have been an English subject. Her collection of *Lays*, or romantic love tales, was immensely popular both in France and England. Both in her *Fables* and *Lays* she utilized old materials. *The Lay of the Two Lovers* is one of the most charming of the French *Lays*.

The present version is translated by Eugene Mason, in the volume *French Medieval Romances from the Lays of Marie de France*. Published in Everyman's Library, J. M. Dent and Sons, by whose permission it is here reprinted.

THE LAY OF THE TWO LOVERS

Once upon a time there lived in Normandy two lovers, who were passing fond, and were brought by Love to Death. The story of their love was bruited so abroad, that the Bretons made a song in their own tongue, and named this song the Lay of the Two Lovers.

In Neustria—that men call Normandy—there is verily a high and marvelously great mountain, where lie the relics of the Two Children. Near this high place the King of those parts caused to be built a certain fair and cunning city, and since he was lord of the Pistrians, it was known as Pistres. The town yet endures, with its towers and houses, to bear witness to the truth; moreover the country thereabouts is known to us all as the Valley of Pistres.

This King had one fair daughter, a damsel sweet of face and gracious of manner, very near to her father's heart, since he had lost his Queen.

The maiden increased in years and favor, but he took no heed to her trothing, so that men—yea, even his own people—blamed him greatly for this thing. When the King heard thereof he was passing heavy and dolent, and considered within himself how he might be delivered from this grief. So then, that none should carry off his child, he caused it to be proclaimed, both far and near, by script and trumpet, that he alone should wed the maid, who would bear her in his arms to the pinnacle of the great and perilous mountain, and that without rest or stay. When this news was noised about the country, many came upon the quest. But strive as they would they might not enforce themselves more than they were able. However mighty they were of body, at the last they failed upon the mountain, and fell with their burthen to the ground. Thus, for a while, was none so bold as to seek the high Princess.

Now in this country lived a squire, son to a certain count of that realm, seemly of semblance and courteous, and right desirous to win that prize, which was so coveted of all. He was a welcome guest at the Court, and the King talked with him very willingly. This squire had set his heart upon the daughter of the King, and many a time spoke in her ear, praying her to give him again the love he had bestowed upon her. So seeing him brave and courteous, she esteemed him for the gifts which gained him the favor of the King, and they loved together in their youth. But they hid this matter from all about the Court. This thing was very grievous to them, but the damoiseau thought within himself that it were good to bear the pains he knew, rather than to seek out others that might prove sharper still. Yet in the end, altogether distraught by love, this prudent varlet sought his friend, and showed her his case, saying that he urgently required of her that she would flee with him, for no longer could he endure the weariness of his days. Should he ask her of the King, well he knew that by reason of his love he would refuse the gift, save he bore her in his arms up the steep mount. Then the maiden made answer to her lover, and said:

"Fair friend, well I know you may not carry me to that high place. Moreover should we take to flight, my father would suffer wrath and sorrow beyond measure, and go heavily all his days. Certainly my love is too fond to plague him thus, and we must seek another counsel, for this is not to my heart. Hearken well. I have kindred in Salerno, of rich estate. For more than thirty years my aunt has studied there the art of medicine, and knows the secret gift of every root and herb. If you hasten to her, bearing letters from me, and show her your adventure, certainly she will find counsel and cure. Doubt not that she will discover some cunning simple, that will strengthen your body, as well as comfort your heart. Then return to this realm with your potion, and ask me at my father's hand. He will deem you but a stripling, and set forth the terms of his bargain, that to him alone shall I be given who knows how to climb the perilous mountain, without pause or rest, bearing his lady between his arms."

When the varlet heard this cunning counsel of the maiden, he rejoiced greatly, and thanking her sweetly for her rede, craved permission to depart. He returned to his own home, and gathering together a goodly store of silken cloths most precious, he bestowed his gear upon the pack horses, and made him ready for the road. So with a little company of men, mounted on swift palfreys, and most privy to his mind, he arrived at Salerno. Now the squire made no long stay at his lodging, but as soon as he might, went to the damsel's kindred to open out his mind. He delivered to the aunt the letters he carried from his friend, and bewailed their evil case. When the dame had read these letters with him, line by line, she charged him to lodge with her awhile, till she might do according to his wish. So by her sorceries, and for the love of her maid, she brewed such a potion that no man, however wearied and outworn, but by drinking this philter, would not be refreshed in heart and blood and bones. Such virtue had this medicine, directly it were drunken. This simple she poured within a little flacket, and gave it to the varlet, who received the gift with great joy and delight, and returned swiftly to his own land.

The varlet made no long sojourn in his home. He repaired straightway to the Court, and, seeking out the King, required of him his fair daughter in marriage, promising, for his part, that were she given him, he would bear her in his arms to the summit of the mount. The King was no wise wroth at his presumption. He smiled rather at his folly, for how should one so young and slender succeed in a business wherein so many mighty men had failed? Therefore he appointed a certain day for this judgment. Moreover he caused letters to be written to his vassals and his friends—passing none by—bidding them to see the end of this adventure. Yea, with public cry and sound of trumpet he bade all who would, come to behold the stripling carry his fair daughter to the pinnacle of the mountain. And from every region round about men came to learn the issue of this thing. But for her part the fair maiden did all that she was able to bring her love to a good end. Ever was it fast day and fleshless day with her, so that by any means she might lighten the burden that her friend must carry in his arms.

Now on the appointed day this young dansellon came very early to the appointed place, bringing the flacket with him. When the great company were fully met together, the King led forth his daughter before them; and all might see that she was arrayed in nothing but her smock. The varlet took the maiden in his arms, but first he gave her the flacket with the precious brewage to carry, since for pride he might not endure to drink therefrom, save at utmost peril. The squire set forth at a great pace, and climbed briskly till he was halfway up the mount. Because of the joy he had in clasping his burden, he gave no thought to the potion. But she—she knew the strength was failing in his heart.

"Fair friend," said she, "well I know that you tire: drink now, I pray you, of the flacket, and so shall your manhood come again at need."

But the varlet answered:

"Fair love, my heart is full of courage; nor for any reason will I pause, so long as I can hold upon my way. It is the noise of all this folk—the tumult and the shouting—that makes my steps uncertain. Their cries distress me, I do not dare to stand."

But when two-thirds of the course was won, the grasshopper would have tripped him off his feet. Urgently and often the maiden prayed him, saying:

"Fair friend, drink now of thy cordial."

But he would neither hear, nor give credence to her words. A mighty anguish filled his bosom. He climbed upon the summit of the mountain, and pained himself grievously to bring his journey to an end. This he might not do. He reeled and fell, nor could he rise again, for the heart had burst within his breast.

When the maiden saw her lover's piteous plight, she deemed that he had swooned by reason of his pain. She kneeled hastily at his side, and put the enchanted brewage to his lips, but he could neither drink nor speak, for he was dead, as I have told you. She bewailed his evil lot, with many shrill cries, and flung the useless flacket far away. The precious potion bestrewed the ground, making a garden of that desolate place. For many saving herbs have been found there since that day by the simple folk of that country, which from the magic philter derived all their virtue.

But when the maiden knew that her lover was dead, she made such wondrous sorrow, as no man had ever seen. She kissed his eyes and mouth, and falling upon his body, took him in her arms, and pressed him closely to her breast. There was no heart so hard as not to be touched by her sorrow; for in this fashion died a dame, who was fair and sweet and gracious beyond the wont of the daughters of men.

Now the King and his company, since these two lovers came not again, presently climbed the mountain to learn their end. But when the King came upon them lifeless, and fast in that embrace, incontinent he fell to the ground, bereft of sense. After his speech had returned to him, he was passing heavy, and lamented their doleful case, and thus did all his people with him.

Three days they kept the bodies of these two fair children from earth, with uncovered face. On the third day they sealed them fast in a goodly coffin of marble, and by the counsel of all men, laid them softly to rest on that mountain where they died. Then they departed from them, and left them together, alone.

Since this adventure of the Two Children this hill is known as the Mountain of the Two Lovers, and their story being bruited abroad, the Breton folk have made a Lay thereof, even as I have rehearsed before you.

MARGUERITE DE NAVARRE

(1492–1549)

Marguerite d'Angoulême, daughter of the Duc d'Angoulême and sister of François I, was the second wife of the King of Navarre, and grandmother of Henry IV of France. A woman of culture and learning, and of immense political ability, she was a writer of considerable importance. But among all her varied literary works none is more popular than her famous collection of tales under the title of the *Heptameron*, a volume more or less based on the *Decameron* of Boccaccio. These tales are for the most part intended to teach manners, wisdom and courtesy, and though they are no longer a practical or useful Book of Etiquette, they are still readable. Marguerite was a shrewd observer of men, and showed in the best of her stories a feeling for character and a love of nature. The *Heptameron* was not published until after her death, though the stories circulated in MS. during her lifetime.

The present tale is reprinted from an anonymous translation published in London in 1894. It is the fifty-sixth story, and has for title only a lengthy descriptive paragraph.

THE PIOUS LADY AND THE GRAY FRIAR

(From the *Heptameron*, Tale 56)

A FRENCH lady, whilst sojourning at Padua, was informed that there was a Gray Friar in the Bishop's prison there, and finding that everyone spoke jestingly about him, she inquired the reason. She was told that this Gray Friar, who was an old man, had been confessor to a very honorable and pious widow lady, mother of only one daughter, whom she loved so dearly as to be at all pains to amass riches for her and to find her a good husband. Now, seeing that her daughter was grown up, she was unceasingly anxious to find her a husband who might live with them in peace and quiet, a man, that is, of a good conscience, such as she deemed herself to possess. And since she had heard some foolish preacher say that it were better to do evil by the counsel of theologians than to do well through the belief in the inspiration of the Holy Spirit, she had recourse to her Father Confessor, a man already old, a doctor of theology and one who was held to lead a holy life by the whole town, for she felt sure that, with his counsel and good prayers, she could not fail to find peace both for herself and for her daughter. After she had earnestly begged him to choose for her daughter such a husband as he knew a woman that loved God and her honor ought to desire, he replied that first of all it was needful to implore the grace of the Holy Spirit with prayer and fasting, and then, God guiding his judgment, he hoped to find what she required.

So the Friar retired to think over the matter; and whereas he had heard from the lady that she had got five hundred ducats together to give to her daughter's husband, and that she would take upon herself the charge of maintaining both husband and wife with lodgment, furniture and clothes, he bethought himself that he had a young comrade of handsome figure and pleasant countenance, to whom he might give the fair maiden, the house, the furniture, maintenance and food, whilst he himself kept the five hundred ducats to gratify his burning greed. And when he spoke to his comrade of the matter, he found that they were both of one mind upon it.

He therefore returned to the lady and said:

"I verily believe that God has sent his angel Raphael to me as he did to Tobit, to enable me to find a perfect husband for your daughter. I have in my house the most honorable gentleman in Italy, who has sometimes seen your daughter and is deeply in love with her. And so to-day, whilst I was at prayer, God sent him to me, and he told me of his desire for the marriage, whereupon, knowing his lineage and kindred and notable descent, I promised him to speak to you on the matter. There is, indeed, one defect in him, of which I alone have knowledge, and it is this: Wishing to save one of his friends whom another man was striving to slay, he drew his sword in order to separate them; but it chanced that his friend slew the other, and thus, although he himself had not dealt a blow, yet inasmuch as he had been present at a murder, and had drawn his sword, he became a fugitive from his native town. By the advice of his kinsfolk he came hither in the garb of a scholar, and he dwells here unknown until his kinsfolk shall have ended the matter; and this he hopes will shortly be done. For this reason, then, it would be needful that the marriage should be performed in secret, and that you should suffer him to go in the daytime to the public lectures and return home every evening to sup and sleep."

"Sir," replied the worthy woman, "I look upon what you tell me as of great advantage to myself, for I shall at least have by me what I most desire in the world."

Thereupon the Gray Friar brought his comrade, bravely attired with a crimson satin doublet, and the lady was well pleased with him. And as soon as he was come the betrothal took place, and, immediately after midnight, a mass was said and they were married. Then they went to bed together until daybreak, when the bridegroom told his wife that to escape discovery he must needs return to the college.

After putting on his crimson satin doublet and his long robe, without forgetting his coif of black silk, he bade his wife, who was still in bed, good-bye, promising that he would come every evening to sup with her, but that at dinner they must not wait for him. So he went away and left his wife, who esteemed herself the happiest woman alive to have found so excellent a match. And the young wedded Friar returned to the old father and brought him the five hundred ducats, as had been agreed between them when arranging the marriage.

In the evening he failed not to return and sup with her, who believed him to be her husband, and so well did he make himself liked by her and by his mother-in-law, that they would not have exchanged him for the greatest prince alive.

This manner of life continued for some time, but God in His kindness takes pity upon those that are deceived without fault of their own, and so in His mercy and goodness it came to pass that one morning the lady and her daughter felt a great desire to go and hear mass at St. Francis, and visit their good father confessor through whose means they deemed themselves so well provided, the one with a son-in-law and the other with a husband. It chanced that they did not find the confessor aforesaid nor any other that they knew, and, while waiting to see whether the father would come, they were pleased to hear high mass, which was just beginning. And whilst the young wife was giving close heed to the divine service and its mystery, she was stricken with astonishment on seeing the Priest turn himself about to pronounce the *Dominus vobiscum*, for it seemed to her that it was her husband or else his very fellow. She uttered, however, not a word, but waited till he should turn round again, when, looking still more carefully at him, she had no doubt that it was indeed he. Then she twitched her mother, who was deep in contemplation, and said:

"Alas! madam, what is it that I see?"

"What is it?" said her mother.

"That is my husband," she replied, "who is singing mass, or else 'tis one as like him as can be."

"I pray you, my daughter," replied the mother, who had not carefully observed him, "do not take such a thought into your head. It is impossible that men who are so holy should have practised such deceit. You would sin grievously against God if you believed such a thing."

Nevertheless the mother did not cease looking at him, and when it came to the *Ita missa est* she indeed perceived that no two sons of the same mother were ever so much alike. Yet she was so simple that she would fain have said, "O God, save me from believing what I see." Since her daughter was concerned in the matter, however, she would not suffer it to remain in uncertainty, and resolved to learn the truth.

When evening was come, and the husband (who had perceived nothing of them) was about to return, the mother said to her daughter:

"We shall now, if you are willing, find out the truth concerning your husband. When he is in bed I will go to him, and then, while he is not thinking, you will pluck off his coif from behind, and we shall see whether he be tonsured like the Friar who said mass."

As it was proposed, so was it done. As soon as the wicked husband was in bed, the old lady came and took both his hands as though in sport—her daughter took off his coif, and there he was with his fine tonsure. At this both mother and daughter were as greatly astonished as might be, and forthwith they called their servants to seize him and bind him fast till the morning, nor did any of his excuses or fine speeches avail him aught.

When day was come, the lady sent for her confessor, making as though she had some great secret to tell him, whereupon he came with all speed, and then, reproaching him for the deceit that he had practised on her, she had him seized like the other. Afterwards she sent for the officers of justice, in whose hands she placed them both. It is to be supposed that if the judges were honest men they did not suffer the offense to go unpunished.

FRANÇOIS RABELAIS

(149-?-1553?)

Rabelais was born at Chinon in Touraine during the last years of the Fifteenth Century. He studied medicine at Montpellier and then went to Lyon, where he practised and began writing. It was during the 30's that he began publishing *Gargantua and Pantagruel*. Somewhat later, he was physician to Cardinal Du Bellay, and toward the end of his life he entered the priesthood, though after a short while he left it. He died about 1553.

A great scholar and Humanist, one of the giant figures of literature, Rabelais sang the praises of life in his magnificent books. In these are found occasional episodes, like the two included in this collection, that entitle Rabelais to an important place among the writers of short tales.

The present version of these tales is from the old translation of *The Lives, Heroic Deeds . . . of Gargantua and His Son Pantagruel*, by Sir Thomas Urquhart and Peter Le Motteux. The first story is from Chapter XXXIV, the second from Chapter XXXVII, of the Third Book. Neither story has any title in the original.

HE WHO MARRIED A DUMB WIFE

(From *Gargantua and Pantagruel*, Book 3)

WELCOME, in good faith, my dear Master, welcome; it did me good to hear you talk, the Lord be praised for all. I do not remember to have seen you before now, since the last time that you acted at Montpellier, with our ancient friends, Anthony Saporra, Guy Bourguyer, Balthasar Noyer, Tolly, Jhon Quentin, Francis Robinet, Jhon Perdrier, and Francis Rabelais, the Moral Comedy of him who had espoused and married a Dumb Wife. I was there, quoth Epistemon; the good honest man, her husband, was very earnestly urgent to have the fillet of her tongue untied, and would needs have her speak by all means: At his desire some pains were taken on her, and partly by the industry of the physician, other part by the expertness of the surgeon, the encyliglotte, which she had under her tongue, being cut, she spoke and spoke again; yea, within few hours she spoke so loud, so much, so fiercely, and so long, that her poor husband returned to the same physician for a recipe to make her hold her peace: There are (quoth the physician) many proper remedies in our art, to make dumb women speak, but there are none, that ever I could learn therein, to make them silent. The only cure which I have found out, is their husband's deafness. The wretch became within few weeks thereafter, by virtue of some drugs, charms or enchantments, which the physician had prescribed unto him, so deaf, that he could not have heard the thundering of nineteen hundred cannons at a salvo. His wife, perceiving that indeed he was as deaf as a door-nail, and that her scolding was but in vain, sith that he heard her not, she grew stark mad. Some time after, the doctor asked for his fee of the husband; who answered, That truly he was deaf, and so was not able to understand what the tenure of his demand might be. Whereupon the leech bedusted him with a little, I know not what, sort of powder; which rendered him a fool immediately: so great was the stiltificating virtue of that strange kind of pulverized dose. Then did this fool of a husband and his mad wife join together, falling on the doctor and the surgeon, did so scratch, bethwack, and bang them, that they were left half dead upon the place, so furious were the blows which they received: I never in my lifetime laughed so much, as at the acting of that buffoonery.

THE ROAST-MEAT SELLER

AT Paris, in the Roast-meat Cookery of the Petit Chastelet, before the cook-shop of one of the roast-meat sellers of that lane, a certain hungry porter was eating his bread, after he had by parcels kept it awhile above the reek and steam of a fat goose on the spit, turning at a great fire, and found it so besmoaked with the vapor, to be savory; which the Cook observing, took no notice, till after having ravined his Penny Loaf, whereof no Morsel has been unsmoakified, he was about discamping and going away; but by your leave, as the Fellow thought to have departed thence shot-free, the Master-Cook laid hold upon him by the Gorget, demanded payment for the smoak of his roast-meat. The Porter answered, that he had sustained no loss at all; that by what he had done there was no diminution made of the flesh, that he had taken nothing of his, and that therefore he was not indebted to him in anything: As for the smoak in question, that, although he had not been there, it would howsoever have been evaporated: Besides that, before that time it had never been seen nor heard, that roast-meat smoak was sold upon the streets of Paris. The Cook hereto replied, That he was not obliged nor any way bound to feed and nourish for nought a Porter whom he had never seen before with the smoak of his roast-meat; and thereupon swore, that if he would not forthwith content and satisfie him with present payment for the repast which he had thereby got, that he would take his crooked staves from off his back; which instead of having loads thereafter laid upon them, should serve for fuel to his kitchen fires. Whilst he was going about so to do, and to have pulled them to him by one of the bottom rungs, which he had caught in his hand, the sturdy Porter got out of his gripes, drew forth the knotty cudgel, and stood to his own defence. The altercation waxed hot in words, which moved the gaping hoydens of the sottish Parisians to run from all parts thereabouts to see what the issue would be of that babling strife and contention. In the interim of this dispute, to very good purpose, Seiny Jhon the Fool and Citizen of Paris, hapened to be there, whom the Cook perceiving, said to the Porter, Wilt thou refer and submit unto the noble Seiny Jhon, the decision of the difference and controversie which is betwixt us? Yes, by the blood of a goose, answered the Porter, I am content. Seiny Jhon the Fool, finding that the Cook and Porter had compromised the determination of their variance and debate to the discretion of his award and arbitrament; after that the reasons on either side whereupon was grounded the mutual fierceness of their brawling jar had been to the full displayed and laid open before him, commanded the Porter to draw out of the fab of his belt a piece of money, if he had it. Whereupon the Porter immediately without delay, in reverence to the authority of such a judicious umpire, put the tenth part of a silver Phillip into his hand. This little Phillip Seiny Jhon took, then set it on his left shoulder, to try by feeling if it was of a sufficient weight; after that, laying it on the palm of his hand he made it ring and tingle, to understand by the ear if it was of a good alloy in the metal whereof it was composed: Thereafter he put it to the ball or apple of his left eye, to explore by the sight if it was well stamped and marked; all which being done, in a profound silence of the whole doltish people, who were there spectators of this pageantry, to the great hope of the Cooks, and despair of the Porters Prevalency in the suit that was in agitation, he finally caused the Porter to make it sound several times upon the stal of the Cooks Shop. Then with a presidential majesty holding his Bable (scepter-like) in his Hand, muffling his head with a hood of marten skins, each side whereof had the resemblance of an ape's face, sprucified up with ears of pasted paper, and having about his neck a buckled ruff, raised, furrowed, and ridged, with ponting sticks of the shape and fashion of small organ-pipes; he first, with all the force of his lungs, coughed two or three times, and then with an audible voice pronounced this following sentence, The Court declareth, That the Porter, who ate his Bread at the Smoak of the Roast, hath civilly paid the Cook with the Sound of his Money: And the said Court Ordaineth, That every one return to his own Home, and attend his proper Businesss, without Cost and Charges, and for a Cause. This verdict, award and arbitrament of the Parisian Fool, did appear so equitable, yea, so admirable to the aforesaid doctors, that they very much doubted, if the matter had been brought before the Sessions for Justice of the said Place, or that the Judges of the Rota at Rome had been umpires therein; or yet that the Areopagites themselves had been the deciders thereof, if by any one part, or all of them together, it had been so judicially sententiated and awarded.

CHARLES PERRAULT

(1628–1703)

PERRAULT, one of several talented brothers who graced the age of Louis XIV, was a scholar, government official, and writer. He lived a life devoid of extraordinary events, except for the celebrated Quarrel of the Ancients and Moderns in which he fought a long contest with Boileau and other believers in the superiority of the ancient over the modern writers. Toward the end of his life he wrote eleven fairy tales (published 1697), based on traditional stories. He was the first to give a literary form to *Little Red Riding-Hood*, *Cinderella*, *Puss in Boots*, *The Sleeping Beauty*, and half a dozen other household stories, which are destined to last as long as children enjoy fairy tales.

The present version, revised from an early English translation, is reprinted from an anonymously translated edition of the *Fairy Tales of Perrault*, London, no date.

LITTLE RED RIDING-HOOD

(From *Tales of My Mother Goose*)

ONCE upon a time there lived in a certain village a little country girl, the prettiest creature was ever seen. Her mother was excessively fond of her, and her grandmother doted on her still more. This good woman got made for her a little red riding-hood; which became the girl so extremely well that everybody called her Little Red Riding-Hood.

One day her mother, having made some custards, said to her:

"Go, my child, and see how thy grandmamma does, for I hear she has been very ill; carry her a custard, and this little pot of butter."

Little Red Riding-Hood set out immediately to go to her grandmother, who lived in another village. As she was going through the wood, she met with Gaffer Wolf, who had a very great mind to eat her up, but he durst not, because of some fagot-makers hard by in the forest. He asked her whither she was going. The poor child, who did not know that it was dangerous to stay and hear a wolf talk, said to him:

"I am going to see my grandmamma, and carry her a custard and a little pot of butter from my mamma."

"Does she live far off?" said the wolf.

"Oh, ay," answered Little Red Riding-Hood. "It is beyond that mill you see there, at the first house in the village."

"Well," said the wolf, "and I'll go and see her too. I'll go this way and you go that, and we shall see who will be there soonest."

The wolf began to run as fast as he could, taking the nearest way, and the little girl went by that farthest about, diverting herself in gathering nuts, running after butterflies, and making nosegays of such little flowers as she met with. The wolf was not long before he got to the old woman's house. He knocked at the door—tap, tap!

"Who's there?"

"Your grandchild, Little Red Riding-Hood," replied the wolf, counterfeiting her voice, "who has brought you a custard and a little pot of butter, sent you by mamma."

The good grandmother, who was in bed, because she was somewhat ill, cried out:

"Pull the bobbin and the latch will go up." The wolf pulled the bobbin, and the door opened; and then presently he fell upon the good woman and ate her up in a moment, for it was above three days that he had not touched a bit. He then shut the door, and went into the grandmother's bed, expecting Little Red Riding-Hood, who came sometime afterward and knocked at the door—tap, tap!

"Who's there?"

Little Red Riding-Hood, hearing the big voice of the wolf, was at first afraid; but, believing her grandmother had got a cold and was hoarse, answered:

"'Tis your grandchild, Little Red Riding-Hood, who has brought you a custard and little pot of butter mamma sends you."

The wolf cried out to her, softening his voice as much as he could:

"Pull the bobbin and the latch will go up."

Little Red Riding-Hood pulled the bobbin, and the door opened. The wolf, seeing her come in, said to her, hiding himself under the bed-clothes:

"Put the custard and the little pot of butter upon the stool, and come and lie down with me."

Little Red Riding-Hood undressed herself and went into bed, when, being greatly amazed to see how her grandmother looked in her night-clothes, she said to her:

"Grandmamma, what great arms you have got!"

"That is the better to hug thee, my dear!"

"Grandmamma, what great legs you have got!"

"That is to run the better, my child!"

"Grandmamma, what great ears you have got!"

"That is to hear the better, my child!"

"Grandmamma, what great eyes you have got!"

"It is to see the better, my child!"

"Grandmamma, what great teeth you have got!"

"That is to eat thee up!"

And, saying these words, this wicked wolf fell upon Little Red Riding-Hood, and ate her all up.

JEAN DE LA FONTAINE

(1621–1695)

One of the great figures of the age of Louis XIV, Jean de La Fontaine was born at Château-Thierry in 1621. He studied at Rheims and Paris, though he returned to his home afterward. In 1647 he married and entered the government service. He left his wife shortly after his marriage, and placed himself under the protection of several persons of rank and power. In 1668 the first collection of his *Fables* was published, and the following year his *Tales* in verse. He wrote a romance and several plays besides, was elected to membership in the French Academy, and died in 1695.

La Fontaine's *Fables* are by all counts his greatest achievement. These are, in the words of Lanson, "a picture of human life and French society." Based on Æsop and Phædrus and the other fabulists, the little masterpieces of La Fontaine are highly artistic literary performances. *The Four Friends* represents the ultimate perfection of this type of fable.

The present version is translated by Barrett H. Clark, and appears for the first time in this collection.

THE FOUR FRIENDS

(From *The Fables*)

A RAT, a raven, a tortoise, and a gazelle were once upon a time the greatest friends imaginable. This happy friendship first began in a home which was unknown to any human being. However, there is no place safe from humankind, be it in the densest wood, under the deepest river, or on the highest peaks where eagles perch. One day the graceful gazelle was disporting herself when by ill-luck a barking hound (that ferocious servant of ferocious man) found her trail and followed the scent. The gazelle ran on and on.

At meal-time the rat addressed his friends: "Brothers, how comes it that we are only three to-day? Is Miss Gazelle so fickle that she has forgotten us?" Up spoke the tortoise: "Now, if I were a bird, like the raven, I would at once take flight and learn what accident had befallen our fleet-footed sister, and where. My dear rat, it is shameful to doubt her affection for us." Whereupon the raven flew off, and from a distance caught sight of the unfortunate gazelle—he could recognize her face—all tangled up in a snare, and suffering agonies. So back he flew and gave the alarm. He was no fool, and he thought it would be foolish to ask the why and wherefore, the when and how of the poor sufferer, as would some pedantic schoolmaster, and thereby lose the chance of saving the victim.

The three friends, on hearing the sad news, took counsel and deliberated. Two voted to hurry to the spot where the poor gazelle was lying. "Our friend with the shell," said the raven, "might very well remain here to keep watch over the house; when would such a slow creeper reach the spot? Why, the gazelle would be dead." So without further discussion the other two flew to the assistance of the gazelle. But the tortoise was also set on going. Bewailing his inability to walk fast and cursing fate for having made him carry his house on his back, he trudged on behind the others.

Rongemail (that was the rat's name) cut the snare. Was not that fortunate? But just then the huntsman came along. "Who has set loose my gazelle?" he cried. Rongemail quickly scurried into a hole in the ground; the raven flew up into a tree, and the gazelle ran off into the woods. The huntsman, now very angry and seeing no trace of his prey, caught sight of the tortoise and forgot his anger. "Why," he asked himself, "lose courage because my snare has not worked this time? Here is something for my supper." And so saying, he put the tortoise into his bag.

The poor tortoise would have met his fate had not the raven told the gazelle, who came forth from her hiding-place, pretending to be lame. The man, eager for the chase, threw his bag to one side, and Rongemail immediately opened it as he had opened the snare, thus depriving the huntsman of a supper on his friend the tortoise

---

VOLTAIRE

(*François-Marie Arouet*)

(1694–1779)

VOLTAIRE was born in Paris in 1694. His early education was received at a Jesuit school. He began writing verses at an early age, and though his father wished him to study law, he continued to write. He was several times imprisoned for libellous verses and often forced to go into exile. A good part of his life he spent away from France. For over half a century he dominated the intellectual and artistic life of Europe, writing plays, histories, pamphlets, stories and satires. He was one of the greatest French writers and one of the most influential thinkers of modern times. His stories, of which he wrote a fairly large number, are philosophical and satirical tracts cast into narrative form. *Memnon* is what is known as a philosophical tale: it is one of the keenest satires Voltaire ever wrote.

The present version, anonymously translated, appeared originally in *Romances, Tales, and Smaller Pieces of M. de Voltaire*, vol. I, London, 1794.

MEMNON THE PHILOSOPHER, OR HUMAN WISDOM

MEMNON one day took it into his head to become a great philosopher. There are few men who have not, at some time or other, conceived the same wild project. Says Memnon to himself, To be a perfect philosopher, and of course to be perfectly happy, I have nothing to do but to divest myself entirely of passions; and nothing is more easy, as everybody knows. In the first place, I will never be in love; for, when I see a beautiful woman, I will say to myself, These cheeks will one day grow wrinkled, these eyes be encircled with vermilion, that bosom become flabby and pendant, that head bald and palsied. Now I have only to consider her at present in imagination, as she will afterwards appear; and certainly a fair face will never turn my head.

In the second place, I will be always temperate. It will be in vain to tempt me with good cheer, with delicious wines, or the charms of society. I will have only to figure to myself the consequences of excess, an aching head, a loathing stomach, the loss of reason, of health, and of time. I will then only eat to supply the waste of nature; my health will be always equal, my ideas pure and luminous. All this is so easy that there is no merit in accomplishing it.

But, says Memnon, I must think a little of how I am to regulate my fortune: why, my desires are moderate, my wealth is securely placed with the Receiver General of the finances of Nineveh: I have wherewithal to live independent; and that is the greatest of blessings. I shall never be under the cruel necessity of dancing attendance at court: I will never envy anyone, and nobody will envy me; still, all this is easy. I have friends, continued he, and I will preserve them, for we shall never have any difference; I will never take amiss anything they may say or do; and they will behave in the same way to me. There is no difficulty in all this.

Having thus laid his little plan of philosophy in his closet, Memnon put his head out of the window. He saw two women walking under the plane trees near his house. The one was old, and appeared quite at her ease. The other was young, handsome, and seemingly much agitated: she sighed, she wept, and seemed on that account still more beautiful. Our philosopher was touched, not, to be sure, with the beauty of the lady (he was too much determined not to feel any uneasiness of that kind) but with the distress which he saw her in. He came downstairs and accosted the young Ninevite in the design of consoling her with philosophy. That lovely person related to him, with an air of great simplicity, and in the most affecting manner, the injuries she sustained from an imaginary uncle; with what art he had deprived her of some imaginary property, and of the violence which she pretended to dread from him. "You appear to me," said she, "a man of such wisdom that if you will condescend to come to my house and examine into my affairs, I am persuaded you will be able to draw me from the cruel embarrassment I am at present involved in." Memnon did not hesitate to follow her, to examine her affairs philosophically and to give her sound counsel.

The afflicted lady led him into a perfumed chamber, and politely made him sit down with her on a large sofa, where they both placed themselves opposite to each other in the attitude of conversation, their legs crossed; the one eager in telling her story, the other listening with devout attention. The lady spoke with downcast eyes, whence there sometimes fell a tear, and which, as she now and then ventured to raise them, always met those of the sage Memnon. Their discourse was full of tenderness, which redoubled as often as their eyes met. Memnon took her affairs exceedingly to heart, and felt himself every instant more and more inclined to oblige a person so virtuous and so unhappy. By degrees, in the warmth of conversation, they ceased to sit opposite; they drew nearer; their legs were no longer crossed. Memnon counseled her so closely and gave her such tender advices that neither of them could talk any longer of business nor well knew what they were about.

At this interesting moment, as may easily be imagined, who should come in but the uncle; he was armed from head to foot, and the first thing he said was, that he would immediately sacrifice, as was just, the sage Memnon and his niece; the latter, who made her escape, knew that he was well enough disposed to pardon, provided a good round sum were offered to him. Memnon was obliged to purchase his safety with all he had about him. In those days people were happy in getting so easily quit. America was not then discovered, and distressed ladies were not nearly as dangerous as they are now.

Memnon, covered with shame and confusion, got home to his own house; there he found a card inviting him to dinner with some of his intimate friends. If I remain at home alone, said he, I shall have my mind so occupied with this vexatious adventure that I shall not be able to eat a bit, and I shall bring upon myself some disease. It will therefore be prudent in me to go to my intimate friends, and partake with them of a frugal repast. I shall forget in the sweets of their society that folly I have this morning been guilty of. Accordingly, he attends the meeting; he is discovered to be uneasy at something, and he is urged to drink and banish care. A little wine, drunk in moderation, comforts the heart of god and man: so reasons Memnon the philosopher, and he becomes intoxicated. After the repast, play is proposed. A little play with one's intimate friends is a harmless pastime. He plays and loses all that is in his purse, and four times as much on his word. A dispute arises on some circumstances in the game, and the disputants grow warm:

one of his intimate friends throws a dice box at his head, and strikes out one of his eyes. The philosopher Memnon is carried home to his house, drunk and penniless, with the loss of an eye.

He sleeps out his debauch, and when his head has got a little clear, he sends his servant to the Receiver General of the finances of Nineveh to draw a little money to pay his debts of honor to his intimate friends. The servant returns and informs him that the Receiver General had that morning been declared a fraudulent bankrupt and that by this means an hundred families are reduced to poverty and despair. Memnon, almost beside himself, puts a plaster on his eye and a petition in his pocket, and goes to court to solicit justice from the king against the bankrupt. In the saloon he meets a number of ladies all in the highest spirits, and sailing along with hoops four-and-twenty feet in circumference. One of them, who knew him a little, eyed him askance, and cried aloud, "Ah! What a horrid monster!" Another, who was better acquainted with him, thus accosts him, "Good-morrow, Mr. Memnon. I hope you are very well, Mr. Memnon. La, Mr. Memnon, how did you lose your eye?" And, turning upon her heel, she tripped away without waiting an answer. Memnon hid himself in a corner and waited for the moment when he could throw himself at the feet of the monarch. That moment at last arrived. Three times he kissed the earth, and presented his petition. His gracious majesty received him very favorably, and referred the paper to one of his satraps, that he might give him an account of it. The satrap takes Memnon aside and says to him with a haughty air and satirical grin, "Hark ye, you fellow with the one eye, you must be a comical dog indeed, to address yourself to the king rather than to me; and still more so, to dare to demand justice against an honest bankrupt, whom I honor with my protection, and who is nephew to the waiting-maid of my mistress. Proceed no further in this business, my good friend, if you wish to preserve the eye you have left."

Memnon, having thus in his closet resolved to renounce women, the excesses of the table, play and quarreling, but especially having determined never to go to court, had been in the short space of four-and-twenty hours, duped and robbed by a gentle dame, had got drunk, had gamed, had been engaged in a quarrel, had got his eye knocked out, and had been at court where he was sneered at and insulted.

Petrified with astonishment, and his heart broken with grief, Memnon returns homeward in despair. As he was about to enter his house, he is repulsed by a number of officers who are carrying off his furniture for the benefit of his creditors: he falls down almost lifeless under a plane tree. There he finds the fair dame, of the morning, who was walking with her dear uncle; and both set up a loud laugh on seeing Memnon with his plaster. The night approached, and Memnon made his bed on some straw near the walls of his house. Here the ague seized him, and he fell asleep in one of the fits, when a celestial spirit appeared to him in a dream.

It was all resplendent with light: it had six beautiful wings, but neither feet nor head nor tail, and could be likened to nothing. "What art thou?" said Memnon. "Thy good genius," replied the spirit. "Restore to me then my eye, my health, my fortune, my reason," said Memnon; and he related how he had lost them all in one day. "These are adventures which never happen to us in the world we inhabit," said the spirit. "And what world do you inhabit?" said the man of affliction. "My native country," replied the other, "is five hundred millions of leagues distant from the sun, in a little star near Sirius, which you see from hence." "Charming country!" said Memnon. "And are there indeed no jades to dupe a poor devil, no intimate friends that win his money, and knock out an eye for him, no fraudulent bankrupts, no satraps that make a jest of you while they refuse you justice?" "No," said the inhabitant of the star, "we have nothing of what you talk of; we are never duped by women, because we have none among us; we never commit excesses at table, because we neither eat nor drink; we have no bankrupts, because with us there is neither silver nor gold; our eyes cannot be knocked out because we have not bodies in the form of yours; and satraps never do us injustice because in our world we are all equal." "Pray, my lord," then said Memnon, "without women and without eating how do you spend your time?" "In watching," said the genius, "over the other worlds that are entrusted to us; and I am now come to give you consolation." "Alas!" replied Memnon, "why did you not come yesterday to hinder me from committing so many indiscretions?" "I was with your elder brother Hassan," said the celestial being. "He is still more to be pitied than you are. His Most Gracious Majesty the Sultan of the Indies, in whose court he has the honor to serve, has caused both his eyes to be put out for some small indiscretion; and he is now in a dungeon, his hands and feet loaded with chains." " 'Tis a happy thing truly," said Memnon, "to have a good genius in one's family, when out of two brothers one is blind of an eye, the other blind of both: one stretched upon straw, the other in a dungeon." "Your fate will soon change," said the animal of the star. "It is true, you will never recover your eye, but, except that, you may be sufficiently happy if you never again take it into your head to be a perfect philosopher." "It is then impossible?" said Memnon. "As impossible as to be perfectly wise, perfectly strong, perfectly powerful, perfectly happy. We ourselves are very far from it. There is a world indeed where all this is possible; but, in the hundred thousand millions of worlds dispersed over the regions of space, everything goes on by degrees. There is less philosophy, and less enjoyment on the second than in the first, less in the third than in the second, and so forth till the last in the scale, where all are completely fools." "I am afraid," said Memnon, "that our little terraqueous globe here is the madhouse of those hundred thousand millions of worlds of which Your Lordship does me the honor to speak." "Not quite," said the spirit, "but very nearly: everything must be in its proper place." "But are those poets and philosophers wrong, then, who tell us that everything is for the best?" "No, they are right, when we consider things in relation to the gradation to the whole universe." "Oh! I shall never believe it till I recover my eye again," said poor Memnon.

J. F. MARMONTEL

(1723–1799)

MARMONTEL, born in the Limousin of artisan parents, came early into popular esteem, and, when only a boy, was awarded several prizes for poetry. He wrote to Voltaire, who thought his verses showed an aptitude for finance, and got him a position in Paris. There until the eve of the Revolution he lived a happy and prosperous life. He wrote plays, verses, romances, tales, literary criticism. Popular at court, protected by powerful nobles, he enjoyed the society of the philosophers and writers of his time. His *Moral Tales*, from which *Lausus and Lydia* is taken, were widely read throughout Europe. Strange as it may seem, *Lausus and Lydia* was considered a very pathetic story in its day. It does, however, possess merits of clarity and skilful construction. It may be considered a good example of a much-practised type of story in vogue in the Eighteenth Century, in which the author employs a foreign background—often of some imaginary Oriental land—for the purpose of exemplifying a moral or philosophical point.

The present version is reprinted from *Moral Tales by M. Marmontel*, translated by C. Dennis and R. Lloyd, London, 1771.

LAUSUS AND LYDIA

(From the *Moral Tales*)

THE character of Mezentius, King of Tyrrhene, is well known. A bad prince and a good father, cruel and tender by turns. He had nothing of the tyrant, nothing that showed violence as long as his desires knew no obstacle; but the calm of this haughty soul was the repose of a lion.

Mezentius had a son named Lausus, whose valor and beauty rendered him famous among the young heroes of Italy. Lausus had attended

Mezentius in the war against the King of Præneste. His father, at the very summit of joy, saw him, covered with blood, fighting and vanquishing by his side. The King of Præneste, driven out of his territories and seeking safety in flight, had left in the hands of the conqueror a treasure more precious than his crown, a princess at that age wherein the heart has only the virtues of nature, and nature has all the charms of innocence and beauty. Everything that the Graces in tears possess, either noble or affecting, was painted on Lydia's countenance. In her grief, courage, and dignity, one might discover the daughter of kings amongst the crowd of slaves. She received the first compliments of her enemies without haughtiness, without acknowledgment, as an homage due to her rank, the noble sentiments of which were not weakened by ill fortune.

She heard her father named, and at that name lifted up to heaven her fine eyes filled with tears. All hearts were moved. Mezentius himself, astonished, forgot his pride and age. Prosperity, which hardens weak souls, softens proud hearts, and nothing can be gentler than an hero after a victory. If the savage heart of old Mezentius was not able to resist the charms of his captive, what was the impression on the virtuous soul of young Lausus? He mourned over his exploits; he reproached himself with his victory: it cost Lydia tears. "Let her avenge herself," said he; "let her hate me as much as I love her; I have deserved it but too much." But an idea still more distressful presents itself to his imagination. He sees Mezentius, astonished, softened, pass on a sudden from rage to clemency. He judged rightly that humanity alone had not effected the revolution, and the fear of having his father for a rival completed his confusion.

At the age of Mezentius jealousy follows closely upon love. The tyrant observed the eyes of Lausus with an uneasy attention; he saw extinguished in them all at once the joy and ardor which had lighted up the face of the young hero on his first victory. He saw him disturbed: he caught some looks which it was but too easy to understand. From that instant he considered himself as betrayed; but nature interposed and suspended his rage. A tyrant, even in his fury, constrains himself to think that he is just; and before he condemned his son Mezentius labored to convict him. He began by dissembling his own passion with so much art that the prince looked on his former fears as vain, and considered the attentions of love as nothing more than the effects of clemency. At first he affected to allow Lydia all the appearances of liberty, but the tyrant's court was full of spies and informers, the usual retinue of men of power who, not being able to make themselves beloved, place their greatness in being feared.

His son was no longer afraid of paying Lydia a respectful homage. He mingled with his sentiments an interest so delicate and tender, that

Lydia very soon began to reproach herself for the hatred which she thought she entertained for the blood of her enemy; while Lausus lamented that he had contributed to Lydia's misfortunes. He called the gods to witness that he would do all in his power to repair them. "The King my father," says he, "is as generous after victory as intractable before battle: satisfied with victory, he is incapable of oppression. It is easier than ever for the King of Præneste to engage him to a peace that shall be glorious to both. That peace will dry up your tears, beautiful Lydia; but will it efface the remembrance of their crime who caused you to shed them? Why did I not see all my blood flow rather than those tears?"

Lydia's replies, which were full of modesty and greatness, betrayed to Lausus no warmer emotion than that of gratitude: though at the bottom of her heart she was but too sensible of the care he took to console her. She sometimes blushed for having listened to him with complaisance; but her father's interests made it a law to her to avail herself of such a support. In the meantime their conference growing more frequent became also more animated, more interesting, more intimate; and love made its way insensibly through respect and gratitude, as a flower which, in order to blow, opens the slight texture in which it is enfolded.

Deceived more and more by the feigned tranquillity of Mezentius, the credulous Lausus flattered himself that he should very soon see his duty accord with his inclination, and nothing in the world, in his opinion, was easier than to reconcile them. The treaty of peace which he had meditated, was reduced to two articles: to restore to the King of Præneste his crown and his territories, and to make his marriage with the princess the bond of union between the two powers. He communicated this project to Lydia. The confidence he placed in it, the advantages he saw accruing from it, the transports of joy which the idea alone inspired him with, surprised the lovely captive into a smile, mingled with tears. "Generous Prince," said she to him, "may Heaven fulfill the wishes you pour out for my father! I shall not be sorry that I am made a pledge of peace and the token of gratitude." This touching reply was accompanied with a look still more touching. The tyrant was informed of all. His first transport would have hurried him to sacrifice his rival, but his son was the only support of his crown, the only barrier between the people and him: the same stroke would have rendered him completely odious to his subjects and have taken from him the only defender whom he could oppose to the public hatred. Fear is the ruling passion of tyrants. Mezentius resolved to dissemble. He ordered his son into his presence, talked to him with good humor and bade him prepare to set out the next day for the frontiers of his territory, where he had left his army. The prince endeavored to conceal the grief which wrung his soul, and set out without having time to take leave of Lydia.

The very day of Lausus' departure, Mezentius had caused honorable conditions of peace to be proposed to the King of Præneste, the first article of which was his marriage with the daughter of the vanquished monarch. That unfortunate monarch hesitated not to consent, and the same ambassador that offered him peace brought back his agreement for an answer.

Lausus had in the court a friend, who had been attached to him from his infancy. A remarkable resemblance to the young prince had been the means of making the fortune of the young man, who was called Phanor, but they resembled each other still more in their disposition than their figure; the same inclinations, the same virtues. Lausus and Phanor seemed to have but one soul. Lausus at parting had confided to Phanor his passion and his despair. The latter was therefore inconsolable on hearing of the marriage of Lydia with Mezentius: he thought it his duty to acquaint the prince with it. The situation of the lover at this news cannot be described; his heart was troubled, his reason forsook him, and in the distraction of blind sorrow, he wrote to Lydia the warmest and most imprudent letter that love ever dictated. Phanor was charged with the delivery of it. He went to her at the hazard of his life, if he should be discovered. He was so. Mezentius, enraged, ordered him to be laden with irons and dragged to a frightful prison.

However, everything was prepared for a celebration of this unhappy marriage. We may justly conclude that the feast was suitable to the character of Mezentius. Wrestling, the cestus, gladiators, combats between men and animals bred up to carnage, everything that barbarity has invented for its amusements was to have graced the pomp: nothing was wanting to this bloody spectacle but persons to fight against the wild beasts; for it was customary to expose to these fights none but criminals condemned to die, and Mezentius, who on any suspicion was always eager to put the innocent to death, retarded still less the punishment of the guilty. There remained in the prisons none but the faithful friend of Lausus. "Let him be exposed," said Mezentius; "let him fall a prey to devouring lions: the traitor deserves a more cruel death, but this best suits his crime and my vengeance, and his punishment is a feast worthy of injured love!"

Lausus having in vain expected the answer of his friend, impatiently gave way to affright. "Should we be discovered," said he, "should I have lost my friend by my fatal imprudence! Lydia herself! Ah, I tremble! No, I cannot live any longer in this dreadful uncertainty." He set out; he disguised himself carefully. He arrived, and heard the reports spread among the people; learned that his friend was in chains, and that the next day was to unite Lydia with Mezentius. He learned that they were preparing the feast which was to precede the festival; they were to see the unhappy Phanor a prey to wild beasts. He shrunk at this recital; a deadly chillness spread through all his veins; he came again to himself, but lost in distraction he fell upon his knees and cried out, "Great gods, restrain my hand, my despair terrifies me! Let me die honorably!" Resolved to deliver his dear Phanor, though he should perish in his stead, he flew to the gates of the prison; but how was he to enter? He addressed himself to the slave whose office it was to carry food to the prisoners. "Open your eyes," said he, "and know me; I am Lausus, I am the son of the King. I expect an important service from you. Phanor is confined here: I will see him, I will. I have but one way to come at him: give me your clothes, and fly! There are the pledges of my acknowledgment. Withdraw yourself from the vengeance of my father. If you betray me, you rush on your ruin; if you assist me in my undertaking, my favor shall find you in the very heart of the deserts."

The weak and timorous slave yielded to his promises and threats. He assisted the prince in disguising himself, and disappeared, after having told him the hour at which he was to present himself, and the conduct he was to observe in order to deceive the vigilance of the guards. Night approached and the moment arrived. Lausus presented himself, assuming the name of the slave. The bolts of the dungeon opened with a dismal sound. By the feeble glimmering of a torch, he penetrated into this mansion of horror; he advanced and listened: the accents of a moaning voice struck his ear; he knew it to be the voice of his friend. He saw him lying down in the corner of the cell covered with rags, consumed with weakness, the paleness of death on his countenance, and the fire of despair in his eyes. "Leave me," said Phanor to him, taking him for the slave; "away with these odious nourishments: suffer me to die. Alas," added he, sending forth cries interrupted by sighs, "alas! my dear Lausus is still more unhappy than I. Oh, gods above! If he knows the state to which he has reduced his friend!" "Yes," cried Lausus, throwing himself on his bosom, "yes, my dear Phanor, he does know it, and he partakes of it!" "What do I see?" cried Phanor, transported. "Ah, Lausus, my Prince!" At these words both of them lost the use of their senses, locked in each other's arms. Their hearts met, and their sighs intermingled. They remained for a long time mute and immovable, stretched out on the floor of the dungeon. Grief stifled their voices, and they answered each other only by embracing more closely, and bathing one another with their tears. Lausus, at last coming to himself, "Let us lose no time," said he; "take these clothes, get hence and leave me here." "What, I! Great gods, can I be so vile! Ah, Lausus, could you believe it? Ought you to propose it to me?" "I know you well," said the Prince, "but you should also know me. The sentence is pronounced, your punishment is prepared, you must die or fly." "Fly!" "Hear me: my father is violent, but he is not without sensibility. Nature asserts her right over his heart. If I deliver you from death I have only to melt him to compassion for myself;

and his arm, when lifted up against a son, will be easily disarmed." "He would strike," said Phanor, "and your death would be my crime: I cannot abandon you." "Well, then," said Lausus, "remain here, but at your death you shall see mine also. Depend not on my father's clemency; it would be in vain for him to pardon me: think not that I would pardon myself. This hand, which wrote the fatal letter that condemns you, this hand which, even after its crime is still the hand of your friend, shall reunite us in your own despite." In vain would Phanor have insisted. "Let us argue no longer," interrupted Lausus; "you can say nothing to me that can equal the shame of surviving my friend, after I have destroyed him. Your pressing earnestness makes me blush, and your prayers are an affront. I will answer for my own safety if you will fly. I swear to die if you will stay and perish. Choose: the moments now are precious."

Phanor knew his friend too well to pretend to shake his resolution. "I consent," said he, "to let you try the only means of safety that is left us; but live if you would have me live: your scaffold shall be mine." "I readily believe it," said Lausus, "and your friend esteems you too much to desire you to survive him." At these words they embraced, and Phanor went out of the dungeon in the habit of the slave, which Lausus had just thrown off.

What a night! What a dreadful night for Lydia! Alas, how shall we paint the emotions that arose in her soul, that divided, tore it between love and virtue? She adored Lausus, she detested Mezentius, she was sacrificing herself to her father's interests, delivering herself up to the object of her hatred, tearing herself forever from an adored lover. They led her to the altar as it were to punishment. Barbarous Mezentius! Thou art content to reign over the heart by violence and fear! It suffices thee that thy consort trembles before thee as a slave before his master. Such is love in the heart of a tyrant. Yet, alas! it is for him alone that she is hereafter to live: it is to him that she is going to be united. If she resists, she must betray her lover and her father: a refusal would discover the secret of her soul, and if Lausus were suspected to be dear to her, he were undone. It was in this cruel agitation that Lydia awaited the day. The terrible day arrived. Lydia, dismayed and trembling, saw herself decked out not as a bride to be presented at the altar of Love and Hymen, but as one of those innocent victims that a barbarous piety crowned with flowers before it sacrificed them.

They led her to the place where the spectacle was to be exhibited; the people assembled there in multitudes, and the sports began. I shall not stop to describe the engagements at the cestus, at wrestling, at the sword: a more dreadful object engages our attention.

An enormous lion advances. At first, with a calm pride, he traverses the arena, throwing his dreadful looks round the amphitheater that environs him; a confused murmur announces the terror that he inspires. In a short time the sound of clarions animates him; he replies by his roarings; his shaggy mane is erected around his monstrous head; he lashes his loins with his tail, and the fire begins to issue from his sparkling eyeballs. The affrighted populace wish and dread to see the wretch appear who is to be delivered up to the rage of this monster. Terror and pity seize on every breast. The combatant, whom Mezentius' guards themselves had taken for Phanor, presents himself. Lydia could not distinguish him. The horror with which she was seized obliged her to turn away her eyes from this spectacle, which shocks the sensibility of her tender soul. Alas! what would she feel if she knew that Phanor, the dear friend of Lausus, was the criminal whom they have selected; if she knew that Lausus himself had taken his friend's place, and that it was he who was going to fight!

Half-naked, his hair disheveled, he walked with an intrepid air; a poniard for the attack, a buckler for defense, are the only arms by which he was protected. Mezentius, prepossessed, sees in him only the guilty Phanor. His own blood is drunk, Nature is blind; it is his own son whom he delivers up to death, and his bowels are not moved. Resentment and revenge stifle every other sentiment. He saw with a barbarous joy the fury of the lion rising by degrees. Lausus, impatient, provoked the monster and urged him to the combat. He advanced toward him; the lion sprang forward. Lausus avoided him. Thrice the enraged animal made toward him with his foaming jaws, and thrice Lausus escaped his murderous fangs.

In the meantime Phanor learned what was happening. He ran up, bearing down the multitude before him, while his piercing cries made the amphitheater resound. "Stop, Mezentius! Save your son, for it is he! It is Lausus who is engaged!" Mezentius looked and knew Phanor, who hastened toward him. "Oh, ye gods, what do I see! My people, assist me! Throw yourselves on the arena, save my son from the jaws of death!" At the name of Lausus, Lydia fell down dead on the steps of the amphitheater: her heart cold, her eyes covered with darkness. Mezentius saw only his son, now in imminent danger. A thousand hands strive in vain for his defense: the monster pursued him and would have devoured him before they could have come to his assistance. But, oh, incredible wonder! Unlooked-for happiness! Lausus, eluding the bounds of the furious animal, struck him a mortal wound and his sword was drawn reeking from the lion's heart. He fell amid torrents of blood spat forth from the foaming jaws. The universal alarm now changed into triumph, and the people replied to Mezentius' doleful cries only by shouts of admiration and joy. These shouts recalled Lydia to life: she opened her eyes and saw Lausus at Mezentius' feet, holding in one hand the bloody dagger, and in the other his dear and faithful Phanor. "It is

I," said he to his father, "I alone who am culpable. Phanor's crime was mine: it was my duty to explain it. I forced him to resign his place, and was about to kill myself if he refused. I live, I owe my life to him, and if your son be still dear to you, you owe your son to him, but if your vengeance is not appeased, our days are in your hands. Strike, we will perish together, our hearts have sworn it." Lydia, trembling at this discourse, viewed Mezentius with suppliant eyes, overflowing with tears. The tyrant's cruelty could not withstand this trial. The cries of Nature and the voice of remorse put to silence jealousy and revenge. He remained for a long time immovable and dumb, casting by turns looks of trouble and confusion on the culprits before him, looks in which love, hatred, indignation, and pity succeeded to one another. All trembled around the tyrant. Lausus, Phanor, Lydia, and a multitude innumerable waited with terror the first words that he was to pronounce. He submitted at last, in spite of himself, to that virtue whose ascendancy overpowered him, and passing of a sudden with impetuous violence from rage to tenderness, he threw himself into his son's arms. "Yes," said he, "I pardon thee, and I pardon also thy friend. Live, love one another; but there remains one sacrifice more for me to make thee, and thou hast just now rendered thyself worthy of it. Receive it, then," said he with a new effort; "receive this hand, the gift of which is dearer to thee than life. It is thy valor which has forced it from me; it is that alone could have obtained it."

HONORÉ DE BALZAC

(1799–1850)

Born at Tours in 1799, Balzac left his native city at an early age and after various attempts at making a living went into the publishing business in Paris. Failing at that, he set to work more earnestly than ever at writing, and until the end of his life he toiled incessantly at the series of novels and tales which have rendered him famous as one of the great novelists of the world. In his *Human Comedy*, Balzac included several short stories, which are among the very first of their kind; in them the short story is at last entirely free of the past. His work has that contemporary quality that is one of the distinguishing marks of all great art.

The Mysterious Mansion is grouped among the *Scenes from Private Life*. It is one of the great stories of modern times.

The present version, anonymously translated, is reprinted from *Great Short Stories*, Collier's Sons, New York. The original title of the story is *La Grande Bretêche*.

THE MYSTERIOUS MANSION

ABOUT a hundred yards from the town of Vendôme, on the borders of the Loire, there is an old gray house, surmounted by very high gables, and so completely isolated that neither tanyard nor shabby hostelry, such as you may find at the entrance to all small towns, exists in its immediate neighborhood.

In front of this building, overlooking the river, is a garden, where the once well-trimmed box borders that used to define the walks now grow wild as they list. Several willows that spring from the Loire have grown as rapidly as the hedge that encloses it, and half conceal the house. The rich vegetation of those weeds that we call foul adorns the sloping shore. Fruit trees, neglected for the last ten years, no longer yield their harvest, and their shoots form coppices. The wall-fruit grows like hedges against the walls. Paths once graveled are overgrown with moss, but, to tell the truth, there is no trace of a path. From the height of the hill, to which cling the ruins of the old castle of the Dukes of Vendôme, the only spot whence the eye can plunge into this enclosure, it strikes you that, at a time not easy to determine, this plot of land was the delight of a country gentleman, who cultivated roses and tulips and horticulture in general, and who was besides a lover of fine fruit. An arbor is still visible, or rather the débris of an arbor, where there is a table that time has not quite destroyed. The aspect of this garden of bygone days suggests the negative joys of peaceful, provincial life, as one might reconstruct the life of a worthy tradesman by reading the epitaph on his tombstone. As if to complete the sweetness and sadness of the ideas that possess one's soul, one of the walls displays a sun-dial decorated with the following commonplace Christian inscription: "Ultimam cogita!" The roof of this house is horribly dilapidated, the shutters are always closed, the balconies are covered with swallows' nests, the doors are perpetually shut, weeds have drawn green lines in the cracks of the flights of steps, the locks and bolts are rusty. Sun, moon, winter, summer, and snow have worn the paneling, warped the boards, gnawed the paint. The lugubrious silence which reigns there is only broken by birds, cats, martins, rats and mice, free to course to and fro, to fight and to eat each other. Everywhere an invisible hand has graven the word *mystery*.

Should your curiosity lead you to glance at this house from the side that points to the road, you would perceive a great door which the children of the place have riddled with holes. I afterward heard that this door had been closed for the last ten years. Through the holes broken by the boys you would have observed the perfect harmony that existed between the façades of both garden and courtyard. In both the same disorder prevails. Tufts of weed encircle the paving-stones. Enormous cracks furrow the walls, round whose blackened crests twine the thousand garlands of the pellitory. The steps are out of joint, the wire of the bell is rusted, the spouts are cracked. What fire from heaven has fallen here? What tribunal has decreed that salt should be strewn on this dwelling? Has God been blasphemed, has France been here betrayed? These are the questions we ask ourselves, but get no answer from the crawling things that haunt the place. The empty and deserted house is a gigantic enigma, of which the key is lost. In bygone times it was a small fief, and bears the name of the Grande Bretêche.

I inferred that I was not the only person to whom my good landlady had communicated the secret of which I was to be the sole recipient, and I prepared to listen.

"Sir," she said, "when the Emperor sent the Spanish prisoners of war and others here, the Government quartered on me a young Spaniard who had been sent to Vendôme on parole. Parole notwithstanding he went out every day to show himself to the sous-préfet. He was a Spanish grandee! Nothing less! His name ended in os and dia, something like Burgos de Férédia. I have his name on my books; you can read it if you like. Oh! but he was a handsome young man for a Spaniard; they are all said to be ugly. He was only five feet and a few inches high, but he was well-grown; he had small hands that he took such care of; ah! you should have seen! He had as many brushes for his hands as a woman for her whole dressing apparatus! He had thick black hair, a fiery eye, his skin was rather bronzed, but I liked the look of it. He wore the finest linen I have ever seen on any one, although I have had princesses staying here, and, among others, General Bertrand, the Duke and Duchess d'Abrantès, Monsieur Decazes, and the King of Spain. He didn't eat much; but his manners were so polite, so amiable, that one could not owe him a grudge. Oh! I was very fond of him, although he didn't open his lips four times in the day, and it was impossible to keep up a conversation with him. For if you spoke to him, he did not answer. It was a fad, a mania with them all, I heard say. He read his breviary like a priest, he went to Mass and to all the services regularly. Where did he sit? Two steps from the chapel of Madame de Merret. As he took his place there the first time he went to church, nobody suspected him of any intention in so doing. Besides, he never raised his eyes from his prayer-book, poor young man! After that, sir, in the evening he would walk on the mountains, among the castle ruins. It was the poor man's only amusement, it reminded him of his country. They say that Spain is all mountains! From the commencement of his imprisonment he stayed out late. I was anxious when I found that he did not come home before midnight; but we got accustomed to this fancy of his. He took the key of the door, and we left off sitting up for him. He lodged in a house of ours in the Rue des Casernes. After that, one of our stable-men told us that in the evening when he led the horses to the water, he thought he had seen the Spanish grandee swimming far down the river like a live fish. When he returned, I told him to take care of the rushes; he appeared vexed to have been seen in the water. At last, one day, or rather one morning, we did not find him in his room; he had not returned. After searching everywhere, I found some writing in the drawer of a table, where there were fifty gold pieces of Spain that are called doubloons and were worth about five thousand francs; and ten thousand francs' worth of diamonds in a small sealed box. The writing said, that in case he did not return, he left us the money and the diamonds, on condition of paying for Masses to thank God for his escape, and for his salvation. In those days my husband had not been taken from me; he hastened to seek him everywhere.

"And now for the strange part of the story. He brought home the Spaniard's clothes, that he had discovered under a big stone, in a sort of pilework by the river-side near the castle, nearly opposite to the Grande Bretêche. My husband had gone there so early that no one had seen him. After reading the letter, he burned the clothes, and according to Count Férédia's desire we declared that he had escaped. The sous-préfet sent all the gendarmerie in pursuit of him; but brust! they never caught him. Lepas believed that the Spaniard had drowned himself. I, sir, don't think so; I am more inclined to believe that he had something to do with the affair of Madame de Merret, seeing that Rosalie told me that the crucifix that her mistress thought so much of, that she had it buried with her, was of ebony and silver. Now in the beginning of his stay here, Monsieur de Férédia had one in ebony and silver, that I never saw him with later. Now, sir, don't you consider that I need have no scruples about the Spaniard's fifteen thousand francs, and that I have a right to them?"

"Certainly; but you haven't tried to question Rosalie?" I said.

"Oh, yes, indeed, sir; but to no purpose! the girl's like a wall. She knows something, but it is impossible to get her to talk."

After exchanging a few more words with me, my landlady left me a prey to vague and gloomy thoughts, to a romantic curiosity, and a religious terror not unlike the profound impression produced on us when by night, on entering a dark church, we perceive a faint light under high arches; a vague figure glides by—the rustle of a robe or cassock is heard, and we shudder.

Suddenly the Grande Bretêche and its tall weeds, its barred windows, its rusty ironwork, its closed doors, its deserted apartments, appeared like a fantastic apparition before me. I essayed to penetrate the mysterious dwelling, and to find the knot of its dark story—the drama that had killed three persons. In my eyes Rosalie became the most interesting person in Vendôme. As I studied her, I discovered the traces of secret care, despite the radiant health that shone in her plump countenance.

There was in her the germ of remorse or hope; her attitude revealed a secret, like the attitude of a bigot who prays to excess, or of the infanticide who ever hears the last cry of her child. Yet her manners were rough and ingenuous—her silly smile was not that of a criminal, and could you but have seen the great kerchief that encompassed her portly bust, framed and laced in by a lilac and blue cotton gown, you would have dubbed her innocent. No, I thought, I will not leave Vendôme without learning the history of the Grande Bretêche. To gain my ends I will strike up a friendship with Rosalie, if needs be.

"Rosalie," said I, one evening.

"Sir?"

"You are not married?"

She started slightly.

"Oh, I can find plenty of men, when the fancy takes me to be made miserable," she said, laughing.

She soon recovered from the effects of her emotion, for all women, from the great lady to the maid of the inn, possess a composure that is peculiar to them.

"You are too good-looking and well favored to be short of lovers. But tell me, Rosalie, why did you take service in an inn after leaving Madame de Merret? Did she leave you nothing to live on?"

"Oh, yes! But, sir, my place is the best in all Vendôme."

The reply was one of those that judges and lawyers would call evasive. Rosalie appeared to me to be situated in this romantic history like the square in the midst of a chessboard. She was at the heart of the truth and chief interest; she seemed to me to be bound in the very knot of it. The conquest of Rosalie was no longer to be an ordinary siege—in this girl was centered the last chapter of a novel, therefore from this moment Rosalie became the object of my preference.

One morning I said to Rosalie: "Tell me all you know about Madame de Merret."

"Oh!" she replied in terror, "do not ask that of me, Monsieur Horace."

Her pretty face fell—her clear, bright color faded—and her eyes lost their innocent brightness.

"Well, then," she said, at last, "if you must have it so, I will tell you about it; but promise to keep my secret!"

"Done! my dear girl, I must keep your secret with the honor of a thief, which is the most loyal in the world."

Were I to transcribe Rosalie's diffuse eloquence faithfully, an entire volume would scarcely contain it; so I shall abridge.

The room occupied by Madame de Merret at the Bretêche was on the ground floor. A little closet about four feet deep, built in the thickness of the wall, served as her wardrobe. Three months before the eventful evening of which I am about to speak, Madame de Merret had been so seriously indisposed that her husband had left her to herself in her own apartment, while he occupied another on the first floor. By one of those chances that it is impossible to foresee, he returned home from the club (where he was accustomed to read the papers and discuss politics with the inhabitants of the place) two hours later than usual. His wife supposed him to be at home, in bed and asleep. But the invasion of France had been the subject of a most animated discussion; the billiard-match had been exciting, he had lost forty francs, an enormous sum for Vendôme, where every one hoards, and where manners are restricted within the limits of a praiseworthy modesty, which perhaps is the source of the true happiness that no Parisian covets. For some time past Monsieur de Merret had been satisfied to ask Rosalie if his wife had gone to bed; and on her reply, which was always in the affirmative, had immediately gained his own room with the good temper engendered by habit and confidence. On entering his house, he took it into his head to go and tell his wife of his misadventure, perhaps by way of consolation. At dinner he found Madame de Merret most coquettishly attired. On his way to the club it had occurred to him that his wife was restored to health, and that her convalescence had added to her beauty. He was, as husbands are wont to be, somewhat slow in making this discovery. Instead of calling Rosalie, who was occupied just then in watching the cook and coachman play a difficult hand at brisque, Monsieur de Merret went to his wife's room by the light of a lantern that he deposited on the first step of the staircase. His unmistakable step resounded under the vaulted corridor. At the moment that the Count turned the handle of his wife's door, he fancied he could hear the door of the closet I spoke of close; but when he entered Madame de Merret was alone before the fireplace. The husband thought ingenuously that Rosalie was in the closet, yet a suspicion that jangled in his ear put him on his guard. He looked at his wife and saw in her eyes I know not what wild and hunted expression.

"You are very late," she said. Her habitually pure, sweet voice seemed changed to him.

Monsieur de Merret did not reply, for at that moment Rosalie entered. It was a thunderbolt for him. He strode about the room, passing from one window to the other, with mechanical motion and folded arms.

"Have you heard bad news, or are you unwell?" inquired his wife timidly, while Rosalie undressed her.

He kept silent.

"You can leave me," said Madame de Merret to her maid; "I will put my hair in curl papers myself."

From the expression of her husband's face she foresaw trouble, and wished to be alone with him. When Rosalie had gone, or was supposed to have gone (for she stayed in the corridor for a few minutes), Monsieur de Merret came and stood in front of his wife, and said coldly to her:

"Madame, there is someone in your closet!" She looked calmly at her husband and replied simply:

"No, sir."

This answer was heartrending to Monsieur de Merret; he did not believe in it. Yet his wife had never appeared to him purer or more saintly than at that moment. He rose to open the closet door; Madame de Merret took his hand, looked at him with an expression of melancholy, and said in a voice that betrayed singular emotion:

"If you find no one there, remember this, all will be over between us!" The extraordinary dignity of his wife's manner restored the Count's profound esteem for her, and inspired him with one of those resolutions that only lack a vaster stage to become immortal.

"No," said he, "Josephine, I will not go there. In either case it would separate us forever. Hear me, I know how pure you are at heart, and that your life is a holy one. You would not commit a mortal sin to save your life."

At these words Madame de Merret turned a haggard gaze upon her husband.

"Here, take your crucifix," he added. "Swear to me before God that there is no one in there; I will believe you, I will never open that door."

Madame de Merret took the crucifix and said:

"I swear."

"Louder," said the husband, "and repeat 'I swear before God that there is no one in that closet.' "

She repeated the sentence calmly.

"That will do," said Monsieur de Merret, coldly.

After a moment of silence:

"I never saw this pretty toy before," he said, examining the ebony crucifix inlaid with silver, and most artistically chiseled.

"I found it at Duvivier's, who bought it of a Spanish monk when the prisoners passed through Vendôme last year."

"Ah!" said Monsieur de Merret, as he replaced the crucifix on the nail, and he rang. Rosalie did not keep him waiting. Monsieur de Merret went quickly to meet her, led her to the bay window that opened on to the garden and whispered to her:

"Listen! I know that Gorenflot wishes to marry you, poverty is the only drawback, and you told him that you would be his wife if he found the means to establish himself as a master mason. Well! go and fetch him, tell him to come here with his trowel and tools. Manage not to awaken any one in his house but himself; his fortune will be more than your desires. Above all, leave this room without babbling, otherwise—" He frowned. Rosalie went away, he recalled her.

"Here, take my latchkey," he said. "Jean!" then cried Monsieur de Merret, in tones of thunder in the corridor. Jean, who was at the same time his coachman and his confidential servant, left his game of cards and came.

"Go to bed, all of you," said his master, signing to him to approach; and the Count added, under his breath: "When they are all asleep—*asleep*, d'ye hear?—you will come down and tell me." Monsieur de Merret, who had not lost sight of his wife all the time he was giving his orders, returned quietly to her at the fireside and began to tell her of the game of billiards and the talk of the club. When Rosalie returned she found Monsieur and Madame de Merret conversing very amicably.

The Count had lately had all the ceilings of his reception rooms on the ground floor repaired. Plaster of Paris is difficult to obtain in Vendôme; the carriage raises its price. The Count had therefore bought a good deal, being well aware that he could find plenty of purchasers for whatever might remain over. This circumstance inspired him with the design he was about to execute.

"Sir, Gorenflot has arrived," said Rosalie in low tones.

"Show him in," replied the Count in loud tones.

Madame de Merret turned rather pale when she saw the mason.

"Gorenflot," said her husband, "go and fetch bricks from the coach-house, and bring sufficient to wall up the door of this closet; you will use the plaster I have over to coat the wall with." Then calling Rosalie and the workman aside:

"Listen, Gorenflot," he said in an undertone, "you will sleep here to-night. But to-morrow you will have a passport to a foreign country, to a town to which I will direct you. I shall give you six thousand francs for your journey. You will stay ten years in that town; if you do not like it, you may establish yourself in another, provided it be in the same country. You will pass through Paris, where you will await me. There I will insure you an additional six thousand francs by contract, which will be paid to you on your return, provided you have fulfilled the conditions of our bargain. This is the price for your absolute silence as to what you are about to do to-night. As to you, Rosalie, I will give you ten thousand francs on the day of your wedding, on condition of your marrying Gorenflot; but if you wish to marry, you must hold your tongues; or—no dowry."

"Rosalie," said Madame de Merret, "do my hair."

The husband walked calmly up and down, watching the door, the mason, and his wife, but without betraying any insulting doubts. Madame de Merret chose a moment when the workman was unloading bricks and her husband was at the other end of the room to say to Rosalie: "A thousand francs a year for you, my child, if you can tell Gorenflot to leave a chink at the bottom." Then out loud, she added coolly:

"Go and help him!"

Monsieur and Madame de Merret were silent all the time that Gorenflot took to brick up the door. This silence, on the part of the husband, who did not choose to furnish his wife with a pretext for saying things of a double meaning, had its purpose; on the part of Madame de Merret it was either pride or prudence. When the wall was about half-way up, the sly workman took advantage of a moment when the Count's back was turned, to strike a blow with his trowel in one of the glass panes of the closet-door. This act informed Madame de Merret that Rosalie had spoken to Gorenflot.

All three then saw a man's face; it was dark and gloomy with black hair and eyes of flame. Before her husband turned, the poor woman had time to make a sign to the stranger that signified: Hope!

At four o'clock, toward dawn, for it was the month of September, the construction was finished. The mason was handed over to the care of Jean, and Monsieur de Merret went to bed in his wife's room.

On rising the following morning, he said carelessly:

"The deuce! I must go to the Mairie for the passport." He put his hat on his head, advanced three steps toward the door, altered his mind and took the crucifix.

His wife trembled for joy. "He is going to Duvivier," she thought. As soon as the Count had left, Madame de Merret rang for Rosalie; then in a terrible voice:

"The trowel, the trowel!" she cried, "and quick to work! I saw how Gorenflot did it; we shall have time to make a hole and to mend it again."

In the twinkling of an eye, Rosalie brought a sort of mattock to her mistress, who with unparalleled ardor set about demolishing the wall. She had already knocked out several bricks and was preparing to strike a more decisive blow when she perceived Monsieur de Merret behind her. She fainted.

"Lay Madame on her bed," said the Count coldly. He had foreseen what would happen in his absence and had set a trap for his wife; he had simply written to the mayor, and had sent for Duvivier. The jeweler arrived just as the room had been put in order.

"Duvivier," inquired the Count, "did you buy crucifixes of the Spaniards who passed through here?"

"No, sir."

"That will do, thank you," he said, looking at his wife like a tiger. "Jean," he added, "you will see that my meals are served in the Countess's room; she is ill, and I shall not leave her until she has recovered."

The cruel gentleman stayed with his wife for twenty days. In the beginning, when there were sounds in the walled closet, and Josephine attempted to implore his pity for the dying stranger, he replied, without permitting her to say a word:

"You have sworn on the cross that there is no one there."

PROSPER MERIMÉE

(1803–1870)

Born in Paris in 1803, Mérimée spent the greater part of his life in the government service and in travelling. In later years he became a senator. His chief works are his stories and the novel *Carmen*. Mérimée was one of the earliest authors who were content to write for the purpose of giving esthetic pleasure, and is considered, with Gautier, one of the chief exponents of the Art for Art's Sake theory. His stories are written with great deliberation and care. *Mateo Falcone* is a masterpiece of its kind.

The present version, anonymously translated, is reprinted by permission from *International Short Stories*, P. F. Collier's Sons, New York. Copyright, 1910.

MATEO FALCONE

On leaving Porto-Vecchio from the northwest and directing his steps towards the interior of the island, the traveler will notice that the land rises rapidly, and after three hours' walking over tortuous paths obstructed by great masses of rock and sometimes cut by ravines, he will find himself on the border of a great mâquis. The mâquis is the domain of the Corsican shepherds and of those who are at variance with justice. It must be known that, in order to save himself the trouble of manuring his field, the Corsican husbandman sets fire to a piece of woodland. If the flame spread farther than is necessary, so much the worse! In any case he is certain of a good crop from the land fertilized by the ashes of the trees which grow upon it. He gathers only the heads of his grain, leaving the straw, which it would be unnecessary labor to cut. In the following spring the roots that have remained in the earth without being destroyed send up their tufts of sprouts, which in a few years reach a height of seven or eight feet. It is this kind of tangled thicket that is called a mâquis. They are made up of different kinds of trees and shrubs, so crowded and mingled together at the caprice of nature that only with an ax in hand can a man open a passage through them, and mâquis are frequently seen so thick and bushy that the wild sheep themselves cannot penetrate them.

If you have killed a man, go into the mâquis of Porto-Vecchio. With a good gun and plenty of powder and balls, you can live there in safety. Do not forget a brown cloak furnished with a hood, which will serve you for both cover and mattress. The shepherds will give you chestnuts, milk and cheese, and you will have nothing to fear from justice nor the relatives of the dead except when it is necessary for you to descend to the city to replenish your ammunition.

When I was in Corsica in 18—, Mateo Falcone had his house half a league from this mâquis. He was rich enough for that country, living in noble style—that is to say, doing nothing—on the income from his flocks, which the shepherds, who are a kind of nomads, lead to pasture here and there on the mountains. When I saw him, two years after the event that I am about to relate, he appeared to me to be about fifty years old or more. Picture to yourself a man, small but robust, with curly hair, black as jet, an aquiline nose, thin lips, large, restless eyes, and a complexion the color of tanned leather. His skill as a marksman was considered extraordinary even in his country, where good shots are so common. For example, Mateo would never fire at a sheep with buck-shot; but at a hundred and twenty paces, he would drop it with a ball in the head or shoulder, as he chose. He used his arms as easily at night as during the day. I was told this feat of his skill, which will, perhaps, seem impossible to those who have not traveled in Corsica. A lighted candle was placed at eighty paces, behind a paper transparency about the size of a plate. He would take aim, then the candle would be extinguished, and, at the end of a moment, in the most complete darkness, he would fire and hit the paper three times out of four.

With such a transcendent accomplishment, Mateo Falcone had acquired a great reputation. He was said to be as good a friend as he was a dangerous enemy; accommodating and charitable, he lived at peace with all the world in the district of Porto-Vecchio. But it is said of him that in Corte, where he had married his wife, he had disembarrassed himself very vigorously of a rival who was considered as redoubtable in war as in love; at least, a certain gun-shot which surprised this rival as he was shaving before a little mirror hung in his window was attributed to Mateo. The affair was smoothed over and Mateo was married. His wife Giuseppa had given him at first three daughters (which infuriated him), and finally a son, whom he named Fortunato, and who became the hope of his family, the inheritor of the name. The daughters were well married: their father could count at need on the poniards and carbines of his sons-in-law. The son was only ten years old, but he already gave promise of fine attributes.

On a certain day in autumn, Mateo set out at an early hour with his wife to visit one of his flocks in a clearing of the mâquis. The little Fortunato wanted to go with them, but the clearing was too far away;

moreover, it was necessary someone should stay to watch the house; therefore the father refused: it will be seen whether or not he had reason to repent.

He had been gone some hours, and the little Fortunato was tranquilly stretched out in the sun, looking at the blue mountains, and thinking that the next Sunday he was going to dine in the city with his uncle, the Caporal, when he was suddenly interrupted in his meditations by the firing of a musket. He got up and turned to that side of the plain whence the noise came. Other shots followed, fired at irregular intervals, and each time nearer; at last, in the path which led from the plain to Mateo's house, appeared a man wearing the pointed hat of the mountaineers, bearded, covered with rags, and dragging himself along with difficulty by the support of his gun. He had just received a wound in his thigh.

This man was an outlaw, who, having gone to the town by night to buy powder, had fallen on the way into an ambuscade of Corsican light-infantry. After a vigorous defense he was fortunate in making his retreat, closely followed and firing from rock to rock. But he was only a little in advance of the soldiers, and his wound prevented him from gaining the mâquis before being overtaken.

He approached Fortunato and said: "You are the son of Mateo Fal cone?"—"Yes."

"I am Gianetto Saupiero. I am followed by the yellow-collars. Hide me, for I can go no farther."

"And what will my father say if I hide you without his permission?"

"He will say that you have done well."

"How do you know?"

"Hide me quickly; they are coming."

"Wait till my father gets back."

"How can I wait? Malediction! They will be here in five minutes. Come, hide me, or I will kill you."

Fortunato answered him with the utmost coolness:

"Your gun is empty, and there are no more cartridges in your belt."

"I have my stiletto."

"But can you run as fast as I can?"

He gave a leap and put himself out of reach.

"You are not the son of Mateo Falcone! Will you then let me be captured before your house?"

The child appeared moved.

"What will you give me if I hide you?" said he, coming nearer.

The outlaw felt in a leather pocket that hung from his belt, and took out a five-franc piece, which he had doubtless saved to buy ammunition with. Fortunato smiled at the sight of the silver piece; he snatched it, and said to Gianetto:

"Fear nothing."

Immediately he made a great hole in a pile of hay that was near the house. Gianetto crouched down in it and the child covered him in such a way that he could breathe without it being possible to suspect that the hay concealed a man. He bethought himself further, and, with the subtlety of a tolerably ingenious savage, placed a cat and her kittens on the pile, that it might not appear to have been recently disturbed. Then, noticing the traces of blood on the path near the house, he covered them carefully with dust, and, that done, he again stretched himself out in the sun with the greatest tranquillity.

A few moments afterwards, six men in brown uniforms with yellow collars, and commanded by an Adjutant, were before Mateo's door. This Adjutant was a distant relative of Falcone's. (In Corsica the degrees of relationship are followed much further than elsewhere.) His name was Tiodoro Gamba; he was an active man, much dreaded by the outlaws, several of whom he had already entrapped.

"Good day, little cousin," said he, approaching Fortunato; "how tall you have grown. Have you seen a man go past here just now?"

"Oh! I am not yet so tall as you, my cousin," replied the child with a simple air.

"You soon will be. But haven't you seen a man go by here, tell me?"

"If I have seen a man go by?"

"Yes, a man with a pointed hat of black velvet, and a vest embroidered with red and yellow."

"A man with a pointed hat, and a vest embroidered with red and yellow?"

"Yes, answer quickly, and don't repeat my questions!"

"This morning the curé passed before our door on his horse, Piero. He asked me how papa was, and I answered him—"

"Ah, you little scoundrel, you are playing sly! Tell me quickly which way Gianetto went? We are looking for him, and I am sure he took this path."

"Who knows?"

"Who knows? It is I know that you have seen him."

"Can any one see who passes when they are asleep?"

"You were not asleep, rascal; the shooting woke you up."

"Then you believe, cousin, that your guns make so much noise? My father's carbine has the advantage of them."

"The devil take you, you cursed little scapegrace! I am certain that you have seen Gianetto. Perhaps, even, you have hidden him. Come, comrades, go into the house and see if our man is there. He could only go on one foot, and the knave has too much good sense to try to reach the mâquis limping like that. Moreover, the bloody tracks stop here."

"And what will papa say?" asked Fortunato with a sneer. "What will he say if he knows that his house has been entered while he was away?"

"You rascal," said the Adjutant, taking him by the ear, "do you know that it only remains for me to make you change your tone? Perhaps you will speak differently after I have given you twenty blows with the flat of my sword."

Fortunato continued to sneer.

"My father is Mateo Falcone," said he with emphasis.

"You little scamp, you know very well that I can carry you off to Corte or to Bastia. I will make you lie in a dungeon, on straw, with your feet in shackles, and I will have you guillotined if you don't tell me where Gianetto is."

The child burst out laughing at this ridiculous menace. He repeated: "My father is Mateo Falcone."

"Adjutant," said one of the soldiers in a low voice, "let us have no quarrels with Mateo."

Gamba appeared evidently embarrassed. He spoke in an undertone with the soldiers who had already visited the house. This was not a very long operation, for the cabin of a Corsican consists only of a single square room, furnished with a table, some benches, chests, housekeeping utensils and those of the chase. In the meantime, little Fortunato petted his cat and seemed to take a wicked enjoyment in the confusion of the soldiers and of his cousin.

One of the men approached the pile of hay. He saw the cat, and gave the pile a careless thrust with his bayonet, shrugging his shoulders as if he felt that his precaution was ridiculous. Nothing moved; the boy's face betrayed not the slightest emotion.

The Adjutant and his troop were cursing their luck. Already they were looking in the direction of the plain, as if disposed to return by the way they had come, when their chief, convinced that menaces would produce no impression on Falcone's son, determined to make a last effort, and try the effect of caresses and presents.

"My little cousin," said he, "you are a very wide-awake little fellow. You will get along. But you are playing a naughty game with me; and if I wasn't afraid of making trouble for my cousin, Mateo, the devil take me, but I would carry you off with me."

"Bah!"

"But when my cousin comes back I shall tell him about this, and he will whip you till the blood comes for having told such lies."

"You don't say so!"

"You will see. But hold on!—be a good boy and I will give you something."

"Cousin, let me give you some advice: if you wait much longer Gianetto will be in the mâquis and it will take a smarter man than you to follow him."

The Adjutant took from his pocket a silver watch worth about ten crowns, and noticing that Fortunato's eyes sparkled at the sight of it, said, holding the watch by the end of its steel chain:

"Rascal! you would like to have such a watch as that hung around your neck, wouldn't you, and to walk in the streets of Porto-Vecchio proud as a peacock? People would ask you what time it was, and you would say: 'Look at my watch.'"

"When I am grown up, my uncle, the Caporal, will give me a watch."

"Yes; but your uncle's little boy has one already; not so fine as this either. But then, he is younger than you."

The child sighed.

"Well! Would you like this watch, little cousin?"

Fortunato, casting sidelong glances at the watch, resembled a cat that has been given a whole chicken. It feels that it is being made sport of, and does not dare to use its claws; from time to time it turns its eyes away so as not to be tempted, licking its jaws all the while, and has the appearance of saying to its master, "How cruel your joke is!"

However, the Adjutant seemed in earnest in offering his watch. Fortunato did not reach out his hand for it, but said with a bitter smile:

"Why do you make fun of me?"

"Good God! I am not making fun of you. Only tell me where Gianetto is and the watch is yours."

Fortunato smiled incredulously, and fixing his black eyes on those of the Adjutant tried to read there the faith he ought to have had in his words.

"May I lose my epaulettes," cried the Adjutant, "if I do not give you the watch on this condition. These comrades are witnesses; I cannot deny it."

While speaking he gradually held the watch nearer till it almost touched the child's pale face, which plainly showed the struggle that was going on in his soul between covetousness and respect for hospitality. His breast swelled with emotion; he seemed about to suffocate. Meanwhile the watch was slowly swaying and turning, sometimes brushing against his cheek. Finally, his right hand was gradually stretched toward it; the ends of his fingers touched it; then its whole weight was in his hand, the Adjutant still keeping hold of the chain. The face was light blue; the cases newly burnished. In the sunlight it seemed to be all on fire. The temptation was too great. Fortunato raised his left hand and pointed over his shoulder with his thumb at the hay against which he was reclining. The Adjutant understood him at once. He dropped the end of the chain and Fortunato felt himself the sole possessor of the watch. He sprang up with the agility of a deer and stood ten feet from the pile, which the soldiers began at once to overturn.

There was a movement in the hay, and a bloody man with a poniard in his hand appeared. He tried to rise to his feet, but his stiffened leg would not permit it and he fell. The Adjutant at once grappled with him and took away his stiletto. He was immediately secured, notwithstanding his resistance.

Gianetto, lying on the earth and bound like a fagot, turned his head towards Fortunato, who had approached.

"Son of —!" said he, with more contempt than anger.

The child threw him the silver piece which he had received, feeling that he no longer deserved it; but the outlaw paid no attention to the movement, and with great coolness said to the Adjutant:

"My dear Gamba, I cannot walk; you will be obliged to carry me to the city."

"Just now you could run faster than a buck," answered the cruel captor; "but be at rest. I am so pleased to have you that I would carry you a league on my back without fatigue. Besides, comrade, we are going to make a litter for you with your cloak and some branches, and at the Crespoli farm we shall find horses."

"Good," said the prisoner. "You will also put a little straw on your litter that I may be more comfortable."

While some of the soldiers were occupied in making a kind of stretcher out of some chestnut boughs and the rest were dressing Gianetto's wound, Mateo Falcone and his wife suddenly appeared at a turn in the path that led to the mâquis. The woman was staggering under the weight of an enormous sack of chestnuts, while her husband was sauntering along, carrying one gun in his hands, while another was slung across his shoulders, for it is unworthy of a man to carry other burdens than his arms.

At the sight of the soldiers Mateo's first thought was that they had come to arrest him. But why this thought? Had he then some quarrels with justice? No. He enjoyed a good reputation. He was said to have a particularly good name, but he was a Corsican and a highlander, and there are few Corsican highlanders who, in scrutinizing their memory, cannot find some peccadillo, such as a gun-shot, dagger-thrust, or similar trifles. Mateo more than others had a clear conscience; for more than ten years he had not pointed his carbine at a man, but he was always prudent, and put himself into a position to make a good defense if necessary. "Wife," said he to Giuseppa, "put down the sack and hold yourself ready."

She obeyed at once. He gave her the gun that was slung across his shoulders, which would have bothered him, and, cocking the one he held in his hands, advanced slowly towards the house, walking among the trees that bordered the road, ready at the least hostile demonstration, to hide behind the largest, whence he could fire from under cover. His wife followed closely behind, holding his reserve weapon and his cartridge-box. The duty of a good housekeeper, in case of a fight, is to load her husband's carbines.

On the other side the Adjutant was greatly troubled to see Mateo advance in this manner, with cautious steps, his carbine raised, and his finger on the trigger.

"If by chance," thought he, "Mateo should be related to Gianetto, or if he should be his friend and wish to defend him, the contents of his two guns would arrive amongst us as certainly as a letter in the post; and if he should see me, notwithstanding the relationship!"

In this perplexity he took a bold step. It was to advance alone towards Mateo and tell him of the affair while accosting him as an old acquaintance, but the short space that separated him from Mateo seemed terribly long.

"Hello! old comrade," cried he. "How do you do, my good fellow? It is I, Gamba, your cousin."

Without answering a word, Mateo stopped, and in proportion as the other spoke, slowly raised the muzzle of his gun so that it was pointing upward when the Adjutant joined him.

"Good-day, brother," said the Adjutant, holding out his hand. "It is a long time since I have seen you."

"Good-day, brother."

"I stopped while passing, to say good-day to you and to cousin Pepa here. We have had a long journey to-day, but have no reason to complain, for we have captured a famous prize. We have just seized Gianetto Saupiero."

"God be praised!" cried Giuseppa. "He stole a milch goat from us last week."

These words reassured Gamba.

"Poor devil!" said Mateo. "He was hungry."

"The villain fought like a lion," continued the Adjutant, a little mortified. "He killed one of my soldiers, and not content with that, broke Caporal Chardon's arm; but that matters little, he is only a Frenchman. Then, too, he was so well hidden that the devil couldn't have found him. Without my little cousin, Fortunato, I should never have discovered him."

"Fortunato!" cried Mateo.

"Fortunato!" repeated Giuseppa.

"Yes, Gianetto was hidden under the hay-pile yonder, but my little cousin showed me the trick. I shall tell his uncle, the Caporal, that he may send him a fine present for his trouble. Both his name and yours will be in the report that I shall send to the Attorney-general."

"Malediction!" said Mateo in a low voice.

They had rejoined the detachment. Gianetto was already lying on the litter ready to set out. When he saw Mateo and Gamba in company he smiled a strange smile, then, turning his head towards the door of the house, he spat on the sill, saying:

"House of a traitor."

Only a man determined to die would dare pronounce the word traitor to Falcone. A good blow with the stiletto, which there would be no need of repeating, would have immediately paid the insult. However, Mateo made no other movement than to place his hand on his forehead like a man who is dazed.

Fortunato had gone into the house when his father arrived, but now he reappeared with a bowl of milk which he handed with downcast eyes to Gianetto.

"Get away from me!" cried the outlaw, in a loud voice. Then, turning to one of the soldiers, he said:

"Comrade, give me a drink."

The soldier placed his gourd in his hands, and the prisoner drank the water handed to him by a man with whom he had just exchanged bullets. He then asked them to tie his hands across his breast instead of behind his back.

"I like," said he, "to lie at my ease."

They hastened to satisfy him; then the Adjutant gave the signal to start, said adieu to Mateo, who did not respond, and descended with rapid steps towards the plain.

Nearly ten minutes elapsed before Mateo spoke. The child looked with restless eyes, now at his mother, now at his father, who was leaning on his gun and gazing at him with an expression of concentrated rage.

"You begin well," said Mateo at last with a calm voice, but frightful to one who knew the man.

"Oh, father!" cried the boy, bursting into tears, and making a forward movement as if to throw himself on his knees. But Mateo cried, "Away from me!"

The little fellow stopped and sobbed, immovable, a few feet from his father.

Giuseppa drew near. She had just discovered the watch-chain, the end of which was hanging out of Fortunato's jacket.

"Who gave you that watch?" demanded she in a severe tone.

"My cousin, the Adjutant."

Falcone seized the watch and smashed it in a thousand pieces against a rock.

"Wife," said he, "is this my child?"

Giuseppa's cheeks turned a brick-red.

"What are you saying, Mateo? Do you know to whom you speak?"

"Very well, this child is the first of his race to commit treason."

Fortunato's sobs and gasps redoubled as Falcone kept his lynx-eyes upon him. Then he struck the earth with his gun-stock, shouldered the weapon, and turned in the direction of the mâquis, calling to Fortunato to follow. The boy obeyed. Giuseppa hastened after Mateo and seized his arm.

"He is your son," said she with a trembling voice, fastening her black eyes on those of her husband to read what was going on in his heart.

"Leave me alone," said Mateo. "I am his father."

Giuseppa embraced her son, and bursting into tears entered the house. She threw herself on her knees before an image of the Virgin and prayed ardently. In the meanwhile Falcone walked some two hundred paces along the path and only stopped when he reached a little ravine which he descended. He tried the earth with the butt-end of his carbine, and found it soft and easy to dig. The place seemed to be convenient for his design.

"Fortunato, go close to that big rock there."

The child did as he was commanded, then he kneeled.

"Say your prayers."

"Oh, father, father, do not kill me!"

"Say your prayers!" repeated Mateo in a terrible voice.

The boy, stammering and sobbing, recited the Pater and the Credo. At the end of each prayer the father loudly answered, "Amen!"

"Are those all the prayers you know?"

"Oh! father, I know the Ave Maria and the litany that my aunt taught me."

"It is very long, but no matter."

The child finished the litany in a scarcely audible tone.

"Are you finished?"

"Oh! my father, have mercy! Pardon me! I will never do so again. I will beg my cousin, the Caporal, to pardon Gianetto."

He was still speaking. Mateo raised his gun, and, taking aim, said:

"May God pardon you!"

The boy made a desperate effort to rise and grasp his father's knees, but there was not time. Mateo fired and Fortunato fell dead.

Without casting a glance on the body, Mateo returned to the house for a spade with which to bury his son. He had gone but a few steps when he met Giuseppa, who, alarmed by the shot, was hastening hither.

"What have you done?" cried she.

"Justice."

"Where is he?"

"In the ravine. I am going to bury him. He died a Christian. I shall have a mass said for him. Have my son-in-law, Tiodoro Bianchi, sent for to come and live with us."

THÉOPHILE GAUTIER

(1811–1872)

THÉOPHILE GAUTIER was born at Tarbes in the south of France in 1811. He came to Paris as an infant. In 1830 he published his first volume of poems. He was, with Victor Hugo and others, one of the prominent initiators of the so-called Romantic Movement in French literature. His finest novel, *Mlle. de Maupin*, appeared in 1835. For many years he wrote art, dramatic, and literary criticisms, poems, stories, ballets and pantomimes, and a number of charming impressionistic travel books. Gautier is one of the most accomplished poets of the external and visible world: his style is vivid, jewelled, and sensuous. His short stories are exotic, highly polished literary exercises, though some of them, like *The Mummy's Foot*, are intrinsically fascinating for their plot and atmosphere.

The present version, translated by Lafcadio Hearn, is reprinted, by permission of the publisher, from the volume, *One of Cleopatra's Nights*, published by Brentano's.

THE MUMMY'S FOOT

I HAD entered, in an idle mood, the shop of one of those curiosity-venders, who are called *marchands de bric-à-brac* in that Parisian *argot* which is so perfectly unintelligible elsewhere in France.

You have doubtless glanced occasionally through the windows of some of these shops, which have become so numerous now that it is fashionable to buy antiquated furniture, and that every petty stockbroker thinks he must have his *chambre au moyen âge*.

There is one thing there which clings alike to the shop of the dealer in old iron, the wareroom of the tapestry-maker, the laboratory of the chemist, and the studio of the painter:—in all those gloomy dens where a furtive daylight filters in through the window-shutters, the most manifestly ancient thing is dust;—the cobwebs are more authentic than the guimp laces; and the old pear-tree furniture on exhibition is actually younger than the mahogany which arrived but yesterday from America.

The warehouse of my *bric-à-brac* dealer was a veritable Capharnaum; all ages and all nations seemed to have made their rendezvous there; an Etruscan lamp of red clay stood upon a Boule cabinet, with ebony panels, brightly striped by lines of inlaid brass; a duchess of the court of Louis XV nonchalantly extended her fawn-like feet under a massive table of the time of Louis XIII with heavy spiral supports of oak, and carven designs of chimeras and foliage intermingled.

Upon the denticulated shelves of several sideboards glittered immense Japanese dishes with red and blue designs relieved by gilded hatching; side by side with enameled works by Bernard Palissy, representing serpents, frogs, and lizards in relief.

From disemboweled cabinets escaped cascades of silver-lustrous Chinese silks and waves of tinsel, which an oblique sunbeam shot through with luminous beads; while portraits of every era, in frames more or less tarnished, smiled through their yellow varnish.

The striped breastplate of a damascened suit of Milanese armor glittered in one corner; Loves and Nymphs of porcelain; Chinese Grotesques, vases of *céladon* and crackle-ware; Saxon and old Sèvres cups encumbered the shelves and nooks of the apartment.

The dealer followed me closely through the tortuous way contrived between the piles of furniture; warding off with his hand the hazardous sweep of my coat-skirts; watching my elbows with the uneasy attention of an antiquarian and a usurer.

It was a singular face, that of the merchant:—an immense skull, polished like a knee, and surrounded by a thin aureole of white hair, which brought out the clear salmon tint of his complexion all the more strikingly, lent him a false aspect of patriarchal *bonhomie*, counteracted, however, by the scintillation of two little yellow eyes which trembled in their orbits like two louis-d'or upon quicksilver. The curve of his nose presented an aquiline silhouette, which suggested the Oriental or Jewish type. His hands—thin, slender, full of nerves which projected like strings upon the finger-board of a violin, and armed with claws like those on the terminations of bats' wings—shook with senile trembling; but those convulsively agitated hands became firmer than steel pincers or lobsters' claws when they lifted any precious article—an onyx cup, a Venetian glass, or a dish of Bohemian crystal. This strange old man had an aspect so thoroughly rabbinical and cabalistic that he would have been burnt on the mere testimony of his face three centuries ago.

"Will you not buy something from me to-day, sir? Here is a Malay kreese with a blade undulating like flame: look at those grooves contrived for the blood to run along, those teeth set backwards so as to tear out the entrails in withdrawing the weapon—it is a fine character of ferocious arm, and will look well in your collection: this two-handed sword is very beautiful—it is the work of Josepe de la Hera; and this *colichemarde*, with its fenestrated guard—what a superb specimen of handicraft!"

"No; I have quite enough weapons and instruments of carnage;—I want a small figure, something which will suit me as a paper-weight; for I cannot endure those trumpery bronzes which the stationers sell, and which may be found on everybody's desk."

The old gnome foraged among his ancient wares, and finally arranged before me some antique bronzes—so-called, at least; fragments of malachite; little Hindoo or Chinese idols—a kind of poussah toys in jadestone, representing the incarnations of Brahma or Vishnoo, and wonderfully appropriate to the very undivine office of holding papers and letters in place.

I was hesitating between a porcelain dragon, all constellated with warts—its mouth formidable with bristling tusks and ranges of teeth—and an abominable little Mexican fetish, representing the god Zitziliputzili *au naturel*, when I caught sight of a charming foot, which I at first took for a fragment of some antique Venus.

It had those beautiful ruddy and tawny tints that lend to Florentine bronze that warm living look so much preferable to the gray-green aspect of common bronzes, which might easily be mistaken for statues in a state of putrefaction: satiny gleams played over its rounded forms, doubtless polished by the amorous kisses of twenty centuries; for it seemed a Corinthian bronze, a work of the best era of art—perhaps molded by Lysippus himself.

"That foot will be my choice," I said to the merchant, who regarded me with an ironical and saturnine air, and held out the object desired that I might examine it more fully.

I was surprised at its lightness; it was not a foot of metal, but in sooth a foot of flesh—an embalmed foot—a mummy's foot: on examining it still more closely the very grain of the skin, and the almost imperceptible lines impressed upon it by the texture of the bandages, became perceptible. The toes were slender and delicate, and terminated by perfectly formed nails, pure and transparent as agates; the great toe, slightly separated from the rest, afforded a happy contrast, in the antique style, to the position of the other toes, and lent it an aerial lightness—the grace of a bird's foot;—the sole, scarcely streaked by a few almost imperceptible cross lines, afforded evidence that it had never touched the bare ground, and had only come in contact with the finest matting of Nile rushes, and the softest carpets of panther skin.

"Ha, ha!—you want the foot of the Princess Hermonthis,"—exclaimed the merchant, with a strange giggle, fixing his owlish eyes upon me—"ha, ha, ha!—for a paper-weight!—an original idea!—artistic idea! Old Pharaoh would certainly have been surprised had some one told him that the foot of his adored daughter would be used for a paper-weight after he had had a mountain of granite hollowed out as a receptacle for the triple coffin, painted and gilded—covered with hieroglyphics and beautiful paintings of the Judgment of Souls,"—continued the queer little merchant, half audibly, as though talking to himself!

"How much will you charge me for this mummy fragment?"

"Ah, the highest price I can get; for it is a superb piece: if I had the match of it you could not have it for less than five hundred francs; —the daughter of a Pharaoh! nothing is more rare."

"Assuredly that is not a common article; but, still, how much do you want? In the first place let me warn you that all my wealth consists of just five louis: I can buy anything that costs five louis, but nothing dearer;—you might search my vest pockets and most secret drawers without even finding one poor five-franc piece more."

"Five louis for the foot of the Princess Hermonthis! that is very little, very little indeed; 'tis an authentic foot," muttered the merchant, shaking his head, and imparting a peculiar rotary motion to his eyes. "Well, take it, and I will give you the bandages into the bargain," he added, wrapping the foot in an ancient damask rag—"very fine! real damask—Indian damask which has never been redyed; it is strong, and yet it is soft," he mumbled, stroking the frayed tissue with his fingers, through the trade-acquired habit which moved him to praise even an object of so little value that he himself deemed it only worth the giving away.

He poured the gold coins into a sort of mediæval alms-purse hanging at his belt, repeating:

"The foot of the Princess Hermonthis, to be used for a paper-weight!"

Then turning his phosphorescent eyes upon me, he exclaimed in a voice strident as the crying of a cat which has swallowed a fish-bone:

"Old Pharaoh will not be well pleased; he loved his daughter—the dear man!"

"You speak as if you were a contemporary of his: you are old enough, goodness knows! but you do not date back to the Pyramids of Egypt," I answered, laughingly, from the threshold.

I went home, delighted with my acquisition.

With the idea of putting it to profitable use as soon as possible, I placed the foot of the divine Princess Hermonthis upon a heap of papers scribbled over with verses, in themselves an undecipherable mosaic work of erasures; articles freshly begun; letters forgotten, and posted in the table drawer instead of the letter-box—an error to which absent-minded people are peculiarly liable. The effect was charming, *bizarre*, and romantic.

Well satisfied with this embellishment, I went out with the gravity and pride becoming one who feels that he has the ineffable advantage over all the passers-by whom he elbows, of possessing a piece of the Princess Hermonthis, daughter of Pharaoh.

I looked upon all who did not possess, like myself, a paper-weight so authentically Egyptian, as very ridiculous people; and it seemed to me that the proper occupation of every sensible man should consist in the mere fact of having a mummy's foot upon his desk.

Happily I met some friends, whose presence distracted me in my infatuation with this new acquisition: I went to dinner with them; for I could not very well have dined with myself.

When I came back that evening, with my brain slightly confused by a few glasses of wine, a vague whiff of Oriental perfume delicately titillated my olfactory nerves: the heat of the room had warmed the natron, bitumen, and myrrh in which the *paraschistes,* who cut open the bodies of the dead, had bathed the corpse of the princess;—it was a perfume at once sweet and penetrating—a perfume that four thousand years had not been able to dissipate.

The Dream of Egypt was Eternity: her odors have the solidity of granite, and endure as long.

I soon drank deeply from the black cup of sleep: for a few hours all remained opaque to me; Oblivion and Nothingness inundated me with their somber waves.

Yet light gradually dawned upon the darkness of my mind; dreams commenced to touch me softly in their silent flight.

The eyes of my soul were opened; and I beheld my chamber as it actually was; I might have believed myself awake, but for a vague consciousness which assured me that I slept, and that something fantastic was about to take place.

The odor of the myrrh had augmented in intensity: and I felt a slight headache, which I very naturally attributed to several glasses of champagne that we had drunk to the unknown gods and our future fortunes.

I peered through my room with a feeling of expectation which I saw nothing to justify: every article of furniture was in its proper place; the lamp, softly shaded by its globe of ground crystal, burned upon its bracket; the water-color sketches shone under their Bohemian glass; the curtains hung down languidly; everything wore an aspect of tranquil slumber.

After a few moments, however, all this calm interior appeared to become disturbed; the woodwork cracked stealthily; the ash-covered log suddenly emitted a jet of blue flame; and the disks of the pateras seemed like great metallic eyes, watching, like myself, for the things which were about to happen.

My eyes accidentally fell upon the desk where I had placed the foot of the Princess Hermonthis.

Instead of remaining quiet—as behooved a foot which had been embalmed for four thousand years—it commenced to act in a nervous manner; contracted itself, and leaped over the papers like a startled frog;—one would have imagined that it had suddenly been brought into contact with a galvanic battery: I could distinctly hear the dry sound made by its little heel, hard as the hoof of a gazelle.

I became rather discontented with my acquisition, inasmuch as I wished my paper-weights to be of a sedentary disposition, and thought it very unnatural that feet should walk about without legs; and I commenced to experience a feeling closely akin to fear.

Suddenly I saw the folds of my bed-curtain stir; and heard a bumping sound, like that caused by some person hopping on one foot across the floor. I must confess I became alternately hot and cold; that I felt a strange wind chill my back; and that my suddenly rising hair caused my nightcap to execute a leap of several yards.

The bed-curtains opened and I beheld the strangest figure imaginable before me.

It was a young girl of a very deep coffee-brown complexion, like the bayadere Amani, and possessing the purest Egyptian type of perfect beauty: her eyes were almond-shaped and oblique, with eyebrows so black that they seemed blue; her nose was exquisitely chiseled, almost Greek in its delicacy of outline; and she might indeed have been taken for a Corinthian statue of bronze, but for the prominence of her cheek-bones and the slightly African fulness of her lips, which compelled one to recognize her as belonging beyond all doubt to the hieroglyphic race which dwelt upon the banks of the Nile.

Her arms, slender and spindle-shaped, like those of very young girls, were encircled by a peculiar kind of metal bands and bracelets of glass beads; her hair was all twisted into little cords; and she wore upon her bosom a little idol-figure of green paste, bearing a whip with seven lashes, which proved it to be an image of Isis: her brow was adorned with a shining plate of gold; and a few traces of paint relieved the coppery tint of her cheeks.

As for her costume, it was very odd indeed.

Fancy a *pagne* or skirt all formed of little strips of material bedizened with red and black hieroglyphics, stiffened with bitumen, and apparently belonging to a freshly unbandaged mummy.

In one of those sudden flights of thought so common in dreams I heard the hoarse falsetto of the *bric-à-brac* dealer, repeating like a monotonous refrain the phrase he had uttered in his shop with so enigmatical an intonation:

"Old Pharaoh will not be well pleased: he loved his daughter, the dear man!"

One strange circumstance, which was not at all calculated to restore my equanimity, was that the apparition had but one foot; the other was broken off at the ankle!

She approached the table where the foot was starting and fidgeting about more than ever, and there supported herself upon the edge of the desk. I saw her eyes fill with pearly-gleaming tears.

Although she had not as yet spoken, I fully comprehended the thoughts which agitated her: she looked at her foot—for it was indeed her own—with an exquisitely graceful expression of coquettish sadness; but the foot leaped and ran hither and thither, as though impelled on steel springs.

Twice or thrice she extended her hand to seize it, but could not succeed.

Then commenced between the Princess Hermonthis and her foot—which appeared to be endowed with a special life of its own—a very fantastic dialogue in a most ancient Coptic tongue, such as might have been spoken thirty centuries ago in the syrinxes of the land of Ser: luckily, I understood Coptic perfectly well that night.

The Princess Hermonthis cried, in a voice sweet and vibrant as the tones of a crystal bell:

"Well, my dear little foot, you always flee from me; yet I always took good care of you. I bathed you with perfumed water in a bowl of alabaster; I smoothed your heel with pumice-stone mixed with palm oil; your nails were cut with golden scissors and polished with a hippopotamus tooth; I was careful to select *tatbebs* for you, painted and embroidered and turned up at the toes, which were the envy of all the young girls in Egypt: you wore on your great toe rings bearing the device of the sacred Scarabæus; and you supported one of the lightest bodies that a lazy foot could sustain."

The foot replied, in a pouting and chagrined tone:

"You know well that I do not belong to myself any longer;—I have been bought and paid for; the old merchant knew what he was about; he bore you a grudge for having refused to espouse him;—this is an ill turn which he has done you. The Arab who violated your royal coffin in the subterranean pits of the necropolis of Thebes was sent thither by him: he desired to prevent you from being present at the reunion of the shadowy nations in the cities below. Have you five pieces of gold for my ransom?"

"Alas, no!—my jewels, my rings, my purses of gold and silver, they were all stolen from me," answered the Princess Hermonthis, with a sob.

"Princess," I then exclaimed, "I never retained anybody's foot unjustly;—even though you have not got the five louis which it cost me, I present it to you gladly: I should feel unutterably wretched to think that I were the cause of so amiable a person as the Princess Hermonthis being lame."

I delivered this discourse in a royally gallant, troubadour tone, which must have astonished the beautiful Egyptian girl.

She turned a look of deepest gratitude upon me; and her eyes shone with bluish gleams of light.

She took her foot—which surrendered itself willingly this time—

like a woman about to put on her little shoe, and adjusted it to her leg with much skill.

This operation over, she took a few steps about the room, as though to assure herself that she was really no longer lame.

"Ah, how pleased my father will be!—he who was so unhappy because of my mutilation, and who from the moment of my birth set a whole nation at work to hollow me out a tomb so deep that he might preserve me intact until that last day, when souls must be weighed in the balance of Amenthi! Come with me to my father;—he will receive you kindly; for you have given me back my foot."

I thought this proposition natural enough. I arrayed myself in a dressing-gown of large-flowered pattern, which lent me a very Pharaonic aspect; hurriedly put on a pair of Turkish slippers, and informed the Princess Hermonthis that I was ready to follow her.

Before starting, Hermonthis took from her neck the little idol of green paste, and laid it on the scattered sheets of paper which covered the table.

"It is only fair," she observed smilingly, "that I should replace your paper-weight."

She gave me her hand, which felt soft and cold, like the skin of a serpent; and we departed.

We passed for some time with the velocity of an arrow through a fluid and grayish expanse, in which half-formed silhouettes flitted swiftly by us, to right and left.

For an instant we saw only sky and sea.

A few moments later obelisks commenced to tower in the distance: pylons and vast flights of steps guarded by sphinxes became clearly outlined against the horizon.

We had reached our destination.

The princess conducted me to the mountain of rose-colored granite, in the face of which appeared an opening so narrow and low that it would have been difficult to distinguish it from the fissures in the rock, had not its location been marked by two stelæ wrought with sculptures.

Hermonthis kindled a torch, and led the way before me.

We traversed corridors hewn through the living rock: their walls, covered with hieroglyphics and paintings of allegorical processions, might well have occupied thousands of arms for thousands of years in their formation;—these corridors, of interminable length, opened into square chambers, in the midst of which pits had been contrived, through which we descended by cramp-irons or spiral stairways;—these pits again conducted us into other chambers, opening into other corridors, likewise decorated with painted sparrow-hawks, serpents coiled in circles, the symbols of the *tau* and *pedum*—prodigious works of art which no living eye can ever examine—interminable legends of granite which only the dead have time to read through all eternity.

At last we found ourselves in a hall so vast, so enormous, so immeasurable, that the eye could not reach its limits; files of monstrous columns stretched far out of sight on every side, between which twinkled livid stars of yellowish flame;—points of light which revealed further depths incalculable in the darkness beyond.

The Princess Hermonthis still held my hand, and graciously saluted the mummies of her acquaintance.

My eyes became accustomed to the dim twilight, and objects became discernible.

I beheld the kings of the subterranean races seated upon thrones—grand old men, though dry, withered, wrinkled like parchment, and blackened with naphtha and bitumen—all wearing *pshents* of gold, and breastplates and gorgets glittering with precious stones; their eyes immovably fixed like the eyes of sphinxes, and their long beards whitened by the snow of centuries. Behind them stood their peoples, in the stiff and constrained posture enjoined by Egyptian art, all eternally preserving the attitude prescribed by the hieratic code. Behind these nations, the cats, ibises, and crocodiles contemporary with them—rendered monstrous of aspect by their swathing bands—mewed, flapped their wings, or extended their jaws in a saurian giggle.

All the Pharaohs were there—Cheops, Chephrenes, Psammetichus, Sesostris, Amenotaph—all the dark rulers of the pyramids and syrinxes:—on yet higher thrones sat Chronos and Xixouthros—who was contemporary with the deluge; and Tubal Cain, who reigned before it.

The beard of King Xixouthros had grown seven times around the granite table, upon which he leaned, lost in deep reverie—and buried in dreams.

Further back, through a dusty cloud, I beheld dimly the seventy-two pre-Adamite Kings, with their seventy-two peoples—forever passed away.

After permitting me to gaze upon this bewildering spectacle a few moments, the Princess Hermonthis presented me to her father Pharaoh, who favored me with a most gracious nod.

"I have found my foot again!—I have found my foot!" cried the Princess, clapping her little hands together with every sign of frantic joy: "it was this gentleman who restored it to me."

The races of Kemi, the races of Nahasi—all the black, bronzed, and copper-colored nations repeated in chorus:

"The Princess Hermonthis has found her foot again!"

Even Xixouthros himself was visibly affected.

He raised his heavy eyelids, stroked his mustache with his fingers, and turned upon me a glance weighty with centuries.

"By Oms, the dog of Hell, and Tmei, daughter of the Sun and of Truth! this is a brave and worthy lad!" exclaimed Pharaoh, pointing to me with his scepter, which was terminated with a lotus-flower.

"What recompense do you desire?"

Filled with that daring inspired by dreams in which nothing seems impossible, I asked him for the hand of the Princess Hermonthis;—the hand seemed to me a very proper antithetic recompense for the foot.

Pharaoh opened wide his great eyes of glass in astonishment at my witty request.

"What country do you come from? and what is your age?"

"I am a Frenchman; and I am twenty-seven years old, venerable Pharaoh."

"——Twenty-seven years old! and he wishes to espouse the Princess Hermonthis, who is thirty centuries old!" cried out at once all the Thrones and all the Circles of Nations.

Only Hermonthis herself did not seem to think my request unreasonable.

"If you were even only two thousand years old," replied the ancient King, "I would willingly give you the Princess; but the disproportion is too great; and, besides, we must give our daughters husbands who will last well: you do not know how to preserve yourselves any longer; even those who died only fifteen centuries ago are already no more than a handful of dust;—behold! my flesh is solid as basalt; my bones are bars of steel!

"I shall be present on the last day of the world, with the same body and the same features which I had during my lifetime: my daughter Hermonthis will last longer than a statue of bronze.

"Then the last particles of your dust will have been scattered abroad by the winds; and even Isis herself, who was able to find the atoms of Osiris, would scarce be able to recompose your being.

"See how vigorous I yet remain, and how mighty is my grasp," he added, shaking my hand in the English fashion with a strength that buried my rings in the flesh of my fingers.

He squeezed me so hard that I awoke, and found my friend Alfred shaking me by the arm to make me get up.

"O you everlasting sleeper!—must I have you carried out into the middle of the street, and fireworks exploded in your ears? It is after noon; don't you recollect your promise to take me with you to see M. Aguado's Spanish pictures?"

"God! I forgot all, all about it," I answered, dressing myself hurriedly; "we will go there at once; I have the permit lying on my desk."

I started to find it;—but fancy my astonishment when I beheld, instead of the mummy's foot I had purchased the evening before, the little green paste idol left in its place by the Princess Hermonthis!

VILLIERS DE L'ISLE ADAM

(1838–1889)

COUNT VILLIERS DE L'ISLE ADAM, born in Brittany in 1838, led a strange life. "Born without average will-power," says Huneker, "except the will to imagine beautiful and strange things, all his years he fought the contending impulses of his dual nature." He was the very model of a bohemian. His strange tales, the best of which are collected under the title *Cruel Tales*, are fantastic prose poems in the manner of Poe. *The Torture of Hope*, according to Huneker, recalls Poe at his best.

The present version, anonymously translated, is reprinted from an American collection of tales, not dated. It is from the volume of *Cruel Tales*.

THE TORTURE OF HOPE

MANY years ago, as evening was closing in, the venerable Pedro Arbuez d'Espila, sixth prior of the Dominicans of Segovia, and third Grand Inquisitor of Spain, followed by a *fra redemptor*, and preceded by two familiars of the Holy Office, the latter carrying lanterns, made their way to a subterranean dungeon. The bolt of a massive door creaked, and they entered a mephitic *in pace*, where the dim light revealed between rings fastened to the wall a bloodstained rack, a brazier, and a jug. On a pile of straw, loaded with fetters and his neck encircled by an iron carcan, sat a haggard man, of uncertain age, clothed in rags.

This prisoner was no other than Rabbi Aser Abarbanel, a Jew of Aragon, who—accused of usury and pitiless scorn for the poor—had been daily subjected to torture for more than a year. Yet "his blindness was as dense as his hide," and he had refused to abjure his faith.

Proud of a filiation dating back thousands of years, proud of his ancestors—for all Jews worthy of the name are vain of their blood—he descended Talmudically from Othoniel and consequently from Ipsiboa, the wife of the last judge of Israel, a circumstance which had sustained his courage amid incessant torture. With tears in his eyes at the thought of this resolute soul rejecting salvation, the venerable Pedro Arbuez d'Espila, approaching the shuddering rabbi, addressed him as follows:

"My son, rejoice: your trials here below are about to end. If in the presence of such obstinacy I was forced to permit, with deep regret, the use of great severity, my task of fraternal correction has its limits. You are the fig tree which, having failed so many times to bear fruit, at last withered, but God alone can judge your soul. Perhaps Infinite Mercy will shine upon you at the last moment! We must hope so. There are examples. So sleep in peace to-night. To-morrow you will be included in the *auto da fé:* that is, you will be exposed to the *quémadero,* the symbolical flames of the Everlasting Fire: it burns, as you know, only at a distance, my son; and Death is at least two hours (often three) in coming, on account of the wet, iced bandages with which we protect the heads and hearts of the condemned. There will be forty-three of you. Placed in the last row, you will have time to invoke God and offer to Him this baptism of fire, which is of the Holy Spirit. Hope in the Light, and rest."

With these words, having signed to his companions to unchain the prisoner, the prior tenderly embraced him. Then came the turn of the *fra redemptor,* who, in a low tone, entreated the Jew's forgiveness for what he had made him suffer for the purpose of redeeming him; then the two familiars silently kissed him. This ceremony over, the captive was left, solitary and bewildered, in the darkness.

Rabbi Aser Abarbanel, with parched lips and visage worn by suffering, at first gazed at the closed door with vacant eyes. Closed? The word unconsciously roused a vague fancy in his mind, the fancy that he had seen for an instant the light of the lanterns through a chink between the door and the wall. A morbid idea of hope, due to the weakness of his brain, stirred his whole being. He dragged himself toward the strange *appearance.* Then, very gently and cautiously, slipping one finger into the crevice, he drew the door toward him. Marvelous! By an extraordinary accident the familiar who closed it had turned the huge key an instant before it struck the stone casing, so that the rusty bolt not having entered the hole, the door again rolled on its hinges.

The rabbi ventured to glance outside. By the aid of a sort of luminous dusk he distinguished at first a semicircle of walls indented by winding stairs; and opposite to him, at the top of five or six stone steps, a sort of black portal, opening into an immense corridor, whose first arches only were visible from below.

Stretching himself flat he crept to the threshold. Yes, it was really a corridor, but endless in length. A wan light illumined it: lamps suspended from the vaulted ceiling lightened at intervals the dull hue of the atmosphere—the distance was veiled in shadow. Not a single door appeared in the whole extent! Only on one side, the left, heavily grated loopholes, sunk in the walls, admitted a light which must be that of evening, for crimson bars at intervals rested on the flags of the pavement. What a terrible silence! Yet, yonder, at the far end of that passage there might be a doorway of escape! The Jew's vacillating hope was tenacious, for it was *the last.*

Without hesitating, he ventured on the flags, keeping close under the loopholes, trying to make himself part of the blackness of the long walls. He advanced slowly, dragging himself along on his breast, forcing back the cry of pain when some raw wound sent a keen pang through his whole body.

Suddenly the sound of a sandaled foot approaching reached his ears. He trembled violently, fear stifled him, his sight grew dim. Well, it was over, no doubt. He pressed himself into a niche and, half lifeless with terror, waited.

It was a familiar hurrying along. He passed swiftly by, holding in his clenched hand an instrument of torture—a frightful figure—and vanished. The suspense which the rabbi had endured seemed to have suspended the functions of life, and he lay nearly an hour unable to move. Fearing an increase of tortures if he were captured, he thought of returning to his dungeon. But the old hope whispered in his soul that divine *perhaps*, which comforts us in our sorest trials. A miracle had happened. He could doubt no longer. He began to crawl toward the chance of escape. Exhausted by suffering and hunger, trembling with pain, he pressed onward. The sepulchral corridor seemed to lengthen mysteriously, while he, still advancing, gazed into the gloom where there *must* be some avenue of escape.

Oh! oh! He again heard footsteps, but this time they were slower, more heavy. The white and black forms of two inquisitors appeared, emerging from the obscurity beyond. They were conversing in low tones, and seemed to be discussing some important subject, for they were gesticulating vehemently.

At this spectacle Rabbi Aser Abarbanel closed his eyes: his heart beat so violently that it almost suffocated him; his rags were damp with the cold sweat of agony; he lay motionless by the wall, his mouth wide open, under the rays of a lamp, praying to the God of David.

Just opposite to him the two inquisitors paused under the light of the lamp—doubtless owing to some accident due to the course of their argument. One, while listening to his companion, gazed at the rabbi! And, beneath the look—whose absence of expression the hapless man did not at first notice—he fancied he again felt the burning pincers scorch his flesh, he was to be once more a living wound. Fainting, breathless, with fluttering eyelids, he shivered at the touch of the monk's floating robe. But—strange yet natural fact—the inquisitor's gaze was evidently that of a man deeply absorbed in his intended reply, engrossed by what he was hearing; his eyes were fixed—and seemed to look at the Jew *without seeing him.*

In fact, after the lapse of a few minutes, the two gloomy figures slowly pursued their way, still conversing in low tones, toward the place whence the prisoner had come; HE HAD NOT BEEN SEEN! Amid the horrible confusion of the rabbi's thoughts, the idea darted through his brain: "Can I be already dead that they did not see me?" A hideous impression roused him from his lethargy: in looking at the wall against which his face was pressed, he imagined he beheld two fierce eyes watching him! He flung his head back in a sudden frenzy of fright, his hair fairly bristling! Yet, no! No. His hand groped over the stones: it was the *reflection* of the inquisitor's eyes, still retained in his own, which had been refracted from two spots on the wall.

Forward! He must hasten toward that goal which he fancied (absurdly, no doubt) to be deliverance, toward the darkness from which he was now barely thirty paces distant. He pressed forward faster on his knees, his hands, at full length, dragging himself painfully along, and soon entered the dark portion of this terrible corridor.

Suddenly the poor wretch felt a gust of cold air on the hands resting upon the flags; it came from under the little door to which the two walls led.

Oh, Heaven, if that door should open outward. Every nerve in the miserable fugitive's body thrilled with hope. He examined it from top to bottom, though scarcely able to distinguish its outlines in the surrounding darkness. He passed his hand over it: no bolt, no lock! A latch! He started up, the latch yielded to the pressure of his thumb: the door silently swung open before him.

"Halleluia!" murmured the rabbi in a transport of gratitude as, standing on the threshold, he beheld the scene before him.

The door had opened into the gardens, above which arched a starlit sky, into spring, liberty, life! It revealed the neighboring fields, stretching toward the sierras, whose sinuous blue lines were relieved against the horizon. Yonder lay freedom! Oh, to escape! He would journey all night through the lemon groves, whose fragrance reached him. Once in the mountains and he was safe! He inhaled the delicious air; the breeze revived him, his lungs expanded! He felt in his swelling heart the *Veni foràs* of Lazarus! And to thank once more the God who had bestowed this mercy upon him, he extended his arms, raising his eyes toward Heaven. It was an ecstasy of joy!

Then he fancied he saw the shadow of his arms approach him—fancied that he felt these shadowy arms inclose, embrace him—and that he was pressed tenderly to someone's breast. A tall figure actually did stand directly before him. He lowered his eyes—and remained motionless, gasping for breath, dazed, with fixed eyes, fairly driveling with terror.

Horror! He was in the clasp of the Grand Inquisitor himself, the venerable Pedro Arbuez d'Espila, who gazed at him with tearful eyes, like a good shepherd who had found his stray lamb.

The dark-robed priest pressed the hapless Jew to his heart with so fervent an outburst of love, that the edges of the monachal haircloth rubbed the Dominican's breast. And while Aser Abarbanel with protruding eyes gasped in agony in the ascetic's embrace, vaguely comprehending that *all the phases of this fatal evening were only a prearranged torture, that of* Hope, the Grand Inquisitor, with an accent of touching reproach and a look of consternation, murmured in his ear, his breath parched and burning from long fasting:

"What, my son! On the eve, perchance, of salvation—you wished to leave us?"

ALPHONSE DAUDET

(1840–1897)

Alphonse Daudet, one of the masters of the Naturalistic School of modern France, was born at Nîmes in 1840. He made his literary début in 1858 with a volume of verses. He was both novelist and short story writer, but the *Contes du Lundi* and *Lettres de mon Moulin* are now read in preference to *Sappho* and *Jack*. The Tartarin books are perhaps an exception: they are little masterpieces of humour and observation. The *Contes du Lundi* (1873) contain some of Daudet's most delicate and appealing stories. In *The Last Lesson* there is a spontaneity and feeling which is characteristic of all his best work.

The present version, anonymously translated, is reprinted from *Great Short Stories*, P. F. Collier Sons, New York, 1909. Copyright, 1909, by the Frank A. Munsey Co., by whose permission it is here used.

THE LAST LESSON

I STARTED for school very late that morning and was in great dread of a scolding, especially because M. Hamel had said that he would question us on participles, and I did not know the first word about them. For a moment I thought of running away and spending the day out of doors. It was so warm, so bright! The birds were chirping at the edge of the woods; and in the open field back of the saw-mill the Prussian soldiers were drilling. It was all much more tempting than the rule for participles, but I had the strength to resist, and hurried off to school.

When I passed the town hall there was a crowd in front of the bulletin-board. For the last two years all our bad news had come from there—the lost battles, the draft, the orders of the commanding officer —and I thought to myself, without stopping:

"What can be the matter now?"

Then, as I hurried by as fast as I could go, the blacksmith, Wachter, who was there, with his apprentice, reading the bulletin, called after me:

"Don't go so fast, bub; you'll get to your school in plenty of time!"

I thought he was making fun of me, and reached M. Hamel's little garden all out of breath.

Usually, when school began, there was a great bustle, which could be heard out in the street, the opening and closing of desks, lessons repeated in unison, very loud, with our hands over our ears to understand better, and the teacher's great ruler rapping on the table. But now it was all so still! I had counted on the commotion to get to my desk without being seen; but, of course, that day everything had to be as quiet as Sunday morning. Through the window I saw my classmates, already in their places, and M. Hamel walking up and down with his terrible iron ruler under his arm. I had to open the door and go in before everybody. You can imagine how I blushed and how frightened I was.

But nothing happened. M. Hamel saw me and said very kindly:

"Go to your place quickly, little Franz. We were beginning without you."

I jumped over the bench and sat down at my desk. Not till then, when I had got a little over my fright, did I see that our teacher had on his beautiful green coat, his frilled shirt, and the little black silk cap, all embroidered, that he never wore except on inspection and prize days. Besides, the whole school seemed so strange and solemn. But the thing that surprised me most was to see, on the back benches that were always empty, the village people sitting quietly like ourselves; old Hauser, with his three-cornered hat, the former mayor, the former postmaster, and several others besides. Everybody looked sad; and Hauser had brought an old primer, thumbed at the edges, and he held it open on his knees with his great spectacles lying across the pages.

While I was wondering about it all, M. Hamel mounted his chair, and, in the same grave and gentle tone which he had used to me, said:

"My children, this is the last lesson I shall give you. The order has come from Berlin to teach only German in the schools of Alsace and Lorraine. The new master comes to-morrow. This is your last French lesson. I want you to be very attentive."

What a thunderclap these words were to me!

Oh, the wretches; that was what they had put up at the town-hall!

My last French lesson! Why, I hardly knew how to write! I should never learn any more! I must stop there, then! Oh, how sorry I was for not learning my lessons, for seeking birds' eggs, or going sliding on the Saar! My books, that had seemed such a nuisance a while ago, so heavy to carry, my grammar, and my history of the saints, were old friends now that I couldn't give up. And M. Hamel, too; the idea that he was going away, that I should never see him again, made me forget all about his ruler and how cranky he was.

Poor man! It was in honor of this last lesson that he had put on his fine Sunday clothes, and now I understood why the old men of the village were sitting there in the back of the room. It was because they were sorry, too, that they had not gone to school more. It was their way of thanking our master for his forty years of faithful service and of showing their respect for the country that was theirs no more.

While I was thinking of all this, I heard my name called. It was my turn to recite. What would I not have given to be able to say that dreadful rule for the participle all through, very loud and clear, and without one mistake? But I got mixed up on the first words and stood there, holding on to my desk, my heart beating, and not daring to look up. I heard M. Hamel say to me:

"I won't scold you, little Franz; you must feel bad enough. See how it is! Every day we have said to ourselves: 'Bah! I've plenty of time. I'll learn it to-morrow.' And now you see where we've come out. Ah, that's the great trouble with Alsace; she puts off learning till to-morrow. Now those fellows out there will have the right to say to you: 'How is it; you pretend to be Frenchmen, and yet you can neither speak nor write your own language?' But you are not the worst, poor little Franz. We've all a great deal to reproach ourselves with.

"Your parents were not anxious enough to have you learn. They preferred to put you to work on a farm or at the mills, so as to have a little more money. And I? I've been to blame also. Have I not often sent you to water my flowers instead of learning your lessons? And when I wanted to go fishing, did I not just give you a holiday?"

Then, from one thing to another, M. Hamel went on to talk of the French language, saying that it was the most beautiful language in the world—the clearest, the most logical; that we must guard it among us and never forget it, because when a people are enslaved, as long as they hold fast to their language it is as if they had the key to their prison. Then he opened a grammar and read us our lesson. I was amazed to see how well I understood it. All he said seemed so easy, so easy! I think, too, that I had never listened so carefully, and that he had never explained everything with so much patience. It seemed almost as if the poor man wanted to give us all he knew before going away, and to put it all into our heads at one stroke.

After the grammar, we had a lesson in writing. That day M. Hamel had new copies for us, written in a beautiful round hand: France, Alsace, France, Alsace. They looked like little flags floating everywhere in the school-room, hung from the rod at the top of our desks. You ought to have seen how every one set to work, and how quiet it was! The only sound was the scratching of the pens over the paper. Once some beetles flew in; but nobody paid any attention to them, not even the littlest ones, who worked right on tracing their fish-hooks, as if that was French, too. On the roof the pigeons cooed very low, and I thought to myself:

"Will they make them sing in German, even the pigeons?"

Whenever I looked up from my writing I saw M. Hamel sitting motionless in his chair and gazing first at one thing, then at another, as if he wanted to fix in his mind just how everything looked in that little school-room. Fancy! For forty years he had been there in the same place, with his garden outside the window and his class in front of him, just like that. Only the desks and benches had been worn smooth; the walnut-trees in the garden were taller, and the hop-vine that he had planted himself twined about the windows to the roof. How it must have broken his heart to leave it all, poor man; to hear his sister moving about in the room above, packing their trunks! For they must leave the country next day.

But he had the courage to hear every lesson to the very last. After the writing, we had a lesson in history, and then the babies chanted their ba, be, bi, bo, bu. Down there at the back of the room old Hauser had put on his spectacles and, holding his primer in both hands, spelled the letters with them. You could see that he, too, was crying; his voice trembled with emotion, and it was so funny to hear him that we all wanted to laugh and cry. Ah, how well I remember it, that last lesson!

All at once the church-clock struck twelve. Then the Angelus. At the same moment the trumpets of the Prussians, returning from drill, sounded under our windows. M. Hamel stood up, very pale, in his chair. I never saw him look so tall.

"My friends," said he, "I—I—" But something choked him. He could not go on.

Then he turned to the blackboard, took a piece of chalk, and, bearing on with all his might, he wrote as large as he could:

"Vive La France!"

Then he stopped and leaned his head against the wall, and, without a word, he made a gesture to us with his hand:

"School is dismissed—you may go."

EMILE ZOLA

(1840–1903)

Emile Zola was one of the most extraordinary writers of the last century. With limitless energy and scrupulous pains he constructed an imposing edifice of novels and tales, the epic of a certain French family. He preached the doctrine of Naturalism, believing that every novel or story should be based upon what he called a "human document." Opinions still differ as to his importance as an artist. There is no doubt, however, that he influenced most of the fiction writers who have followed him. The prevailing tone of his work is tragic and the details sordid, but he occasionally turned to the purely fantastic. In the *Tales for Nanon* (1864), one of his very earliest productions, he delights in relating a number of delicate fairy tales. *The Fairy Amoureuse* is one of the most charming of these tales.

The present version is translated by Barrett H. Clark, and appears in this collection for the first time in English.

THE FAIRY AMOUREUSE

DO you hear the rain, Nanon, beating against the windows? And the wind sighing through the long corridor? It's a horrid night, a night when poor wretches shiver before the gates of the rich, who dance indoors in rooms bright with many gilded chandeliers. Take off those silk slippers of yours, and come sit on my knee before the blazing hearth. Lay aside your gorgeous finery: I'm going to tell you a pretty fairy tale this evening.

Once upon a time, Nanon, there stood on the top of a mountain an ancient castle, somber and forbidding to look upon. It was a mass of turrets and ramparts and portcullises with heavy clanking chains; men-at-arms clad in steel from top to toe stood guard night and day on its battlements. Of those who came to the castle only warriors found a welcome at the hands of its master, Count Enguerrand.

If you had seen this old warrior stalking through the long galleries, and heard the sudden outbursts of his dry and menacing voice, you would have trembled with fright, just like his niece Odette, a pious and pretty little lady. Have you ever seen an Easter daisy among the nettles and briars open its petals in the early morning to the first kiss of the sun? Odette was like that, living among the rough knights in attendance on her uncle. Whenever she caught sight of him she would suddenly stop playing, and her eyes fill with tears. She had grown tall and fair, and often sighed with a vague desire for she knew not what; and every time the Lord Enguerrand appeared she was seized with an unspeakable and growing dread.

She had her room in a turret in a distant part of the castle, and spent her time embroidering lovely banners; she found repose in praying to God and in looking out of her window at the emerald landscape and the azure sky. How often, at night, had she risen from her bed and gone to the window to gaze at the stars! How often had the heart of this sixteen-year-old child leaped up toward the vasty spaces of the heavens, asking her radiant sisters of the firmament what it was that so troubled her! And after these sleepless nights, these first stirrings of her yet unconscious love, she would have strange promptings urging her to embrace the rough old knight her uncle. But a short answer or a stern glance would check her impulse, and all atremble she would take up her needle again. You are sorry, Nanon, for the poor child: she was like a fresh-scented flower whose loveliness and scent are alike spurned.

One day as poor Odette was sitting at her window following with her eyes the flight of two doves, she heard a soft voice far below her at the foot of the castle wall. She leaned out and saw a handsome young man who, with a song on his lips, demanded hospitality of the inmates of the castle. Though she listened intently, she could not understand what he said, but the sweet voice made her heart heavy, and the tears ran slowly down her cheeks, wetting the sprig of marjoram which she held in her hand.

But the castle gates were not opened, and a man-at-arms cried out from the walls:

"Stand back. Only soldiers are admitted here."

Odette continued to look out of the window. She let slip the flower from her hand, still wet with her tears. It fell near the feet of the singer who, raising his eyes and seeing the fair hair of the girl, kissed the sprig and turned away, though he stopped at every step to look back. After he had disappeared, Odette went to her prie-dieu and prayed a long time. She gave thanks to heaven, she knew not why; she felt happy, though she did not suspect the reason of her happiness. And that night she dreamed a beautiful dream. She saw again the sprig of marjoram she had thrown to the young man. Slowly, out of the midst of the quivering leaves, there emerged a tiny fairy, with flame-colored wings, a crown of myosotis and a long robe of green, the color of hope.

"Odette," said the fairy in a soothing voice, "I am the Fairy Amoureuse. It was I who sent the young man Lois to you this morning—the young man with the enchanting voice. It was I who, seeing your tears, wanted to dry them. I go about the world seeking lonely hearts and bringing together those who sigh in solitude. I visit the peasant's hut as well as the lord's manor, and at times I see fit to unite the shepherd's crook with the king's scepter. I sow flowers under the feet of those I protect. I enthrall them with bonds so precious and sweet that their hearts throb with joy. My home is among the green things that grow, the forest paths, and in winter-time among the glowing logs on the hearth, in the rooms of husbands and wives. Wherever I set my foot there are kisses and tenderness. Cry no more, Odette, I am Amoureuse, the good Fairy, who have come to dry your tears."

Then she disappeared again into her flower, which closed once more and became an ordinary bud.

You know, of course, Nanon, that the Fairy Amoureuse really exists. Watch her dancing in our own home, and pity the poor people who don't believe in her.

When Odette awoke next morning a ray of sunshine lighted up her room, the song of a bird rose to her high tower and the morning breeze, scented with the first kiss of the flowers, caressed her bright tresses. She rose, happy, and spent the whole day singing, hoping that the Fairy's prophecy would come true. Sometimes she would scan the countryside, smiling at each swiftly flying bird, and feeling within her breast something that made her happy and forced her to clap her hands with joy.

When evening came she descended into the great hall. Near the Count Enguerrand was a knight who listened respectfully to what the old man was saying. Odette seated herself before the fireplace, where a cricket was chirping, and busily plied her ivory distaff.

As she worked, she cast glances from time to time at the stranger knight, and once she caught sight of the sprig of marjoram, which he held tight in one hand. By that sign, and by his sweet voice, she recognized Lois. She almost cried aloud for joy, but in order to conceal her blushes she leaned forward toward the glowing logs, and shook the fire with a long iron rod. The flames darted upwards in a brilliant array, and all at once out of the shower of sparks the Fairy Amoureuse sprang up smiling. Shaking from her green silk robe the bits of burning wood that looked like grains of pure gold, she made off into the great hall where, invisible to the Count, she stood just behind the two young people, while the old warrior went on busily relating the details of a frightful battle with the Infidels. The Fairy spoke in a soothing undertone:

"You must love each other, my children. Leave to the old the memories of youth, and the telling of long tales by the fireside. Let your kisses be the only sound to mingle with the crackling logs. Later will be time enough to mitigate the sorrows of old age by remembering the happy hours long past. When you love at sixteen, words are of no avail: a single look tells more than a lengthy discourse. Love each other, my children, and let old age prate."

Then she covered the two with her wings so completely that the Count, who was explaining how the Giant Buch the Iron-headed was killed by a great blow from the hand of Giralda of the Heavy Sword, could not see when Lois implanted his first kiss on the brow of the trembling Odette.

Now I must tell you, Nanon, about those beautiful wings of the Fairy Amoureuse. They were as transparent as glass and as delicate as the wings of a fly. But when two lovers are in danger of being seen, they grow and grow and become so thick and so opaque that they shut off the view of anything behind them and prevent anyone's hearing the kisses. And so the old man went on and on with his wondrous tale, while Lois continued to caress the fair Odette, right in the presence of the wicked old lord.

Good heavens, what wonderful wings they were! Young girls, I am told, discover them for themselves, and more than one has succeeded in concealing herself from her grandparents. Isn't that so, Nanon?

Well, when the Count had at last brought to a close his lengthy discourse, the Fairy Amoureuse disappeared again into the fire, and Lois withdrew after thanking his host and throwing a farewell kiss to Odette. The girl was so happy that she dreamed that night of mountains studded with flowers made bright by millions of stars, each of them a thousand times more radiant than the sun.

Next morning she went down into the garden, wandering from arbor to arbor. In one of them she came upon a man-at-arms, bowed to him and was about to pass on, when she noticed a sprig of marjoram in his hand, still wet with tears, and recognized again her Lois. He had come to the castle under a new disguise. He made her sit down on a grassy bank near a fountain, and they gazed into each other's eyes, delighted to be able to see each other's features by the light of day. The warblers sang, and the two lovers felt that the Fairy Amoureuse must surely be hovering about in the air near them.

I shan't tell you all that the discreet old oak-trees heard that morning. It was pleasant to watch the boy and the girl sitting there chatting hour after hour, so long indeed that one warbler found ample time to build herself a nest in a nearby bush.

Suddenly the heavy footsteps of Count Enguerrand were heard in the garden walk. The lovers trembled, but the water of the fountain rippled more sweetly than ever, and Amoureuse rose out of the crystal stream, a smile on her face. She covered the lovers with her wings, and quickly slipped between them and the Count, who was greatly surprised to hear voices and yet see no one at all.

Holding her friends in her embrace, she repeated to them in a soft undertone:

"I am she who protects love, who closes the eyes and ears of those who no longer love. Fear nothing, dear lovers: love each other in this beautiful clear sunlight, in these garden walks, by the side of these fountains, wherever you happen to be. I am with you, watching over you. God has sent me among men, and they who scoff at sacred things shall never interrupt you. God gave me these beautiful wings, telling me, 'Go, and let the hearts of the young rejoice!' Love each other, while I keep guard over you."

Then she darted off, gathering dew off the foliage (her only nourishment), and taking with her in her joyous round Odette and Lois, whose arms were ever interlaced.

You will ask me what the lovers did next? Really, my dear, I hardly dare tell you. I'm afraid you would not believe me, or be jealous of *their* happiness, and refuse to return my kisses. Naughty girl, you are curious, aren't you? I see I shall have to satisfy your curiosity.

Know then, that the Fairy flew hither and thither until nightfall, and when she tried to separate her lovers, she found them so reluctant that she had to give them a good talking-to. It seems (for her voice was low) that she said things so beautiful that their faces lighted up and their eyes opened wide from happiness. And after she had done speaking and they consented to her proposal, she touched their foreheads with her magic wand.

Suddenly—oh, Nanon, how big your eyes are! And how you would tap your little foot if I were to refuse to tell you the sequel! Suddenly, Lois and Odette were changed into stalks of marjoram, so large and magnificent that only a fairy could have made them so. There they were, side by side, so close that their leaves were entwined. Marvelous flowers they were; they would bloom forever, and eternally mingle their perfumes and their dew.

As for the Count Enguerrand, they say he consoled himself by relating every single night the story of the Giant Buch the Iron-Headed and how he was killed by a great blow from the hand of Giralda of the Heavy Sword.

And now, Nanon, when we go to the country, we shall look for the two magic marjorams and ask them in which flower we may find the Fairy Amoureuse. Perhaps, my dear, there is a little moral hidden in this tale. However, I have told it to you here, as we sit stretched out before the hearth, just in order to make you forget the December rain beating against our windows, and in the hope that it will inspire you to love a little more the young man who told it to you.

FRANÇOIS COPPÉE

(1842–1908)

Coppée, the poet of the poor and humble, lived a long and uneventful life. His volumes of verse are characterized by qualities of sentiment and simplicity. But his novels, plays, and short stories, especially the last, are an integral part of his literary work. These, says Brander Matthews, "have qualities of their own; they have sympathy, poetry, and a power of suggesting pictures not exceeded.

I think, by those of either M. de Maupassant or M. Daudet."

The present version, translated by Walter Learned, is reprinted from *Ten Tales by François Coppée,* by permission of the publisher, Harper & Brothers.

THE SUBSTITUTE

HE was scarcely ten years old when he was first arrested as a vagabond.

He spoke thus to the judge:

"I am called Jean François Leturc, and for six months I was with the man who sings and plays upon a cord of catgut between the lanterns at the Place de la Bastille. I sang the refrain with him, and after that I called, 'Here's all the new songs, ten centimes, two sous!' He was always drunk, and used to beat me. That is why the police picked me up the other night. Before that I was with the man who sells brushes. My mother was a laundress, her name was Adèle. At one time she lived with a man on the ground-floor at Montmartre. She was a good work-woman and liked me. She made money because she had for customers waiters in the cafés, and they use a good deal of linen. On Sundays she used to put me to bed early so that she could go to the ball. On week-days she sent me to Les Frères, where I learned to read. Well, the sergent-de-ville whose beat was in our street used always to stop before our windows to talk with her—a good-looking chap, with a medal from the Crimea. They were married, and after that everything went wrong. He didn't take to me, and turned mother against me. Every one had a blow for me, and so, to get out of the house, I spent whole days in the Place Clichy, where I knew the mountebanks. My father-in-law lost his place, and my mother her work. She used to go out washing to take care of him; this gave her a cough—the steam. . . . She is dead at Lamboisière. She was a good woman. Since that I have lived with the seller of brushes and the catgut scraper. Are you going to send me to prison?"

He said this openly, cynically, like a man. He was a little ragged street-arab, as tall as a boot, his forehead hidden under a queer mop of yellow hair.

Nobody claimed him, and they sent him to the Reform School.

Not very intelligent, idle, clumsy with his hands, the only trade he could learn there was not a good one—that of reseating straw chairs. However, he was obedient, naturally quiet and silent, and he did not seem to be profoundly corrupted by that school of vice. But when, in his seventeenth year, he was thrown out again on the streets of Paris, he unhappily found there his prison comrades, all great scamps, exercising their dirty professions: teaching dogs to catch rats in the sewers, and blacking shoes on ball nights in the passage of the Opera—amateur wrestlers, who permitted themselves to be thrown by the Hercules of the booths—or fishing at noontime from rafts; all of these occupations he followed to some extent, and, some months after he came out of the house of correction, he was arrested again for a petty theft—a pair of old shoes prigged from a shop-window. Result: a year in the prison of Sainte Pélagie, where he served as valet to the political prisoners.

He lived in much surprise among this group of prisoners, all very young, negligent in dress, who talked in loud voices, and carried their heads in a very solemn fashion. They used to meet in the cell of one of the oldest of them, a fellow of some thirty years, already a long time in prison and quite a fixture at Sainte Pélagie—a large cell, the walls covered with colored caricatures, and from the window of which one could see all Paris—its roofs, its spires, and its domes—and far away the distant line of hills, blue and indistinct upon the sky. There were upon the walls some shelves filled with volumes and all the old paraphernalia of a fencing-room: broken masks, rusty foils, breastplates, and gloves that were losing their tow. It was there that the "politicians" used to dine together, adding to the everlasting "soup and beef," fruit, cheese, and pints of wine which Jean François went out and got by the can—a tumultuous repast interrupted by violent disputes, and where, during the dessert, the "Carmagnole" and "Ça Ira" were sung in full chorus. They assumed, however, an air of great dignity on those days when a newcomer was brought in among them, at first entertaining him gravely as a citizen, but on the morrow using him with affectionate familiarity and calling him by his nickname. Great words were used there: Corporation, Responsibility, and phrases quite unintelligible to Jean François—such as this, for example, which he once heard imperiously put forth by a frightful little hunchback who blotted some writing-paper every night:

"It is done. This is the composition of the Cabinet: Raymond, the Bureau of Public Instruction; Martial, the Interior; and for Foreign Affairs, myself."

His time done, he wandered again around Paris, watched afar by the police, after the fashion of cockchafers, made by cruel children to fly at the end of a string. He became one of those fugitive and timid beings whom the law, with a sort of coquetry, arrests and releases by turn—something like those platonic fishers who, in order that they may not exhaust their fish-pond, throw immediately back into the water the fish which has just come out of the net. Without a suspicion on his part that so much honor had been done to so sorry a subject, he had a special bundle of memoranda in the mysterious portfolios of the Rue de Jérusalem. His name was written in round hand on the gray paper of the cover, and the notes and reports, carefully classified, gave him his successive appellations: "Name, Leturc"; "the prisoner Leturc," and, at last, "the criminal Leturc."

He was two years out of prison, dining where he could, sleeping in night lodging-houses and sometimes in lime-kilns, and taking part with his fellows in interminable games of pitch-penny on the boulevards near the barriers. He wore a greasy cap on the back of his head, carpet slippers, and a short white blouse. When he had five sous he had his hair curled. He danced at Constant's at Montparnasse; bought for two sous to sell for four at the door of Bobino, the jack of hearts or the ace of clubs serving as a countermark; sometimes opened the door of a carriage; led horses to the horse-market. From the lottery of all sorts of miserable employments he drew a goodly number. Who can say if the atmosphere of honor which one breathes as a soldier, if military discipline might not have saved him? Taken, in a cast of the net, with some young loafers who robbed drunkards sleeping on the streets, he denied very earnestly having taken part in their expeditions. Perhaps he told the truth, but his antecedents were accepted in lieu of proof, and he was sent for three years to Poissy. There he made coarse playthings for children, was tattooed on the chest, learned thieves' slang and the penal code. A new liberation, and a new plunge into the sink of Paris; but very short this time, for at the end of six months at the most he was again compromised in a night robbery, aggravated by climbing and breaking—a serious affair, in which he played an obscure rôle, half dupe and half fence. On the whole his complicity was evident, and he was sent for five years at hard labor. His grief in this adventure was above all in being separated from an old dog which he had found on a dung-heap, and cured of the mange. The beast loved him.

Toulon, the ball and chain, the work in the harbor, the blows from a stick, wooden shoes on bare feet, soup of black beans dating from Trafalgar, no tobacco money, and the terrible sleep in a camp swarming with convicts; that was what he experienced for five broiling summers and five winters raw with the Mediterranean wind. He came out from there stunned, was sent under surveillance to Vernon, where he worked some time on the river. Then, an incorrigible vagabond, he broke his exile and came again to Paris. He had his savings, fifty-six francs, that is to say, time enough for reflection. During his absence his former wretched companions had dispersed. He was well hidden, and slept in a loft at an old woman's, to whom he represented himself as a sailor, tired of the sea, who had lost his papers in a recent shipwreck, and who wanted to try his hand at something else. His tanned face and his calloused hands, together with some sea phrases which he dropped from time to time, made his tale seem probable enough.

One day when he risked a saunter in the streets, and when chance had led him as far as Montmartre, where he was born, an unexpected memory stopped him before the door of Les Frères, where he had learned to read. As it was very warm the door was open, and by a single glance the passing outcast was able to recognize the peaceable school-room. Nothing was changed: neither the bright light shining in at the great windows, nor the crucifix over the desk, nor the rows of benches with the tables furnished with inkstands and pencils, nor the table of weights and measures, nor the map where pins stuck in still indicated the operations of some ancient war. Heedlessly and without thinking, Jean François read on the blackboard the words of the Evangelist which had been set there as a copy:

"Joy shall be in heaven over one sinner that repenteth, more than over ninety and nine just persons, which need no repentance."

It was undoubtedly the hour for recreation, for the Brother Professor had left his chair, and, sitting on the edge of a table, he was telling a story to the boys who surrounded him with eager and attentive eyes. What a bright and innocent face he had, that beardless young man, in his long black gown, and white necktie, and great ugly shoes, and his badly cut brown hair streaming out behind! All the simple figures of the children of the people who were watching him seemed scarcely less childlike than his; above all when, delighted with some of his own simple and priestly pleasantries, he broke out in an open and frank peal of laughter which showed his white and regular teeth, a peal so contagious that all the scholars laughed loudly in their turn. It was such a sweet, simple group in the bright sunlight, which lighted their dear eyes and their blond curls.

Jean François looked at them for some time in silence, and for the first time in that savage nature, all instinct and appetite, there awoke a mysterious, a tender emotion. His heart, that seared and hardened heart, unmoved when the convict's cudgel or the heavy whip of the watchman fell on his shoulders, beat oppressively. In that sight he saw again his infancy; and closing his eyes sadly, the prey to torturing regret, he walked quickly away.

Then the words written on the blackboard came back to his mind.

"If it wasn't too late, after all!" he murmured; "if I could again, like others, eat honestly my brown bread, and sleep my fill without nightmare! The spy must be sharp who recognizes me. My beard, which I shaved off down there, has grown out thick and strong. One can burrow somewhere in the great ant-hill, and work can be found. Whoever is not worked to death in the hell of the galleys comes out agile and robust, and I learned there to climb ropes with loads upon my back. Building is going on everywhere here, and the masons need helpers. Three francs a day! I never earned so much. Let me be forgotten, and that is all I ask."

He followed his courageous resolution; he was faithful to it, and after three months he was another man. The master for whom he worked called him his best workman. After a long day upon the scaffolding, in the hot sun and the dust, constantly bending and raising his back to take the hod from the man at his feet and pass it to the man over his head, he went for his soup to the cook-shop, tired out, his legs aching, his hands burning, his eyelids stuck with plaster, but content with himself, and carrying his well-earned money in a knot in his handkerchief. He went out now without fear, since he could not be recognized in his white mask, and since he had noticed that the suspicious glances of the policeman were seldom turned on the tired workman. He was quiet and sober. He slept the sound sleep of fatigue. He was free!

At last—oh, supreme recompense!—he had a friend!

He was a fellow-workman like himself, named Savinien, a little peasant with red lips who had come to Paris with his stick over his shoulder and a bundle on the end of it, fleeing from the wine-shops and going to mass every Sunday. Jean François loved him for his piety, for his candor, for his honesty, for all that he himself had lost, and so long ago. It was a passion, profound and unrestrained, which transformed him by fatherly cares and attentions. Savinien, himself of a weak and egotistical nature, let things take their course, satisfied only in finding a companion who shared his horror of the wine-shop. The two friends lived together in a fairly comfortable lodging, but their resources were very limited. They were obliged to take into their room a third companion, an old Auvergnat, gloomy and rapacious, who found it possible out of his meager salary to save something with which to buy a place in his own country. Jean François and Savinien were always together. On holidays they together took long walks in the environs of Paris, and dined under an arbor in one of those small country inns where there are a great many mushrooms in the sauces and innocent rebusses on the napkins. There Jean François learned from his friend all that lore of which they who are born in the city are ignorant; learned the names of the trees, the flowers, and the plants; the various seasons for harvesting; he heard eagerly the thousand details of a laborious country life—the autumn sowing, the winter chores, the splendid celebrations of harvest and vintage days, the sound of the mills at the water-side, and the flails striking the ground, the tired horses led to water, and the hunting in the morning mist; and, above all, the long evenings around the fire of vine-shoots, that were shortened by some marvelous stories. He discovered in himself a source of imagination before unknown, and found a singular delight in the recital of events so placid, so calm, so monotonous.

One thing troubled him, however: it was the fear lest Savinien might learn something of his past. Sometimes there escaped from him some low word of thieves' slang, a vulgar gesture—vestiges of his former horrible existence—and he felt the pain one feels when old wounds reopen; the more because he fancied that he sometimes saw in Savinien the awakening of an unhealthy curiosity. When the young man, already tempted by the pleasures which Paris offers to the poorest, asked him about the mysteries of the great city, Jean François feigned ignorance and turned the subject; but he felt a vague inquietude for the future of his friend.

His uneasiness was not without foundation. Savinien could not long remain the simple rustic that he was on his arrival in Paris. If the gross and noisy pleasures of the wine-shop always repelled him, he was profoundly troubled by other temptations, full of danger for the inexperience of his twenty years. When spring came he began to go off alone, and at first he wandered about the brilliant entrance of some dancing-hall, watching the young girls who went in with their arms around each other's waists, talking in low tones. Then, one evening, when lilacs perfumed the air and the call to quadrilles was most captivating, he crossed the threshold, and from that time Jean François observed a change, little by little, in his manners and his visage. He became more frivolous, more extravagant. He often borrowed from his friend his scanty savings, and he forgot to repay. Jean François, feeling that he was abandoned, jealous and forgiving at the same time, suffered and was silent. He felt that he had no right to reproach him, but with the foresight of affection he indulged in cruel and inevitable presentiments.

One evening, as he was mounting the stairs to his room, absorbed in his thoughts, he heard, as he was about to enter, the sound of angry voices, and he recognized that of the old Auvergnat who lodged with Savinien and himself. An old habit of suspicion made him stop at the landing-place and listen to learn the cause of the trouble.

"Yes," said the Auvergnat, angrily, "I am sure that some one has opened my trunk and stolen from it the three louis that I had hidden in a little box; and he who has done this thing must be one of the two companions who sleep here, if it were not the servant Maria. It concerns you as much as it does me, since you are the master of the house, and I will drag you to the courts if you do not let me at once break open the valises of the two masons. My poor gold! It was here yesterday in its place, and I will tell you just what it was, so that if we find it again nobody can accuse me of having lied. Ah, I know them, my three beautiful gold-pieces, and I can see them as plainly as I see you' One piece was more worn than the others; it was of greenish gold, with a portrait of the great emperor. The other was a great old fellow with a queue and epaulettes; and the third, which had on it a Philippe with whiskers, I had marked with my teeth. They don't trick me. Do you know that

I only wanted two more like that to pay for my vineyard? Come, search these fellows' things with me, or I will call the police! Hurry up!"

"All right," said the voice of the landlord; "we will go and search with Maria. So much the worse for you if we find nothing, and the masons get angry. You have forced me to it."

Jean François' soul was full of fright. He remembered the embarrassed circumstances and the small loans of Savinien and how sober he had seemed for some days. And yet he could not believe that he was a thief. He heard the Auvergnat panting in his eager search, and he pressed his closed fists against his breast as if to still the furious beating of his heart.

"Here they are!" suddenly shouted the victorious miser. "Here they are, my louis, my dear treasure; and in the Sunday vest of that little hypocrite of Limousin! Look, landlord, they are just as I told you. Here is the Napoleon, the man with a queue, and the Philippe that I have bitten. See the dents! Ah, the little beggar with the sanctified air. I should have much sooner suspected the other. Ah, the wretch! Well, he must go to the convict prison."

At this moment Jean François heard the well-known step of Savinien coming slowly up the stairs.

He is going to his destruction, thought he. Three stories. I have time!

And, pushing open the door, he entered the room, pale as death, where he saw the landlord and the servant stupefied in a corner, while the Auvergnat, on his knees, in the disordered heap of clothes, was kissing the pieces of gold.

"Enough of this," he said, in a thick voice; "I took the money, and put it in my comrade's trunk. But that is too bad. I am a thief, but not a Judas. Call the police; I will not try to escape, only I must say a word to Savinien in private. Here he is."

In fact, the little Limousin had just arrived, and seeing his crime discovered, believing himself lost, he stood there, his eyes fixed, his arms hanging.

Jean François seized him forcibly by the neck, as if to embrace him; he put his mouth close to Savinien's ear, and said to him in a low, supplicating voice:

"Keep quiet."

Then turning towards the others:

"Leave me alone with him. I tell you I won't go away. Lock us in if you wish, but leave us alone."

With a commanding gesture he showed them the door.

They went out.

Savinien, broken by grief, was sitting on the bed, and lowered his eyes without understanding anything.

"Listen," said Jean François, who came and took him by the hands. "I understand! You have stolen three gold-pieces to buy some trifle for a girl. That costs six months in prison. But one only comes out from there to go back again, and you will become a pillar of police courts and tribunals. I understand it. I have been seven years at the Reform School, a year at Sainte Pélagie, three years at Poissy, five years at Toulon. Now, don't be afraid. Everything is arranged. I have taken it on my shoulders."

"It is dreadful," said Savinien; but hope was springing up again in his cowardly heart.

"When the elder brother is under the flag, the younger one does not go," replied Jean François. "I am your substitute, that's all. You care for me a little, do you not? I am paid. Don't be childish—don't refuse. They would have taken me again one of these days, for I am a runaway from exile. And then, do you see, that life will be less hard for me than for you. I know it all, and I shall not complain if I have not done you this service for nothing, and if you swear to me that you will never do it again. Savinien, I have loved you well, and your friendship has made me happy. It is through it that, since I have known you, I have been honest and pure, as I might always have been, perhaps, if I had had, like you, a father to put a tool in my hands, a mother to teach me my prayers. It was my sole regret that I was useless to you, and that I deceived you concerning myself. To-day I have unmasked in saving you. It is all right. Do not cry, and embrace me, for already I hear heavy boots on the stairs. They are coming with the *posse*, and we must not seem to know each other so well before those chaps."

He pressed Savinien quickly to his breast, then pushed him from him, when the door was thrown wide open.

It was the landlord and the Auvergnat, who brought the police. Jean François sprang forward to the landing-place, held out his hands for the handcuffs, and said, laughing, "Forward, bad lot!"

To-day he is at Cayenne, condemned for life as an incorrigible.

ANATOLE FRANCE

(*Anatole Thibault*)

(1844–1924)

ANATOLE FRANCE was born at Paris in 1844 and lived there most of his life. He was *par excellence* a man of letters. For over forty years he has written about Paris, the ancient world and the Middle

Ages, endowing each novel or story with the philosophy of enlightened scepticism which is his contribution to modern thought.

Among the several volumes of stories he has written, *L'Etui de nacre* includes some of his very best. From this is taken *Our Lady's Juggler*, which is a retelling of one of the most beautiful of the French mediæval tales.

The present version is translated for this collection by Barrett H. Clark, by permission of Anatole France's English publishers, John Lane, Ltd., the Bodley Head.

OUR LADY'S JUGGLER

IN the days of King Louis there lived a poor juggler by the name of Barnabas, a native of Compiègne, who wandered from city to city performing tricks of skill and prowess.

On fair days he would lay down in the public square a worn and aged carpet, and after having attracted a group of children and idlers by certain amusing remarks which he had learned from an old juggler, and which he invariably repeated in the same fashion without altering a word, he would assume the strangest postures, and balance a pewter plate on the tip of his nose. At first the crowd regarded him with indifference, but when, with his hands and head on the ground he threw into the air and caught with his feet six copper balls that glittered in the sunlight, or when, throwing himself back until his neck touched his heels, he assumed the form of a perfect wheel and in that position juggled with twelve knives, he elicited a murmur of admiration from his audience, and small coins rained on his carpet.

Still, Barnabas of Compiègne, like most of those who exist by their accomplishments, had a hard time making a living. Earning his bread by the sweat of his brow, he bore rather more than his share of those miseries we are all heir to through the fault of our Father Adam.

Besides, he was unable to work as much as he would have liked, for in order to exhibit his wonderful talents, he required—like the trees—the warmth of the sun and the heat of the day. In winter time he was no more than a tree stripped of its leaves, in fact, half-dead. The frozen earth was too hard for the juggler. Like the cicada mentioned by Marie de France, he suffered during the bad season from hunger and cold. But, since he had a simple heart, he suffered in silence.

He had never thought much about the origin of wealth nor about the inequality of human conditions. He firmly believed that if this world was evil the next could not but be good, and this faith upheld him. He was not like the clever fellows who sell their souls to the devil; he never took the name of God in vain; he lived the life of an honest man, and though he had no wife of his own, he did not covet his neighbor's, for woman is the enemy of strong men, as we learn by the story of Samson which is written in the Scriptures.

Verily, his mind was not turned in the direction of carnal desire, and it caused him far greater pain to renounce drinking than to forego the pleasure of women. For, though he was not a drunkard, he enjoyed drinking when the weather was warm. He was a good man, fearing God, and devout in his adoration of the Holy Virgin. When he went into a church he never failed to kneel before the image of the Mother of God and to address her with this prayer:

"My Lady, watch over my life until it shall please God that I die, and when I am dead, see that I have the joys of Paradise."

One evening, after a day of rain, as he walked sad and bent with his juggling balls under his arm and his knives wrapped up in his old carpet seeking some barn where he might go supperless to bed, he saw a monk going in his direction, and respectfully saluted him. As they were both walking at the same pace, they fell into conversation.

"Friend," said the monk, "how does it happen that you are dressed all in green? Are you perchance going to play the part of the fool in some mystery?"

"No, indeed, father," said Barnabas. "My name is Barnabas, and my business is that of juggler. It would be the finest calling in the world if I could eat every day."

"Friend Barnabas," answered the monk, "be careful what you say. There is no finer calling than the monastic. The priest celebrates the praise of God, the Virgin, and the saints; the life of a monk is a perpetual hymn to the Lord."

And Barnabas replied: "Father, I confess I spoke like an ignorant man. My estate cannot be compared to yours, and though there may be some merit in dancing and balancing a stick with a denier on top of it on the end of your nose, it is in no wise comparable to your merit. Father, I wish I might, like you, sing the Office every day, especially the Office of the Very Holy Virgin, to whom I am specially and piously devoted. I would willingly give up the art by which I am known from Soissons to Beauvais, in more than six hundred cities and villages, in order to enter the monastic life."

The monk was touched by the simplicity of the juggler, and as he was not lacking in discernment, he recognized in Barnabas one of those well-disposed men of whom Our Lord has said, "Let peace be with them on earth." And he made answer therefore:

"Friend Barnabas, come with me and I will see that you enter the monastery of which I am the Prior. He who led Mary the Egyptian through the desert put me across your path in order that I might lead you to salvation."

Thus did Barnabas become a monk. In the monastery which he entered, the monks celebrated most magnificently the cult of the Holy Virgin, each of them bringing to her service all the knowledge and skill which God had given him.

The Prior, for his part, wrote books, setting forth, according to the rules of scholasticism, all the virtues of the Mother of God. Brother Maurice copied these treatises with a cunning hand on pages of parchment, while Brother Aléxandre decorated them with delicate miniatures representing the Queen of Heaven seated on the throne of Solomon, with four lions on guard at the foot of it. Around her head, which was encircled by a halo, flew seven doves, the seven gifts of the Holy Spirit: fear, piety, knowledge, power, judgment, intelligence, and wisdom. With her were six golden-haired virgins: Humility, Prudence, Retirement, Respect, Virginity, and Obedience. At her feet two little figures, shining white and quite naked, stood in suppliant attitudes. They were souls imploring, not in vain, Her all-powerful intercession for their salvation. On another page Brother Aléxandre depicted Eve in the presence of Mary, that one might see at the same time sin and its redemption, woman humiliated, and the Virgin exalted. Among the other much-prized pictures in his book were the Well of Living Waters, the Fountain, the Lily, the Moon, the Sun, and the Closed Garden, of which much is said in the Canticle; the Gate of Heaven and the City of God. These were all images of the Virgin.

Brother Marbode, too, was one of the cherished children of Mary. He was ever busy cutting images of stone, so that his beard, his eyebrows and his hair were white with the dust, and his eyes perpetually swollen and full of tears. But he was a hardy and a happy man in his old age, and there was no doubt that the Queen of Paradise watched over the declining days of Her child. Marbode represented Her seated in a pulpit, Her forehead encircled by a halo, with an orb of pearls. He was at great pains to make the folds of Her robe cover the feet of Her of whom the prophet has said, "My beloved is like a closed garden."

At times he represented Her as a graceful child, and Her image seemed to say, "Lord, Thou art My Lord!"

There were also in the Monastery poets who composed prose writings in Latin and hymns in honor of the Most Gracious Virgin Mary; there was, indeed, one among them—a Picard—who translated the Miracles of Our Lady into rimed verses in the vulgar tongue.

Perceiving so great a competition in praise and so fine a harvest of good works, Barnabas fell to lamenting his ignorance and simplicity.

"Alas!" he sighed as he walked by himself one day in the little garden shaded by the Monastery wall, "I am so unhappy because I cannot, like my brothers, give worthy praise to the Holy Mother of God to whom I have consecrated all the love in my heart. Alas, I am a stupid fellow, without art, and for your service, Madame, I have no edifying sermons, no fine treatises nicely prepared according to the rules, no beautiful paintings, no cunningly carved statues, and no verses counted off by feet and marching in measure! Alas, I have nothing!"

Thus did he lament and abandon himself to his misery.

One evening when the monks were talking together by way of diversion, he heard one of them tell of a monk who could not recite anything but the *Ave Maria.* He was scorned for his ignorance, but after he died there sprang from his mouth five roses, in honor of the five letters in the name Maria. Thus was his holiness made manifest.

In listening to this story, Barnabas was conscious once more of the Virgin's beneficence, but he was not consoled by the example of the happy miracle, for his heart was full of zeal and he wanted to celebrate the glory of His Lady in Heaven.

He sought for a way in which to do this, but in vain, and each day brought him greater sorrow, until one morning he sprang joyously from his cot and ran to the chapel, where he remained alone for more than an hour. He returned thither again after dinner, and from that day onward he would go into the chapel every day the moment it was deserted, passing the greater part of the time which the other monks dedicated to the pursuit of the liberal arts and the sciences. He was no longer sad and he sighed no more. But such singular conduct aroused the curiosity of the other monks, and they asked themselves why Brother Barnabas retired alone so often, and the Prior, whose business it was to know everything that his monks were doing, determined to observe Barnabas. One day, therefore, when Barnabas was alone in the chapel, the Prior entered in company with two of the oldest brothers, in order to watch, through the bars of the door, what was going on within.

They saw Barnabas before the image of the Holy Virgin, his head on the floor and his feet in the air, juggling with six copper balls and twelve knives. In honor of the Holy Virgin he was performing the tricks which had in former days brought him the greatest fame. Not understanding that he was thus putting his best talents at the service of the Holy Virgin, the aged brothers cried out against such sacrilege. The Prior knew that Barnabas had a simple soul, but he believed that the man had lost his wits. All three set about to remove Barnabas from the chapel, when they saw the Virgin slowly descend from the altar and, with a fold of her blue mantle, wipe the sweat that streamed over the juggler's forehead.

Then the Prior, bowing his head down to the marble floor, repeated these words:

"Blessed are the pure in heart, for they shall see God."

"Amen," echoed the brothers, bowing down to the floor.

GUY DE MAUPASSANT

(1850–1893)

De Maupassant was born at the Château de Miromesnil in 1850. Distinguished though he is as a master of the novel form, and in spite of the fact that his half-dozen novels are powerful and significant works, it is his stories, of which he wrote several hundred, that constitute his chief claim to immortality. He is one of the first modern writers who consistently applied himself to the development of the short story as a separate literary form.

The Necklace is generally conceded to be one of Maupassant's most highly finished achievements. Though it belongs technically to the "surprise" type so ingeniously utilized at a later date by O. Henry, the surprise which marks the point of the tale is introduced not for its own sake alone, but in order to reveal at a stroke the tragedy through which Mathilde has lived.

The present version, translated by Jonathan Sturges, is reprinted by permission of the publisher, from *The Odd Number*, Harper & Brothers.

THE NECKLACE

SHE was one of those pretty and charming girls who are sometimes, as if by a mistake of destiny, born in a family of clerks. She had no dowry, no expectations, no means of being known, understood, loved, wedded, by any rich and distinguished man; and she let herself be married to a little clerk at the Ministry of Public Instruction.

She dressed plainly because she could not dress well, but she was as unhappy as though she had really fallen from her proper station; since with women there is neither caste nor rank; and beauty, grace, and charm act instead of family and birth. Natural fineness, instinct for what is elegant, suppleness of wit, are the sole hierarchy, and make from women of the people the equals of the very greatest ladies.

She suffered ceaselessly, feeling herself born for all the delicacies and all the luxuries. She suffered from the poverty of her dwelling, from the wretched look of the walls, from the worn-out chairs, from the ugliness of the curtains. All those things, of which another woman of her rank would never even have been conscious, tortured her and made her angry. The sight of the little Breton peasant who did her humble housework aroused in her regrets which were despairing, and distracted dreams. She thought of the silent ante-chambers hung with Oriental tapestry, lit by tall bronze candelabra, and of the two great footmen in knee-breeches who sleep in the big armchairs, made drowsy by the heavy warmth of the hot-air stove. She thought of the long *salons* fitted up with ancient silk, of the delicate furniture carrying priceless curiosities, and of the coquettish perfumed boudoirs made for talks at five o'clock with intimate friends, with men famous and sought after, whom all women envy and whose attention they all desire.

When she sat down to dinner, before the round table covered with a table-cloth three days old, opposite her husband, who uncovered the soup tureen and declared with an enchanted air, "Ah, the good *pot-au-feu!* I don't know anything better than that," she thought of dainty dinners, of shining silverware, of tapestry which peopled the walls with ancient personages and with strange birds flying in the midst of a fairy forest; and she thought of delicious dishes served on marvelous plates, and of the whispered gallantries which you listen to with a sphinx-like smile, while you are eating the pink flesh of a trout or the wings of a quail.

She had no dresses, no jewels, nothing. And she loved nothing but that; she felt made for that. She would so have liked to please, to be envied, to be charming, to be sought after.

She had a friend, a former schoolmate at the convent, who was rich, and whom she did not like to go and see any more, because she suffered so much when she came back.

But, one evening, her husband returned home with a triumphant air, and holding a large envelope in his hand.

"There," said he, "here is something for you."

She tore the paper sharply, and drew out a printed card which bore these words:

> "The Minister of Public Instruction and Mme. Georges Ramponneau request the honor of M. and Mme. Loisel's company at the palace of the Ministry on Monday evening, January 18th."

Instead of being delighted, as her husband hoped, she threw the invitation on the table with disdain, murmuring:

"What do you want me to do with that?"

"But, my dear, I thought you would be glad. You never go out, and this is such a fine opportunity. I had awful trouble to get it. Every one wants to go; it is very select, and they are not giving many invitations to clerks. The whole official world will be there."

She looked at him with an irritated eye, and she said, impatiently:

"And what do you want me to put on my back?"

He had not thought of that; he stammered:

"Why, the dress you go to the theater in. It looks very well, to me."

He stopped, distracted, seeing that his wife was crying. Two great tears descended slowly from the corners of her eyes towards the corners of her mouth. He stuttered:

"What's the matter? What's the matter?"

But, by a violent effort, she had conquered her grief, and she replied, with a calm voice, while she wiped her wet cheeks:

"Nothing. Only I have no dress, and therefore I can't go to this ball. Give your card to some colleague whose wife is better equipped than I."

He was in despair. He resumed:

"Come, let us see, Mathilde. How much would it cost, a suitable dress, which you could use on other occasions, something very simple?"

She reflected several seconds, making her calculations and wondering also what sum she could ask without drawing on herself an immediate refusal and a frightened exclamation from the economical clerk.

Finally, she replied, hesitatingly:

"I don't know exactly, but I think I could manage it with four hundred francs."

He had grown a little pale, because he was laying aside just that amount to buy a gun and treat himself to a little shooting next summer on the plain of Nanterre, with several friends who went to shoot larks down there, of a Sunday.

But he said:

"All right. I will give you four hundred francs. And try to have a pretty dress."

The day of the ball drew near, and Mme. Loisel seemed sad, uneasy, anxious. Her dress was ready, however. Her husband said to her one evening:

"What is the matter? Come, you've been so queer these last three days."

And she answered:

"It annoys me not to have a single jewel, not a single stone, nothing to put on. I shall look like distress. I should almost rather not go at all."

He resumed:

"You might wear natural flowers. It's very stylish at this time of the year. For ten francs you can get two or three magnificent roses."

She was not convinced.

"No; there's nothing more humiliating than to look poor among other women who are rich."

But her husband cried:

"How stupid you are! Go look up your friend Mme. Forestier, and ask her to lend you some jewels. You're quite thick enough with her to do that."

She uttered a cry of joy:

"It's true. I never thought of it."

The next day she went to her friend and told of her distress.

Mme. Forestier went to a wardrobe with a glass door, took out a large jewel-box, brought it back, opened it, and said to Mme. Loisel:

"Choose, my dear."

She saw first of all some bracelets, then a pearl necklace, then a Venetian cross, gold, and precious stones of admirable workmanship. She tried on the ornaments before the glass, hesitated, could not make up her mind to part with them, to give them back. She kept asking:

"Haven't you any more?"

"Why, yes. Look. I don't know what you like."

All of a sudden she discovered, in a black satin box, a superb necklace of diamonds; and her heart began to beat with an immoderate desire. Her hands trembled as she took it. She fastened it around her throat, outside her high-necked dress, and remained lost in ecstasy at the sight of herself.

Then she asked, hesitating, filled with anguish:

"Can you lend me that, only that?"

"Why, yes, certainly."

She sprang upon the neck of her friend, kissed her passionately, then fled with her treasure.

The day of the ball arrived. Mme. Loisel made a great success. She was prettier than them all, elegant, gracious, smiling, and crazy with joy. All the men looked at her, asked her name, endeavored to be introduced. All the attachés of the Cabinet wanted to waltz with her. She was remarked by the minister himself.

She danced with intoxication, with passion, made drunk by pleasure, forgetting all, in the triumph of her beauty, in the glory of her success, in a sort of cloud of happiness composed of all this homage, of all this admiration, of all these awakened desires, and of that sense of complete victory which is so sweet to woman's heart.

She went away about four o'clock in the morning. Her husband had been sleeping since midnight, in a little deserted ante-room, with three other gentlemen whose wives were having a very good time.

He threw over her shoulders the wraps which he had brought, modest wraps of common life, whose poverty contrasted with the elegance of the ball dress. She felt this and wanted to escape so as not to be remarked by the other women, who were enveloping themselves in costly furs.

Loisel held her back.

"Wait a bit. You will catch cold outside. I will go and call a cab."

But she did not listen to him, and rapidly descended the stairs. When they were in the street they did not find a carriage; and they began to look for one, shouting after the cabmen whom they saw passing by at a distance.

They went down towards the Seine, in despair, shivering with cold. At last they found on the quay one of those ancient noctambulant coupés which, exactly as if they were ashamed to show their misery during the day, are never seen round Paris until after nightfall.

It took them to their door in the Rue des Martyrs, and once more, sadly, they climbed up homeward. All was ended for her. And as to him, he reflected that he must be at the Ministry at ten o'clock.

She removed the wraps, which covered her shoulders, before the glass, so as once more to see herself in all her glory. But suddenly she uttered a cry. She had no longer the necklace around her neck!

Her husband, already half-undressed, demanded:

"What is the matter with you?"

She turned madly towards him:

"I have—I have—I've lost Mme. Forestier's necklace."

He stood up, distracted.

"What!—how?—Impossible!"

And they looked in the folds of her dress, in the folds of her cloak, in her pockets, everywhere. They did not find it.

He asked:

"You're sure you had it on when you left the ball?"

"Yes, I felt it in the vestibule of the palace."

"But if you had lost it in the street we should have heard it fall. It must be in the cab."

"Yes. Probably. Did you take his number?"

"No. And you, didn't you notice it?"

"No."

They looked, thunderstruck, at one another. At last Loisel put on his clothes.

"I shall go back on foot," said he, "over the whole route which we have taken, to see if I can't find it."

And he went out. She sat waiting on a chair in her ball dress, without strength to go to bed, overwhelmed, without fire, without a thought.

Her husband came back about seven o'clock. He had found nothing.

He went to Police Headquarters, to the newspaper offices, to offer a reward; he went to the cab companies—everywhere, in fact, whither he was urged by the least suspicion of hope.

She waited all day, in the same condition of mad fear before this terrible calamity.

Loisel returned at night with a hollow, pale face; he had discovered nothing.

"You must write to your friend," said he, "that you have broken the clasp of her necklace and that you are having it mended. That will give us time to turn round."

She wrote at his dictation.

At the end of a week they had lost all hope.

And Loisel, who had aged five years, declared:

"We must consider how to replace that ornament."

The next day they took the box which had contained it, and they went to the jeweler whose name was found within. He consulted his books.

"It was not I, madame, who sold that necklace; I must simply have furnished the case."

Then they went from jeweler to jeweler, searching for a necklace like the other, consulting their memories, sick both of them with chagrin and with anguish.

They found, in a shop at the Palais Royal, a string of diamonds which seemed to them exactly like the one they looked for. It was worth forty thousand francs. They could have it for thirty-six.

So they begged the jeweler not to sell it for three days yet. And they made a bargain that he should buy it back for thirty-four thousand francs, in case they found the other one before the end of February.

Loisel possessed eighteen thousand francs which his father had left him. He would borrow the rest.

He did borrow, asking a thousand francs of one, five hundred of another, five louis here, three louis there. He gave notes, took up ruinous obligations, dealt with usurers, and all the race of lenders. He compromised all the rest of his life, risked his signature without even knowing if he could meet it; and, frightened by the pains yet to come, by the black misery which was about to fall upon him, by the prospect of all the physical privations and of all the moral tortures which he was to suffer, he went to get the new necklace, putting down upon the merchant's counter thirty-six thousand francs.

When Mme. Loisel took back the necklace Mme. Forestier said to her, with a chilly manner:

"You should have returned it sooner, I might have needed it."

She did not open the case, as her friend had so much feared. If she had detected the substitution, what would she have thought, what would she have said? Would she not have taken Mme. Loisel for a thief?

Mme. Loisel now knew the horrible existence of the needy. She took her part, moreover, all on a sudden, with heroism. That dreadful debt must be paid. She would pay it. They dismissed their servant; they changed their lodgings; they rented a garret under the roof.

She came to know what heavy housework meant and the odious cares of the kitchen. She washed the dishes, using her rosy nails on the greasy pots and pans. She washed the dirty linen, the shirts, and the dish-cloths, which she dried upon a line; she carried the slops down to the street every morning, and carried up the water, stopping for breath at every landing. And, dressed like a woman of the people, she went to the fruiterer, the grocer, the butcher, her basket on her arm, bargaining, insulted, defending her miserable money sou by sou.

Each month they had to meet some notes, renew others, obtain more time.

Her husband worked in the evening making a fair copy of some tradesman's accounts, and late at night he often copied manuscript for five sous a page.

And this life lasted ten years.

At the end of ten years they had paid everything, everything, with the rates of usury, and the accumulations of the compound interest.

Mme. Loisel looked old now. She had become the woman of impoverished households—strong and hard and rough. With frowsy hair, skirts askew, and red hands, she talked loud while washing the floor with great swishes of water. But sometimes, when her husband was at the office, she sat down near the window, and she thought of that gay evening of long ago, of that ball where she had been so beautiful and so fêted.

What would have happened if she had not lost that necklace? Who knows? who knows? How life is strange and how changeful! How little a thing is needed for us to be lost or to be saved!

But, one Sunday, having gone to take a walk in the Champs Elysées to refresh herself from the labors of the week, she suddenly perceived a woman who was leading a child. It was Mme. Forestier, still young, still beautiful, still charming.

Mme. Loisel felt moved. Was she going to speak to her? Yes, certainly. And now that she had paid, she was going to tell her all about it. Why not?

She went up.

"Good-day, Jeanne."

The other, astonished to be familiarly addressed by this plain goodwife, did not recognize her at all, and stammered:

"But—madame!—I do not know— You must have mistaken."

"No. I am Mathilde Loisel."

Her friend uttered a cry.

"Oh, my poor Mathilde! How you are changed!"

"Yes, I have had days hard enough, since I have seen you, days wretched enough—and that because of you!"

"Of me! How so?"

"Do you remember that diamond necklace which you lent me to wear at the ministerial ball?"

"Yes. Well?"

"Well, I lost it."

"What do you mean? You brought it back."

"I brought you back another just like it. And for this we have been ten years paying. You can understand that it was not easy for us, us who had nothing. At last it is ended, and I am very glad."

Mme. Forestier had stopped.

"You say that you bought a necklace of diamonds to replace mine?"

"Yes. You never noticed it, then! They were very like."

And she smiled with a joy which was proud and naïve at once.

Mme. Forestier, strongly moved, took her two hands.

"Oh, my poor Mathilde! Why, my necklace was paste. It was worth at most five hundred francs!"